D1582876

MODERN
HOUSING ESTATES

Standard Textbooks for ARCHITECTS, SUR-VEYORS, BUILDERS, etc.

ARCHITECTURAL PRACTICE AND PROCEDURE. By Hamilton H. Turner, F.R.I.C.S.

A review of the business side of an architect's work, and of office organisation. Containing 390 pages, with forms, a model house specification, reports, illustrations, etc. Fourth edition, revised and enlarged.

Demy 8vo. Fourth Edition 18s. *net*

QUANTITIES. By Prof. Banister Fletcher, F.R.I.B.A., and H. Phillips Fletcher, F.R.I.B.A., F.S.I. Revised and Remodelled by A. E. Baylis, F.R.I.C.S. *Twelfth Edition.*

A textbook in tabulated form on the methods of the valuation and measurement of building and engineering works. With chapters on cubing, grouping, repairs, the law, etc., and examples of the complete taking off, abstracting and billing of standard buildings, many specially written and reproduced in facsimile. Mr. Baylis's edition of this famous work to all intents and purposes constitutes a new book, thoroughly in line with the latest conditions. It contains 658 pages and many diagrams.

Demy 8vo. 30s. *net*

LONDON BUILDING LAW. By Horace R. Chanter, F.R.I.B.A., F.R.I.C.S., M.I.Struct.E.

This book, intended as an introduction and guide to the various enactments and byelaws which affect building in London, is written in clear and simple language, as distinct from the exacting phraseology usually adopted in legal textbooks. It provides a comprehensive digest of the essential requirements affecting the construction of London buildings, enabling the reader to gain a clear understanding of the law as it relates to normal practice. It will be found of immense assistance to architects, surveyors, builders, estate agents and property owners, or to any concerned with the design, construction or alteration of buildings in the metropolis.

Medium 8vo. 21s. *net*

MODEL BUILDING BYELAWS ILLUSTRATED. By G. E. Mitchell, M.Inst.M. & Cy.E., A.R.I.B.A.

Second edition, revised and enlarged. Comprising the revised series issued by The Ministry of Health and made under The Public Health Act, 1936.

Royal 8vo. 15s. *net*

DRAINAGE AND SANITATION. A Practical Exposition of the Conditions vital to Healthy Buildings, their Surroundings and Construction, their Ventilation, Heating, Lighting, Water and Waste Services. For the use of Architects, Surveyors, Engineers, Health Officers, and Sanitary Inspectors. By E. H. Blake, F.R.I.C.S., M.R.S.I. *Ninth Edition*, revised by W. R. Jenkins, B.Sc., A.M.I.C.E., F.R.I.C.S.

Large 8vo, cloth 15s. *net*

B. T. BATSFORD LTD
LONDON · NEW YORK · TORONTO · SYDNEY

FRONTISPIECE

BIRD'S-EYE VIEW OF PROPOSED HOUSING AND COMMUNITY DEVELOPMENT AT THE INCH NETHER LIBERTON

For the City and Royal Burgh of Edinburgh

D. STRATTON DAVIS, A.R.I.B.A.
(*Stratton Davis & Yates*, F.S.A.
FF.R.I.B.A., F.R.I.C.S., *Architects*)

MODERN HOUSING ESTATES

A Practical Guide to their Planning, Design and Development for the use of Town Planners, Architects, Surveyors, Engineers, Municipal Officials, Builders and others interested in the technical and legal aspects of the subject

BY

STANLEY GALE

A.M.Inst.M.E., M.R.S.I.

Civil Engineer and Surveyor
Chartered Municipal Engineer

With over 200 illustrations and numerous folding plates from drawings and photographs including many prepared by leading Local Authorities and other bodies

B. T. BATSFORD LTD
LONDON · NEW YORK · TORONTO · SYDNEY

First Published Spring 1949

PRINTED AND BOUND IN ENGLAND
BY WILLIAM CLOWES AND SONS LTD, BECCLES, SUFFOLK
FOR THE PUBLISHERS
B. T. BATSFORD LTD.
LONDON : 15 NORTH AUDLEY ST., W.1
& MALVERN WELLS, WORCESTERSHIRE
NEW YORK : 122 EAST 55TH STREET
TORONTO : 480–6 UNIVERSITY AVENUE
SYDNEY : 156 CASTLEREAGH STREET

PREFACE

The greatest public need at the present time is the adequate provision of houses for the vast number of people in this country desiring to have homes of their own.

With the passing of the Town and Country Planning Act, 1947, the way became clearer for proceeding apace with the herculean task of constructing housing estates both by Local Authorities and private enterprise.

Much has been written, spoken and discussed upon future building schemes and countless reports, memoranda, orders and circulars have been published, but these are apt to bewilder those responsible for carrying out such schemes.

The difficult questions of land acquisition, compensation and betterment have been the cause of much controversy in recent years, and have resulted in the Government providing improved legislative measures to alleviate such difficulties in dealing with the great housing problem.

This book is intended to give the reader a clear and concise outline of all matters affecting the planning and construction of housing estates, the creation of neighbourhood units and the development of satellite towns on garden city principles.

It is hoped that the work will prove of service to Housing Committees and their Officers ; Architects, Surveyors and Town Planners and other professionals interested in estate development, as well as to students preparing for the various professional examinations which relate to town planning, civil engineering, and surveying.

As far as possible as many practical diagrams, plans, and photographs have been given to illustrate the numerous schemes dealt with in the text.

Acknowledgements are due to the kindness of the promoters of various Garden City Estates, and to various important Local Authorities for allowing the publication of notes, plans and photographs of their respective estates, also to the Controller of His Majesty's Stationery Office for permission to publish extracts from numerous Government Acts, Reports, Circulars and Memoranda ; to the Institution of Municipal Engineers for extracts from their Journals and Reports, and to the Proprietors and Editors of " Architectural Design and Construction ". To my publishers, and especially their Director, Mr. W. Hanneford Smith, Hon. A.R.I.B.A., I am greatly indebted for their collaboration in the preparation of the book ; also to Mr. Francis Lucarotti, their Production Manager, for his care and skill in the presentation of the volume. The coloured frontispiece, and dust wrapper, also Plates XV and XVI, illustrating the Inch Nether Liberton Housing and Community Development Scheme, Edinburgh, are reproduced by the kind permission of Messrs. Stratton Davis and Yates, FF.R.I.B.A., the architects responsible for the scheme.

STANLEY GALE

September 1948.

CONTENTS

LIST OF ILLUSTRATIONS

PAGE

CHAPTER I

THE CHOICE AND DESIGN OF ESTATES

Siting Residential Estates

The selection of suitable estates is rather limited because of town planning restrictions on use of land for various purposes, such as industrial areas, open spaces, aerodrome sites, agricultural areas, etc. ; but where any choice is possible sites in healthy surroundings and with convenient means of quick transport to and from places of work and town centres should be chosen.

A local knowledge of the subsoils is desirable, as it is known that variations in the level of subsoil water have been related to disease—by causing impure air from rising subsoil water to penetrate in basements of houses.

A dry gravel or sandy soil is the best choice, but any land if well drained (excepting made-up ground, unless the filling has had several years in which to consolidate) can be used for building upon.

Houses must be built upon good foundations carried down to the firm stratum after the top soil has been removed. Underlying strata of clay, limestone, chalk, or rock foundation are suitable for supporting substantial building loads. In wet and peaty ground it is essential to provide adequate concrete rafts for the building foundations.

Land subject to flooding and mining subsidence should be avoided, and a careful investigation as to the existence of springs and underground streams is advisable. A careful study of local geological survey maps will repay the trouble ; and particular notice should be taken of the conditions of land in winter and summer periods, as often land appears dry and ideal in the summer, whilst in winter the same land may become waterlogged and unsuitable.

Undulating land and gentle hillsides make good sites, whilst hilltops and deep valley areas are not so good because of likely flooding and drainage difficulties.

Flat land may appear ideal for building upon, but deeper drainage will be required to properly drain the properties, and may prove very expensive.

The important points of site selection may therefore be summarised as follows :

(1) Relation to existing or contemplated residential and industrial sites.
(2) The configuration of the ground for economical development : the suitability of the subsoil and the aspect of the site if sloping. (Sites sloping steeply to the north are undesirable.)
(3) Possibility of extension and future development.

(4) Amenities of the site : trees, fertility of the land.

(5) Open spaces in the neighbourhood and adaptability of parts of the site for this purpose and for shops and larger houses.

(6) Convenience and economy in the provision of sewers, sewerage, water supply, electricity and gas services.

(7) Adequate transport facilities from sites to industrial works, offices, schools, and town centres.

With regard to existing watercourses the developer should note that under Public Health Act, 1936, it is a statutory nuisance to obstruct or impede the flow of a watercourse, and that culverting or piping may only be done with the consent of the local authority. The watercourses should not be filled in or allowed to get silted up, as may cause unhealthy nuisances. The Rivers Pollution Prevention Act, 1876, and Land Drainage Act, 1930, also deal with the proper maintenance of watercourses. The developer constructing roads across watercourses or ditches will be advised to consult with local authorities, or drainage boards if necessary, before doing any constructional work that may result in heavy claims for damages against the developer.

Character of Estates

The layout should develop the order and individual character of a good design. By so planning the lines of the roads and disposing the spaces and the buildings as to develop the beauty of vista, arrangement, and proportion, attractiveness may be added to the dwellings at little or no extra cost.

The extent of layout design should not be confined to the limited boundaries of the land immediately to be developed, but the planning should extend to areas adjoining, so that a comprehensive scheme of development is designed to fit into a master plan of the district. Otherwise a layout plan of a confined size planned independently of adjoining areas may not conform to the general scheme of planned development.

It would be advisable for the prospective developer to have an early consultation with the Local Planning Authority's officers or with a professional planning consultant before depositing layout plans, and thereby save much time, energy, and expense.

The Preliminary Survey

The need and value of an accurate survey and contour plan cannot be over-emphasized, and particularly as regards contours of the ground, which decide the positions of the roads, levels of houses, and drainage possibilities. The survey should indicate the positions of boundaries, streams, watercourses, existing buildings, roads, sewers, public services, woods, trees, ponds, marshy lands, railways, quarries, and various natural features.

Ordnance Survey maps to 1/2500 scale have recently been revised, and provide much useful data. The 6-in.-to-the-mile maps are useful for indicating drainage areas ; and as the contours are also shown, they are very useful in planning limits of drainage to the proposed and existing lines of sewers. On such maps could also be shown the transport communications, waterways, built-up areas, agricultural and woodland areas, and relative positions of proposed housing estates to town centres, railway stations, and industrial districts. An important point to consider is the exact location of public footpaths, bridle paths, and rights of way which cross the proposed housing estates, as under the Rights of Way Act, 1932, a public right of way is one that has been used without interruption by the public for at least twenty years. If it is necessary to close or divert any public way application should be made to the local authority or a court of summary jurisdiction, otherwise the developer may incur expense and delay of his development schemes.

Aerial photographic surveys are very useful, as recent development can easily be seen, and they have the quality of revealing hidden features, *e.g.* ancient earth workings, and if used in conjunction with Ordnance maps can present a picture survey of great help to planners.

CONTOURING

A contour survey of potential sites is very necessary in designing lines, gradients, and depths of estates roads and sewers, and well repays careful attention given to it. Contouring may be done by the following methods :

(1) By taking a number of section lines across the site at regular distances, say 20 to 50 ft. apart on even ground and nearer on steep undulating ground.

(2) By taking levels on radiating lines from a fixed position on the highest part of the area, and noting the positions of the levels on a plan ; but this method is only useful for small sites.

(3) By taking spot levels and afterwards surveying their positions.

By the first method a number of sections are ranged across the site and each line is numbered. Levels are taken from an Ordnance bench mark, or a known datum point, and then levels are read on measured points along each section line. The levels are plotted and drawn in sections from which the contour lines can be drawn by extending the level sections on to the plan.

The second method is done in the same way as the first, but that levels are taken at salient points and noted on the plan, and no section lines are laid down.

The third method, that of spot levelling, is suitable on fairly level ground, but not for steep or undulating ground. When the levels are marked on the plan approximate contour lines can be drawn between the spot levels.

An example of a survey and contour plan is shown in Fig. 1, p. 4.

DESIGN OF THE LAYOUT

When a survey and contour plan of the estate has been completed, it must be carefully studied, and several sketch layout designs should

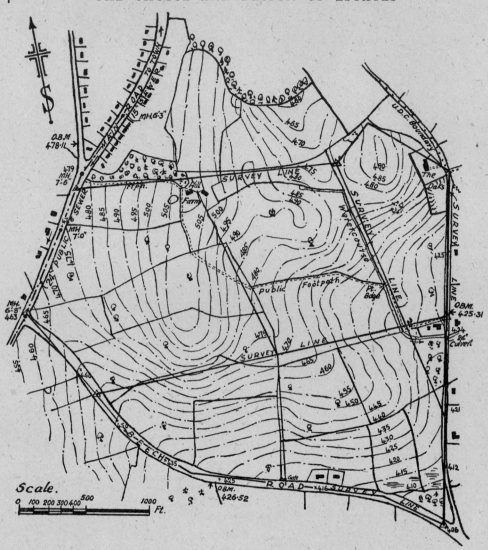

FIG. 1. An example of a survey and contour plan

be considered before deciding on a final design which will comply with all town-planning provisions, housing requirements, and financial factors.

The main points of consideration are as follows :

(1) The requirements of the local and regional town-planning schemes.
(2) Planning of the roads.
(3) Building density.
(4) Open spaces.

(5) Sites for community buildings, shopping centres, schools, churches, etc.

(6) Building lines.

(7) General amenities.

With regard to (2) Planning of the roads, these may be contour roads, normal-to-contour roads, or diagonal roads.

Contour Roads. These run parallel to the contours, and houses on each side are therefore on different levels ; but if land is on a gentle slope there is no objection to houses being lower than road level along one side of the road. Extra foundations are, however, needed if the houses are brought up to road level. Contour roads result in producing houses with their horizontal lines parallel to the roads, and are easy and economical of development. (Fig. 8, p. 14.)

Roads normal to the contours. These make for easier drainage, and houses are approximately level on both sides of a rising road, which looks more pleasing than a level road.

Diagonal Roads. These are sometimes made to produce easier gradients or better routes, but have the big disadvantage of making inconvenient shaped building plots, and on the whole are better avoided.

Steep Sites. On steep slopes of, say, 1 in 8 a form of development which is economical, and a pleasant feature, is obtained by building on the top side of the road only, and making a narrower width of road with only one footpath.

The extra cost of deeper foundations, sewers, and roadworks is at least equivalent to the extra cost per house for this type of road. The houses on the higher side of the road will overlook the top of the houses below, and the general view of this can be pleasing.

Culs-de-sac. These are used instead of through roads for building on irregular pieces and corners of land. The result is saving of roadworks, and they provide attractive variations to a layout of formal through roads. (Fig. 7, p. 12.)

The main points to consider in the design of culs-de-sac are these:

(1) They should rise from entrance to end, which gives a better vista than if the fall were the other way.

(2) They should not be constructed so as to create the impression that they are anything but culs-de-sac. The entrances should not be too wide, and corner houses should be so sited as to avoid view of the back gardens of culs-de-sac.

(3) The end of a cul-de-sac should have a terminal feature, such as a block on the central axis line, with perhaps a prominent porch or gable, to make a focal point. A tree centrally placed at the end of a cul-de-sac makes an attractive feature.

(4) The building lines should be well spaced in culs-de-sac, and low garden fences, or open front lawns can give an air of spaciousness.

(5) Culs-de-sac should not be longer than 500 ft., as otherwise the object is defeated. At the end of a cul-de-sac may be constructed a footpath to afford a short-cut to a through road.

(6) The alignment should be normal to the contour, thus preserving a balanced roof line.

(7) A cul-de-sac should not have another branching off it.

(8) A turning space of at least 30 ft. radius between kerbs is essential and the space can be circular, rectangular, or square-shaped.

An example of a cul-de-sac is shown in Fig. 2.

Other variations of layout design include the close, which comes next in principle to the cul-de-sac, affords greater density, and gives more privacy. Loop roads can also be used and have the advantage of allowing through traffic.

Quadrangles are formed with interior streets up to 1000 ft. long. In shape they can be square or hexagonal, and with central green spaces can be made to look attractive, with blocks of houses built around them.

The double building line, with an equal number of units in front and rear of the site, not only achieves considerable saving in street lengths, but also provides for better shaped units, with wider frontages, and thus assists the planning of the individual houses.

Cross access streets have much to commend them, as they divide the estate into economically-sized units and give satisfactory frontages to most houses, but such streets must not be too long in length.

Illustrations are given in Fig. 3, p. 9, showing various types of street layout designs, which illustrate the above-mentioned points.

Balanced Layouts

Although plans of layouts may look well balanced and geometrical, they may not be so on the site, where a bird's-eye view is not possible, All such natural features as groups of trees, streams, ponds, and dells should be utilised to the best advantage, and emphasised by grouping the houses and buildings in order to obtain pleasing vistas. Corners and bends of streets should be designed to enable houses to be pleasantly grouped together, and small shrubberies and trees can be added with advantage. A good example is shown in Fig. 4, p. 10, of an estate designed by architects of the Bournville Village Trust.

Types of Layout

There are mainly four types of layout that may be used :

(i) Rectangular or grid-iron.

(ii) Spider's-web or radial.

(iii) Geometrical arrangement.

(iv) Contour pattern.

Rectangular or Grid-Iron. In this type of plan the streets are laid out parallel to one another, with communicating streets at right angles. The spaces between the roads are rectangular or square in shape, and on a level site the blocks are simple and convenient for building. It is a type of plan largely used in America until quite recently. It is open to serious objection from the traffic point of view, is monotonous, and is quite unsuitable for undulating land. (See Fig. 5, p. 11.)

FIG. 2. An example of a cul-de-sac

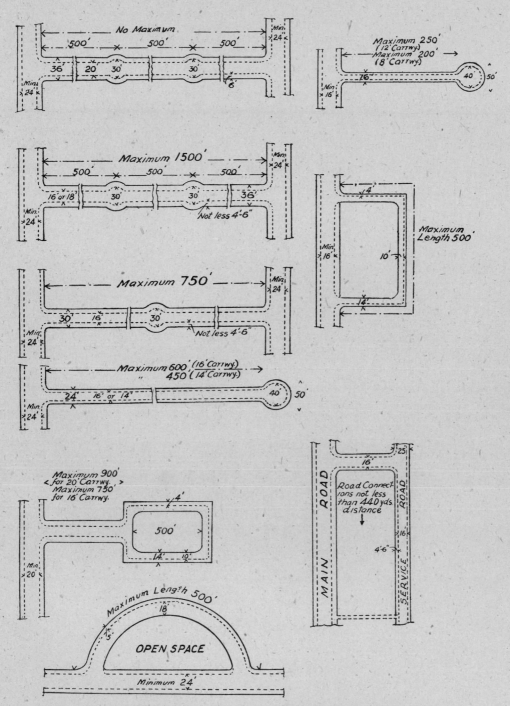

FIG. 3. Illustrations of various types of street layout designs

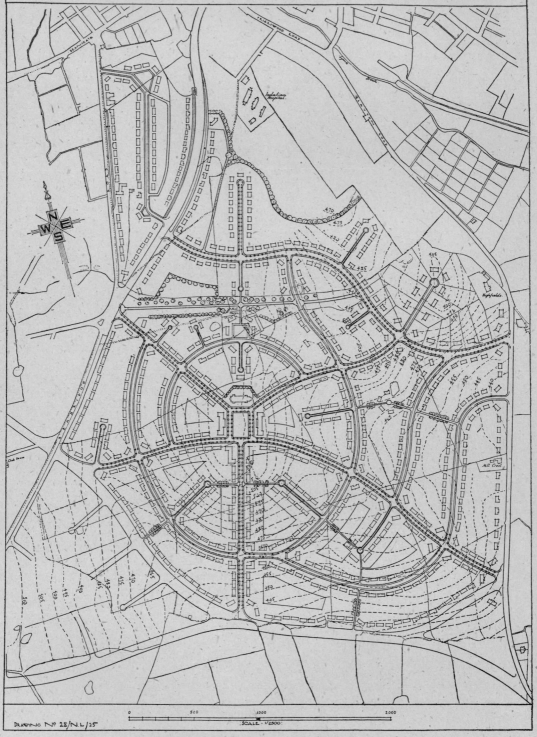

BOROUGH OF NEWCASTLE-UNDER-LYME
PROPOSED DEVELOPMENT OF HILL FARM ESTATE

FIG. 4. A good example of a well-planned housing estate

(By courtesy of Bournville Village Trust Architects Department)
(Based upon the Ordnance Survey map with the sanction of the Controller of His Majesty's Stationery Office)

Spider's-Web or Radial. This is the natural way in which most English towns have developed. The market-place is the centre point, from which roads radiate in all directions to neighbouring towns and villages. The ideal plan on this system, however, had radiating roads connected by

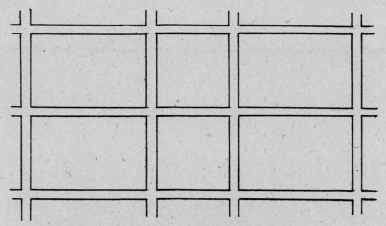

FIG. 5. Rectangular or grid-iron plan

other roads arranged more or less in concentric circles. It is essential that at the centre there should be some universal magnetic attraction, otherwise the roads would lead to a place to which few people wish to go.

The spider's-web plan is readily adaptable to the exigencies of the site, and is no less effective if even considerable divergence is made from the ideal figure. (See Fig. 6, p. 12.)

The Geometrical Type. The feature of this plan is the formal arrangement of the roads in some symmetrical pattern. It offers excellent opportunities for architectural treatment in the formal manner. It requires a level site for success. Often the beauty of the plan is only apparent on paper or from an aeroplane. The expense of constructing roads, sewers, etc., to conform to the plan on undulating ground is not justified by the resulting appearance. (See Fig. 7, p. 12.)

The Contour Type of Plan. This is the type of plan usually adapted at the present time, especially for layouts of land as distinct from whole towns. It is the exact opposite to formal planning. The streets conform as nearly as possible to the contours of the ground. The adaptation of a plan to suit the ground levels results not only in economy in constructing roads and sewers and the foundations of buildings, but also gives individuality in character.

Although the name " contour method " is the usual way of describing this type of plan, it does not mean that the routes of roads slavishly follow the contours. Indeed, this would be impossible, as the roads could not be drained. (See Fig. 8, p. 14.)

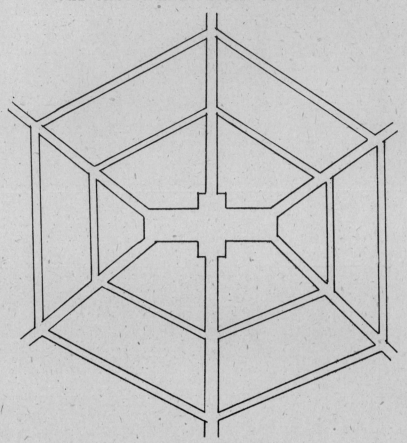

Fɪɢ. 6. Spider's web or radial plan

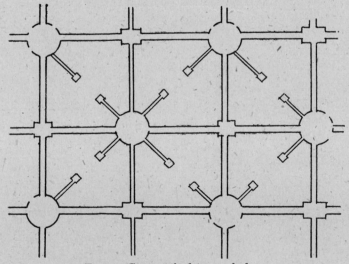

Fɪɢ. 7. Geometrical type of plan

ROAD FRONTAGES

It is well worth while to give considerable care to the planning of estate roads, as much can result in economy with little loss of amenity.

The test of the financial efficiency of development roads is the length of road per house. The total length of the roads in a scheme, of the several widths employed, should be divided by the total number of houses in that scheme ; and when the length of road per house has thus been ascertained, it should be compared with the length per house in alternative layouts for the same land.

When this has been done, it may happen that consideration of amenity may induce the developer to provide a greater length of road per house. By this method of considering the road frontage per house any decision is made with exact knowledge of the cost. The developers are in a position to determine that the amenities secured are worth the cost.

Economy of road frontage may be attained first by skilled design of the development roads and secondly by skilled arrangement of the buildings and houses.

In the design of roads superfluous cross roads should be replaced by culs-de-sac. The loss caused by having great lengths of road that only afford a second frontage for houses fronting on to other roads should be avoided. This means that the number of road junctions must be limited.

The second consideration in economy of road frontage is the arrangement of the houses. The most economical is obviously the continuous block, and the more the block is broken up by gaps between the houses the greater the road frontage per house. The most extravagant in road frontage is the detached house. In housing sites, therefore, it seems desirable to strike a balance and introduce blocks of four and perhaps eight—not only from the point of view of economy of road frontage, but also to relieve the monotony of semi-detached houses. In cases of blocks of houses where there is no secondary road, some of the saving in road frontage will be neutralised, of course, by the cost of covered passages to reach the inner houses of the blocks.

Both in semi-detached and in terrace arrangements broad-fronted houses will give greater continuity to the architectural treatment of the road than houses having a narrow frontage. Very often broad-fronted terrace houses will generally require no more land and be no more expensive in roads and sewers than narrow-fronted houses arranged in pairs.

BUILDING DENSITY

Under the Town Planning Act, 1932, Model Clauses, " density " meant the extent to which land can be covered by buildings. Methods to control this were : (a) prescribing the area of the site of each building ; (b) prescribing an average density over an area of land, termed for convenience as " land unit " ; (c) a combination of the two methods.

As far as dwelling-houses are concerned, the density was given as so many houses to the acre, i.e. 6 to the acre for first-class residential areas and 10 or 12 to the acre for general residential areas.

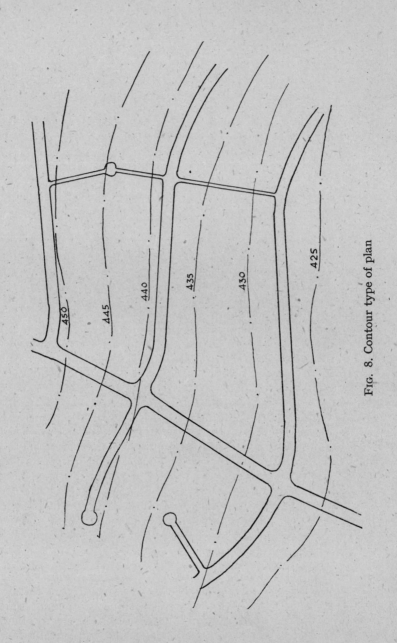

Fig. 8. Contour type of plan

Subsidy houses had to be planned at a maximum of 12 to the acre, and 8 to the acre in agricultural areas. Buildings other than dwelling-houses, such as flats, shops, and business premises, were to be dealt with as dwelling-house units, but in practice this was unworkable. Therefore such buildings as these are excluded from calculations of house densities, and are treated separately on their merits.

Land Units

Each area of land covered by house, garden, and half-width of street-fronting is called a land unit, and density is assessed by the number of land units per acre. A density of, say, 12 houses to the acre means 12 land units to the acre, or approximately 403 sq. yds. per plot. The net area of each plot, however, can vary very much according to the amount of street area and open space area allocated to areas scheduled for development. The Model Clauses give minimum sizes of plots as shown in the following Table:

Density	Size of Plot
12 to acre	250 sq. yds.
8 ,, ,, ...	400 ,, ,,
6 ,, ,, ...	500 ,, ,,

In expensive re-development areas in towns the density of houses can be as high as 20 to the acre, so long as the minimum area of each house is 120 sq. yds.

Density Table

The Density Table, shown on p. 27, gives relative densities of houses in which due allowance has been made for : (a) area of house covering the ground, (b) area of private garden attached to it, (c) area of half-width of street fronting it. The total of these three areas gives the land unit per house, and the number of such units per acre thus given is the calculated building density.

In addition it is desirable to provide " open spaces ", " parking spaces ", " play parks ", and allotments to residential areas, and it has been suggested that the provision of anything up to 7 acres per 1000 population should be allowed for. The addition of these areas will materially alter the density. The number of houses or land units is somewhat reduced, as can be seen by reference to the Density Table.

The effect of this is that house density per acre is greatly reduced in order to allow reasonable open spaces, and a more equitable basis is to calculate density on the number of persons per acre. A reasonable estimate, such as 100 to 150 persons per acre, could be taken as a basis for estimating the number of houses required per acre. It may be difficult to calculate closely the number of people to each house, but for sewerage calculations a basis of 5 persons per house is adopted. A basis of 5 persons per house and 12 houses to the acre would mean a population of 60 per acre, which is by no means overcrowding the area. If a

DENSITY   GRAPH
SHOWING NUMBER OF UNITS TO THE ACRE

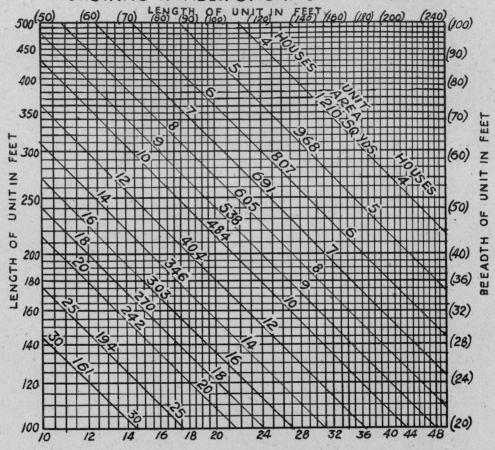

FIG. 9. Density graph and table of building plots

PER UNIT	DENSITIES TO ACRE						
	20	14	12	10	8	AVERAGE	
AREA OF HOUSE ON GROUND	SQ.YDS. 42	SQ.YDS 45	SQ.YDS. 53	SQ.YDS. 56	SQ.YDS. 67	SQ.YDS. 53	13%
AREA OF PRIVATE GARDEN SPACE	156	241	271	338	428	287	68%
AREA OF HALF WIDTH OF STREET	44	60	80	90	110	76	19%
TOTALS	242	346	404	484	605	416	100%

population of, say, only a 100 persons were taken as a basis, this would mean a housing density of 20 to the acre, which is not unreasonable and utilises land for housing estates to a greater extent. In many cases people do not want large gardens, and a garden of about 200 sq. yds. is considered quite ample.

Economical use of precious building land and careful planning of roads and siting of houses result in more houses at a cheaper cost. A housing density from 16 to 20 per acre is, by comparison with existing built-up areas, having densities from 50 to even 80 houses per acre, a vast planning improvement.

DENSITY GRAPH OF LAND UNITS

On p. 16 is given a Graph from which it is possible to read at a glance the length and breadth in feet of land units or building plots according to the building density required. For example, a density of 12 units to the acre requires an area of approximately 400 sq. yds. (which includes half-width of street). If the breadth of the unit is, say, 30 ft., by following the vertical line at 30 ft. at base of the chart until it crosses the density line of 12 to the acre, then following the horizontal line to the left side of the chart, the required length of the unit is read as 120 ft. Thus, size of unit wanted is 120 ft. × 30 ft. = 3600 sq. ft. or 400 sq. yds. Of course, varying measurements of length and breadth can be obtained for any set area of unit.

DENSITIES FOR FLATS

The Model Clauses do not give a definite basis as to number allowed per acre, but suggest a standard of about 100 persons per acre.

A working rule of 25 per cent. of ground space covered by flats has been suggested, provided certain restrictions on height and spacing of flats are observed.

A figure of 30 flats per acre is quoted these days as being reasonable, and if compared to 16 houses to an acre will provide (at 5 persons per house or flat) for 150 persons, as against 80 in houses, an increase of over 80 per cent. The cost of flats, however, may be as much as 50 per cent. higher than that of houses. Flats only benefit financially if cost of land is excessive and the greatest number of people have to be accommodated, as in town centres, where higher rents can be expected.

OPEN SPACES

It is thought very desirable to make provision for recreational facilities on a rough basis of 10 per cent. of the total town area. Playing-fields for young children and for those over 14 years will require, as a minimum, 5 acres per 1000 population ; and in addition adequate ground should be set apart for allotments, motor parks, and public gardens.

In arriving at a suitable building density the degree of benefit may be taken into account of adjoining private open spaces ; but this is sometimes difficult to apportion to density of adjoining properties. Such private open spaces may eventually be developed, and so upset the density

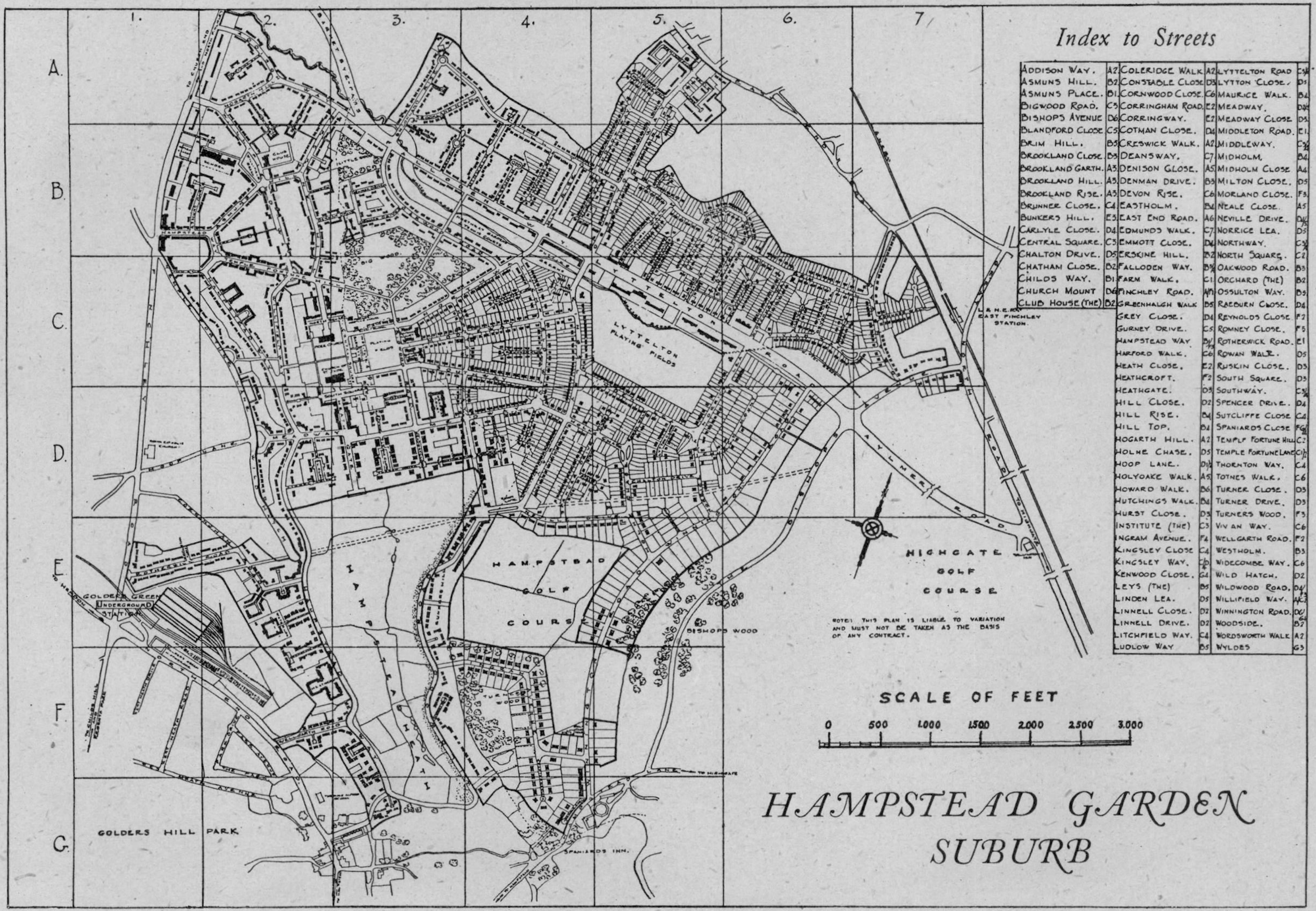

Index to Streets

ADDISON WAY.	A7	COLERIDGE WALK	A2	LYTTELTON ROAD	D4
ASMUNS HILL.	B2	CONSTABLE CLOSE	D3	LYTTON CLOSE.	D1
ASMUNS PLACE.	B1	CORNWOOD CLOSE	C4	MAURICE WALK.	A6
BIGWOOD ROAD.	C3	CORRINGHAM ROAD.	C3	MEADWAY	C3
BISHOPS AVENUE	D6	CORRINGWAY	C4	MEADWAY CLOSE.	C3
BLANDFORD CLOSE	B5	COTMAN CLOSE	C4	MIDDLETON ROAD.	C1
DRUM HILL.	B4	CRESWICK WALK.	A2	MIDDLEWAY.	A7
BROOKLAND CLOSE.	B5	DEANSWAY.	D5	MIDHOLM.	C7
BROOKLAND GARTH.	A5	DENISON CLOSE.	D3	MIDHOLM CLOSE.	C7
BROOKLAND HILL.	A5	DENMAN DRIVE.	A3	MILTON CLOSE.	D6
BROOKLAND RISE.	A5	DEVON RISE.	C2	MORELAND CLOSE.	C4
BUNKERS CLOSE.	A4	DEVON RISE.	C2	NEALE CLOSE.	D4
BUNKERS HILL.	E5	EAST END ROAD.	D1	NEVILLE DRIVE.	A6
CARLYLE CLOSE.	D4	EDMUND WALK.	C3	NORRICE LEA.	C5
CENTRAL SQUARE.	C3	ERSKINE HILL.	C2	NORTH SQUARE.	C3
CHALTON DRIVE.	D4	FALLODEN WAY.	D2	OAKWOOD ROAD.	A3
CHATHAM CLOSE.	D3	FARM WALK.	B2	ORCHARD (The)	C2
CHILDS WAY.	B3	FINCHLEY ROAD.	D7	OSMULTON CLOSE.	A4
CHURCH MOUNT	C2	GRACEMEAGH WALK	D2	RADDEN CLOSE.	D4
CLUB HOUSE (The)	D2			REYNOLDS CLOSE.	D4
		GREY CLOSE.	D1	ROTHERWICK ROAD.	C3
		GURNEY DRIVE.	C4	RUSKIN CLOSE.	D3
		HAMPSTEAD WAY.	B3	SOUTH SQUARE.	C3
		HARPOID WALK.	D2	SOUTHWAY.	D2
		HEATH CLOSE.	C3	SPENCER DRIVE.	D4
		HEATHCROFT.	D5	SUTCLIFFE CLOSE.	D4
		HEATHGATE.	C4	SPANIARDS CLOSE.	D6
		HILL CLOSE.	B4	TEMPLE FORTUNE HILL.	C2
		HILL RISE.	B4	TEMPLE FORTUNE LANE.	C2
		HILL TOP.	B4	THORNTON WAY.	A2
		HOGARTH HILL.	A3	TOTNES WALK.	A5
		HOLME CHASE.	D4	TURNER CLOSE.	D3
		HOOP LANE.	C2	TURNER DRIVE.	D3
		HOLYOAKE WALK.	A2	TURNERS WOOD.	D6
		HOWARD WALK.	A4	VIVIAN WAY.	C5
		HUTCHINGS WALK.	D4	WELLGARTH ROAD.	D6
		HURST CLOSE.	D3	WESTHOLM.	C3
		INSTITUTE. (The)	C3	WIDECOMBE WAY.	D3
		INGRAM AVENUE.	D6	WILD HATCH.	C4
		KINGSLEY CLOSE.	D3	WILDWOOD ROAD.	B5
		KINGSLEY WAY.	D5	WILLIFIELD WAY.	A3
		KENWOOD CLOSE.	D6	WINNINGTON ROAD.	D5
		LEYS (The)	C3	WOODSIDE.	C3
		LINDEN LEA.	C2	LINNELL CLOSE.	D3
		LINNELL CLOSE.	D3	WORDSWORTH WALK.	A2
		LINNELL DRIVE.	C4	WYLDES.	C5
		LITCHFIELD WAY.	C4		
		LUDLOW WAY.	B3		

HAMPSTEAD GARDEN SUBURB

SCALE OF FEET

0   500   1,000   1,500   2,000   2,500   3,000

NOTE: THIS PLAN IS LIABLE TO VARIATION AND MUST NOT BE TAKEN AS THE BASIS OF ANY CONTRACT.

FIG. 10. Hampstead Garden Suburb plan

ARCHITECTS: Barry Parker, F.R.I.B.A.; Sir Raymond Unwin, PP.R.I.B.A. with Sir Edwin Lutyens, R.A.

(By courtesy of Hampstead Garden Suburb, Ltd.)

of adjoining estates. Allowances for open spaces may with advantage be omitted from density calculations and treated separately under Town Planning Control. A more even distribution of garden space to houses is obtained if the housing estate is divided up into land units and areas of open spaces can be kept out of the calculations. It will be seen from the Density Table that in the case of 20 land units or houses to the acre, if allowance of 5 acres for open spaces is included in the calculations, the density is reduced to 10 houses to the acre. In facing the big problem of providing housing accommodation for as many tenants as possible on estates, the important question of density allowance must be carefully considered.

COMMUNITY AND SHOPPING CENTRES

The social life of a large estate is an important factor to its residents, and a centre is most desirable where shops, public buildings, churches, and cinemas can be conveniently grouped together, thus making a small civic centre. Schools should be sited so as to enjoy easy and safe access from all parts of an estate, and care should be taken that road crossings are reduced to a minimum.

The civic centre should be placed on a focal point of the estate, *i.e.* at the top, or at the centre of the main axial road of the estate, and the approach road laid with spacious grass verges and trees to form a pleasing vista.

An example of a typical garden suburb estate is that of Hampstead Garden Suburb, the plan of which is shown in Fig. 10.

The Ministry of Education, in their booklet *Community Centres*,* recognises the important pioneer work of the N.C.S.S. and other voluntary bodies in pre-war years in trying to provide both new and old communities with some form of social and cultural centre. They explain the need for such buildings and the type of activities which experience shows should be carried out under their influence. There is a good discussion of the aims and functions of a community centre, the methods for staffing and maintaining such a building, and finally some notes on planning and accommodation, accompanied by a few suggested " typical plans " (see Figs. 11, 12, pp. 20, 21). The Ministry have based their book on information submitted by witnesses familiar with the various prototypes, such as Y.M.C.A., Y.W.C.A., women's institutes, miners' welfare institutes, village halls, village colleges and Ministry of Labour war-time centres. The Ministry feel that a bold post-war programme is needed and that future community centres should be the responsibility of the local education authority, linking up with more formal provision for adult education and where possible sharing a building with youth service.

DENSITY DEFINITIONS

Scottish Housing Advisory Committee Report, 1944. In this Report, called "Planning our New Houses", the question of density is lightly

* Ministry of Education. *Community Centres.* His Majesty's Stationery Office, 1944.

2

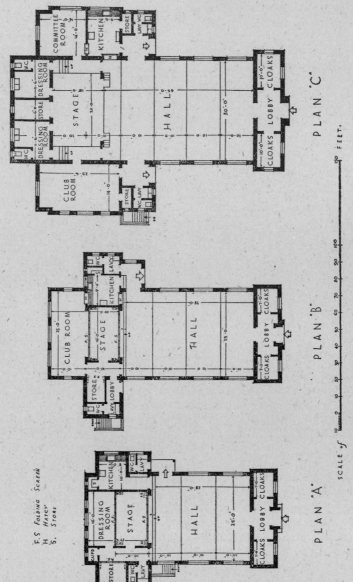

FIG. 11. Plan of typical community centres

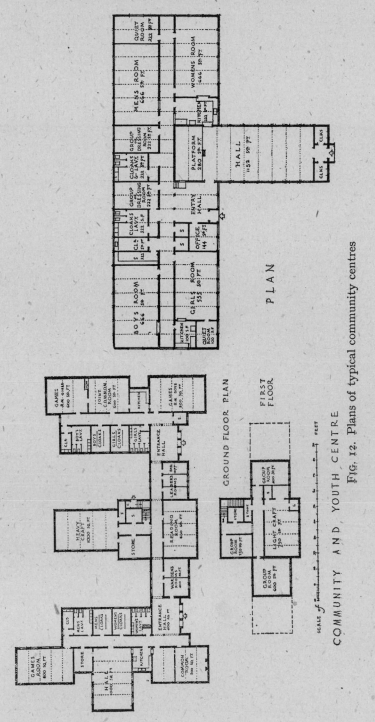

FIG. 12. Plans of typical community centres

discussed as being one for town planning. With regard to flats, however, the Report states "many schemes of flats of comparatively high density were so disposed on the site and were provided with such community services that they were in all respects superior to other schemes of lower density, which simply left blank expanses of open space behind and around flats ".

A note of reservation on this statement has been made by two members of the Committee, to the effect that they cannot agree with this statement, in so far as it confuses density with site planning. They recommend that in relation to housing a full review of density control should be undertaken without delay. Density, properly applied, is one index of healthy living and good social amenity.

Dudley Report on Design of Dwellings, 1944. This Report includes a Report of a Study Group of Ministry of Town and Country Planning which deals with density for a residential neighbourhood for 10,000 population. It states that arriving at reasonable density figures is a most difficult problem.

The higher cost of land, concentration of work-places, and existing housing and community facilities have in the past greatly affected the density of re-development. Certain important amenities, notably open spaces, are quite inadequate in central areas, where they can be introduced only if a long-term planning policy is pursued, for the scale of development is a governing factor.

The Report states that minimum standards of net residential density and gross density per neighbourhood can be set, and gives a table of minimum standards of land areas required in each neighbourhood of 10,000 people.

A RESIDENTIAL NEIGHBOURHOOD OF 10,000 PERSONS

Use	Open Development, acres	Outer ring, acres	Inner ring, acres	Central, acres	Central, acres
Housing	333	200	133	100	83
Primary schools (3–11 yrs. of age) (school and playing-field area)..	17	17	17	17	17
Open space	70	70	60	50	40
Shops, offices, etc...	9	8	7	6	5
Community centre, churches, etc.	7	5	4	3	3
Public buildings	4	3	2	2	2
Service industry and workshops	7	6	5	4	4
Main roads, including half boundary roads, up to a maximum of 20 ft. and parking	35	28	20	17	14
Totals	482	337	248	199	168

Net residential density is defined as the average number of persons per acre of housing area ; which comprises the curtilages of the dwellings, access or internal roads, and half the boundary main roads up to a maximum of 20 ft., where these are contiguous to residential property.

Gross density is the average number of persons per acre of the whole neighbourhood, the acreage of which is shown by the totals.

The Report also recommends that for housing densities generally three measures of density planning or control may be necessary : (1) neighbourhood density as shown in the above table ; (2) there should be a floor-space standard applied to defined areas, *e.g.* areas of 100–300 houses on the lines of land units ; (3) there should be a control safeguarding the lighting and amenity space for every building.

Economies in Layout Design

Estate roads should be so planned as to afford access to as many houses as possible. The cost of estate development is made up of the cost of the land, the houses, and the roads and sewers.

The proof of an efficient and economical scheme is the cost of roads and sewers per house, which cost will determine the sale price or rental of each house. Whilst prospective buyers or renters are willing to pay more for a larger house, they will not pay more because the lengths of roads are greater. Town planning regulations will, of course, determine the maximum number of houses to the acre ; therefore it is most essential that the planning of the layout design to serve these houses should be made with the utmost care possible.

In designing a layout it is more costly to provide short cross roads, as valuable frontage space is lost and the length of the roads per house is greater than actually necessary. It will be found cheaper to provide shorter roads with culs-de-sac leading off them, and access will be obtainable to a greater number of houses.

COMPARATIVE LAYOUT DESIGNS

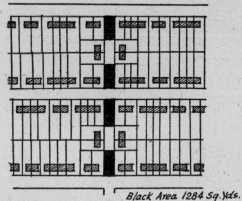

Black Area 1284 Sq.Yds.   Black Area 880 Sq.Yds.

Fig. 13. Cross pattern   Fig. 14. Cul-de-sac pattern

A diagrammatic layout of roads based on cross road pattern is shown in Fig. 13 and an alternative layout is given in Fig. 14. By comparing these two layouts it will be noticed that the roads which only afford a second frontage to houses already fronting other roads, are blacked in, and such loss of frontage is greater in the layout in Fig. 13 than in Fig. 14. The length of redundant frontage in Fig. 13 is approximately 32 per cent. more than in Fig. 14.

Culs-de-sac.   By using culs-de-sac considerable saving in road costs can be made, and access can be afforded to a greater number of houses.

Fig. 15 shows a layout rather wastefully designed, and Fig. 16 shows a better designed layout in the use of culs-de-sac ; and the saving of roads amounts to approximately 30 per cent.

Thus by using culs-de-sac there is access to the same number of houses, and additional land available may be added to the gardens or used as open spaces for play-grounds or allotments.

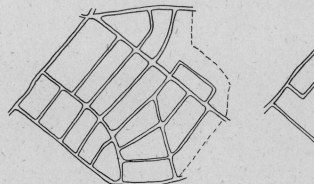 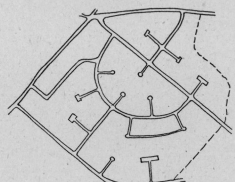

| Fig. 15. Layout wastefully designed | Fig. 16. Better designed Cul-de-sac pattern |

The greater use of culs-de-sac in layout design also helps to reduce traffic dangers by the elimination of through-traffic roads, and enables an estate to be built up in self-contained neighbourhood units.   This is illustrated in Fig. 17, which is a layout consisting practically entirely of culs-de-sac.

If we increase the number of houses for which given lengths of roads and services are sufficient, the maintenance costs such as repairing, cleansing, and lighting are also kept as low as possible.   It becomes, therefore, essential that careful planning of roads should be considered, as the financial gain resulting from an economical layout will also lessen the cost of the houses.

Designs for Various Shaped Areas.   The layout of roads for rectangular-shaped plots should consist of squares having sides 660 ft. long, which gives the minimum possible perimeter.   For triangular blocks, the angles should be limited to 60 degrees; the equilateral form provides the smallest perimeter.

In the case of a trapezium, the minimum perimeter is obtained when the length of the side equals the mean between the top and the base.

For segmental shapes, the semi-circular form of road is most economical. Fig. 17A, p. 26, gives examples of layouts suitable for various shaped plots and can be incorporated with advantage in estate layout plans.

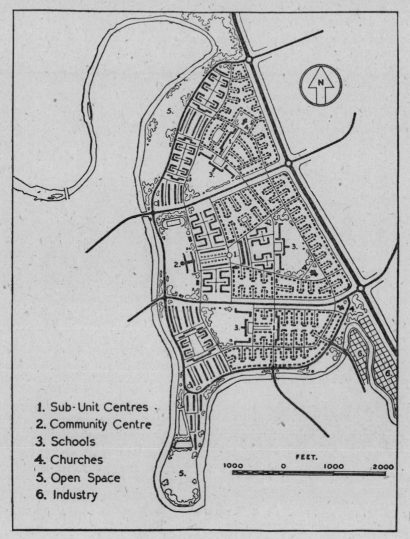

1. Sub-Unit Centres
2. Community Centre
3. Schools
4. Churches
5. Open Space
6. Industry

FIG. 17. Cul-de-sac type of layout

Summary. The most careful planning of estate roads on the outlines suggested above will more than repay the trouble taken. Not only will the capital cost be saved by reducing the lengths of roads and sewers to a minimum to serve the greatest number of houses, but other advantages will result. These are as follows : lower maintenance costs, upkeep, and supervision ; fewer traffic dangers ; pleasanter and quieter residential amenities ; reduced walking distances ; savings on roads and sewers enabling larger houses to be provided—also social centres, recreational and cultural facilities.

Housing Manual 1944.   The grouping of houses in relation to layout design is referred to in this Manual, wherein are stated some principles which should be observed in preparing housing schemes.   These are:

- (*a*) Direct and easy access to the main traffic road, bus route, or railway station connecting places of employment.
- (*b*) Short and direct routes to the shopping centre and groups of communal buildings.
- (*c*) Safe routes to schools and playing-fields.

A level site is usually the most economical ; but a hilly or undulating site offers opportunities which, if used with skill, will give a more distinctive character to the scheme.   In the former case, a layout of a generally

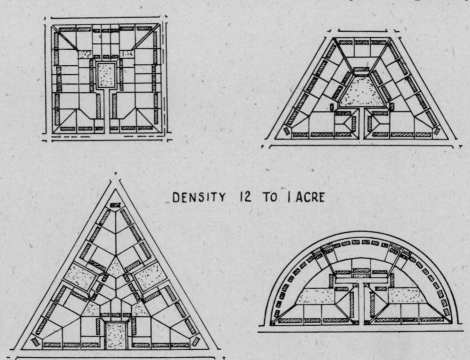

DENSITY 12 TO 1 ACRE

FIG. 17A. Layouts for various shaped areas

rectangular pattern and making for right-angled street junctions is likely to give the best results, diversity being obtained by the use of the square and loop-way on through roads, and, in moderation, of the cul-de-sac, close, or quadrangle.   In the latter case roads may run either with the contours (with buildings on one side only if the slope is steep) or at right angles to the contours (with the buildings on both sides of the road facing down the hill and with access by footpath).

* Published by His Majesty's Stationery Office, 1944 (price 2s.).

TABLE I

HOUSING DENSITIES

Comparative Tables

Total Floor Areas of House, sq. ft.	Cubic Capacity, cu. ft.	Area of Bldg. on Ground, sq. yds.	Area of Private Space or Garden, sq. yds.	Spacing apart of Houses, feet	Area of House Plot, sq. yds.	Area of Street per House, sq. yds.	Total area per House, (land unit) sq. yds.		Resultant Density per acre — 5 Persons a House Popln.	Area of Open Space per 1000 Persons — Acres	Area of Open Space per 1000 Persons — Sq. Yds.	Nett Density per acre	Population 5 per House
750	11,000	40	80	Byelaws	120	40	160	30	150	2½	1815	20	100
800	12,000	42	156	60 ft. between rows	198	44	242	20	100	3	1452	10	50
950	13,520	53	271	70 ft. between rows	324	80	404	12	60	5	1452	6	30
1000	14,100	56	338	Over 70 ft. between rows	394	90	484	10	50	7	1694	4½	22

MODEL CLAUSES

RECOMMENDED DENSITIES

Density	Land Unit
12 per acre	250 sq. yds.
8 ,, ,,	400 ,, ,,
6 ,, ,,	500 ,, ,,

ANALYSIS OF LAYOUT

Density	Buildings Per cent.	Gardens Per cent.	Streets Per cent.
30	25	50	25
20	17	65	18
12	13	67	20
10	11	70	19

The device of placing buildings to close the view at bends and right-angle turns has often been used with advantage, and a similar effect may be obtained in a square if the roads entering it are not opposite to one another. Culs-de-sac and quadrangles should not be narrow, nor, on the other hand, too wide to give a sense of enclosure ; and the dead ends should be connected by footpaths to other streets in order to save long detours.

The sole function of most roads on a housing estate is to give access to the houses, and for these roads a carriageway of 16 ft. is generally sufficient. In larger schemes there will be some roads which need a carriageway of 22 ft., especially if they are likely to become bus routes. For minor roads like culs-de-sac and quadrangles, a satisfactory width is 13 ft. It is essential to have a footpath on one side of the road : the need for footpaths on both sides will depend on local conditions. A footpath should be at least 6 ft. wide.

"The Appearance of Housing Estates," Central Housing Advisory Committee, Report of the Sub-Committee on the Means of Improving the Appearance of Local Authority Housing Estates, published by His Majesty's Stationery Office, June, 1948, is shown on pp. 271–2.

CHAPTER 2

DESIGN AND CONSTRUCTION OF ROADS

Designs for Layout of Roads

When the proposed land for estate development has been surveyed and contoured, the best possible layout must be designed to meet satisfactorily all requirements with reference to new planning ideals. The present tendency is to plan housing estates as complete units or precincts, having within its area its own shopping centre, community centre, church, school, and recreation grounds, to serve a population of between eight and ten thousand people.

In pre-war planning the layout of roads was for sufficiently wide roads to accommodate houses at say, twelve to the acre, but little thought was given to plan the roads on principles of civic township design.

To illustrate this point a hypothetical plan is shown of a layout designed on pre-war town-planning lines, and another plan is shown of the same estate designed on present-day ideals. (See Fig. 18, p. 31.)

It may appear by comparison that there is less amount of roads on the modern design, whereas in fact the total length of roads is practically the same as on the pre-war design.

The greater advantages of the modern layout are apparent. The good points are :

(1) Central axis main boulevard in the centre of the estate.
(2) Along this boulevard the church, community centre, school, and shopping centre are centrally placed, making a pleasing vista.
(3) Recreation grounds and allotments are provided.
(4) There are only two direct access roads to existing main roads.
(5) The whole estate is self-contained, and makes a pleasant little self-contained town, which can be maintained independently by its own residents.
(6) The layout of the roads is not straight, long, and monotonous, as on the pre-war designs ; and the roads afford better spacing, and more pleasing alignment for houses and public buildings.

Road Lines and Gradients

The longitudinal sections of roads should be so fixed to suit levels of adjoining properties, and that the amount of excavation will more or less equal the amount of filling-in required.

Embankments and cuttings should be reduced to a minimum, but a ruling gradient of 1 in 30 should be maintained.

Road Surfaces

The different kinds of traffic using roads require various kinds of surfaces as will suit such kinds of traffic as motors, lorries, omnibuses, vans, cycles, and horses. It is generally considered that an even surface with a sand-paper texture would be the ideal road surface. A good surface should fulfil the following requirements :

(1) Evenness, (2) dustless, (3) non-skid, (4) good riding qualities, (5) good foothold for horses, (6) light colour, (7) durability, (8) resistant to changes of temperature, (9) resilience, (10) economical cost and maintenance.

Carriageway surfaces comprise the following types:

(1) Waterbound macadam; (2) Tarmacadam; (3) Concrete; (4) Cement-bound; (5) Asphalt.

(1) *Waterbound Macadam*. Waterbound macadam surfaces are becoming almost obsolete, being used for rural roads and farm tracks. Where used for roads of light traffic, the waterbound macadam is sealed with a surface coat of tar or bitumen. Cold bituminous emulsions have been found successful for the initial sealing coat of macadam. Waterbound macadam is usually laid to a roller thickness of 4 inches upon a pitched foundation 9 inches deep. A base course of 2 to 2½-inch stone is laid down and well rolled after surface wetting. On this base course another course of 1½ to 2-inch stone is laid and watered and rolled in. Finally a thin binding course of fine stone or gravel and sand is applied, watered and well rolled until complete consolidation is obtained and a fine surface secured.

(2) *Tarmacadam*. This is one of the most used type of surfacing, easily and quickly provided, and has a good life. It is laid about 4 inches thick, and laid in three courses, bottom layer 2 to 2½-inch material, next layer of 1½-in. material, and finally a surface layer of ⅜-in. material. All material is spread with rakes and well rolled until firmly consolidated. The top surfacing is often sealed with a dressing of tarred chippings well rolled in.

B.S. 76 and 802 give detailed specifications in respect of tarmacadam.

(3) *Concrete*. Concrete surfaces are made of a finer and richer mix of concrete laid on the concrete raft forming the main structure of the road. Such wearing surfaces are made of 2 to 3 inches of concrete mixes from 1–2–4 to 1–1½–3, incorporating granite or hard limestone chippings of ½ to ¾-in. gauge. The concrete surfaces are well tamped to correct and smooth crossfalls and sometimes the surface is treated with silicate of soda to " case harden " it to effects of abrasion. (See further notes on p. 39 on concrete road construction.)

(4) *Cement-bound*. Cement-bound surfaces are where cement is used as a binder and are done by (*a*) sandwich system, (*b*) grouting system, (*c*) compressed concrete system. Such surfaces are non-skid and suitable for light traffic but it is important they be laid on a well-consolidated foundation or existing substantial foundation.

The sandwich system consists of a layer of cement sandwiched between two layers of stone which is well consolidated by rolling. Surplus

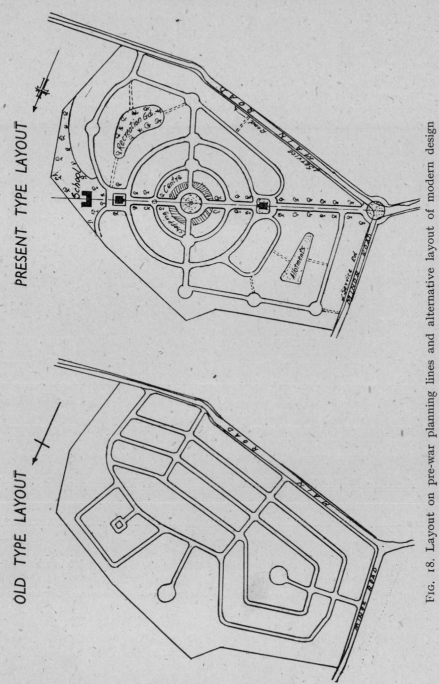

FIG. 18. Layout on pre-war planning lines and alternative layout of modern design

mortar is worked up to the surface and effectively seals it when brushed over it.

(5) *Asphalt.* There are three types of asphalt surfacings used, namely : (1) compressed rock asphalt, (2) rolled asphalt, (3) mastic asphalt. These are usually laid in thicknesses of 1½ to 3 inches thick and finished off with ¾-in. dry or coated chippings well rolled on. Single or two coat asphalt surfaces are laid and the use of cold process asphalt is increasing. They have a long life, exceedingly durable, take heavy traffic easily and wear well in all climates.

B.S. 348, 594, and 596, give detailed specifications for compressed rock asphalt, rolled asphalt, and mastic asphalt surfacings.

KERBS

Kerbs may be of natural stones, *e.g.* granite, limestone, whinstone, or artificial stone, and be of a minimum thickness of 4 in. and exposed face depth between 3 in. and 7 in. and in lengths from 1½ ft. to 3 ft. Kerbs should be laid on and backed with stone chippings or concrete. Concrete kerbs are greatly used, and are specified in B.S. 340 ; they are splayed and chamfered on face.

Kerbs 12 in. × 6 in. laid flat on edges of wide verges greatly add to the line and appearance of the road, and are not so easily damaged by heavy vehicles. B.S. 435 and 706 give specifications for stone kerbs.

CHANNELS

Channels may be constructed of granite setts, 7 in. × 5 in. × 4 in. limestone, or concrete blocks 9 in. to 12 in. wide and 2 ft. to 3 ft. long. For minor roads no special channels are needed if the surfacing can be carried flush to the face of the kerb. The gradients of the channels should not be flatter than 1 in 150, so that gullies can be placed not greater than 200 ft. apart, and preferably have side entrances on face of kerb. Specifications of channels are given in B.S. 340, 435, and 706.

Channels are not always necessary for concrete or asphaltic surfaced carriageways.

FOOTPATHS

Suitable materials for estate footpaths are : gravel chippings 3 in. thick on 3 in. to 4 in. of hardcore ; of tarred stone or clinker surfacing on hardcore or ash foundation 3 in. to 6 in. deep ; 2-in. thick concrete flags or *in situ* on a 3-in. bed of ashes or sand ; various asphalt or bituminous surfacings from 1½ in. to 3 in. thick on an ash or hardcore foundation.

The crossfall on a footpath towards the kerb should not be less than ⅜ in. to 1 ft. Crossings across footpaths can be formed efficiently by depressing the surface level to channel level of the carriageway. Stone sett crossings may be insisted upon where heavy traffic across a footpath is expected. The minimum width of a footpath for pedestrian traffic should be 5 ft. wherever possible, to allow for two lines of pedestrians with allowance for perambulators.

B.S. 1942 gives specifications for tarmacadam paving suitable for footpaths, playgrounds, etc.

VERGES AND TREES

Where necessary good top soil should be provided where grass seed is to be sown or turf laid. Small trees or shrubs on wide verges add rural attractiveness to the roads, and should be planted at regular spacings of about 50 ft. and slightly staggered, to prevent long monotonous rows. Such trees as lime, plane, acacia, scarlet thorn, mountain ash, laburnum, silver birch, and copper beech are suitable for roadways.

The Ministry of Town and Country Planning have issued Circular No. 24 which gives useful points on planting street trees together with a comprehensive list of trees suitable for streets in urban and rural areas.

Gravel or red ash verges are sometimes laid, but they add to the maintenance costs. Verges laid with crazy paving or coloured concrete cost little in maintenance.

LIGHTING OF ROADS

The lighting of roads must be such as to obtain a uniform standard of lighting without undue glare and dark patches of roads. The lamps should be erected on the outside curve of the road bends, and in staggered formation on straight lengths and spaced about 50 yds. apart.

The mounting height should be between 13 and 15 ft. on roads not traffic routes, and lantern output should provide between 600 and 2500 lumens per 100 linear ft., according to local conditions. (Fig. 20, p. 36.)

Central suspension of lights is not always desirable, as it does not clearly illuminate the kerb line.

A Ministry of Transport Departmental Committee on Street Lighting published a comprehensive Report on this subject in August 1937.

Here is a Table, for different classes of roads, of lighting intensities, heights and distances apart of lamp standards.

Class	Illumination Foot Candles	Minimum height of Lamp Standard (= H). ft.	Maximum Spacing ft.
Town centres	2·0	30	5 H
Class " A " roads ..	1·0	25	6 H
Class " B " roads ..	0·5	21	8 H
Through roads	0·2	18	9 H
Town streets	0·1	15	10 H
Residential streets ..	0·05	13	12 H
Side streets	0·02	13	12 H

ROAD WIDTHS

The widths of roads are determined in relation to their length and traffic importance. The widths of estate roads are generally fixed by the town planning regulations, Restriction of Ribbon Development Act, and also by local byelaw requirements, which, generally speaking, are as follows :

16-*ft. wide road*, consisting of 10-ft, carriageway and two 3-ft. footpaths or verges for a maximum length of 500 ft.

24-*ft. wide road*, with 16-ft. carriageway and two 4-ft. footpaths or verges, for maximum length of 650 ft.

30-*ft. wide road*, with 16-ft. carriageway and two 4-ft. 6-in. footpaths and two 2-ft. 6-in. verges, for maximum length of 750 feet.

36-*ft. wide road*, with 18-ft. carriageway, two 4-ft. 6-in. footpaths and verges, for maximum length of 1600 feet.

45-*ft. wide road*, with 24-ft. carriageway, two 7-ft. 6-in. footpaths, and two 3-ft. verges.

Service roads consist of 12-ft. to 16-ft. wide carriageway and one footpath 3-ft. to 6-ft. wide.

Illustrations of sections of the above roads are shown in Fig. 19 on p. 35.

If traffic figures are available, the width of carriageways can be based on amount of traffic it has to take, and traffic lanes 10 ft. to 11 ft. wide are allowed for. Thus, for culs-de-sac a 10-ft. carriageway will be sufficient, and for light traffic a 20-ft. or 22-ft. carriageway will permit two traffic lanes. For heavy traffic routes three lanes or dual carriageways are required.

DRAINAGE OF ROADS

The road gullies should be placed against the kerb, and for concrete roads the side-entrance type are better, as edges of the road slabs are not broken up by projections or the formation of cracks which occur from the corners of the channel type of gullies. Gullies may be constructed of stoneware, concrete, or cast-iron bowls 12 in. to 15 in. diameter and about 2 ft. 6 in. deep, surmounted with cast-iron frame and grid and the whole laid on and surrounded with concrete.

It is essential that double gullies should have a good water-seal tap and be easily accessible for cleaning. Double gullies are sometimes necessary on steep gradients.

Gullies should not be placed at corners of footpath crossings in the path of pedestrians, and should be placed on the higher side of the crossing to prevent surface water flowing downhill over the crossing.

On straight lengths gullies should be placed opposite each other to allow easier connections to the surface-water drains to be made. Gully connections are made by 4-in. or 6-in. pipes laid at an angle of 60 degrees to the drain and cement-jointed. (See Fig. 20, p. 36.)

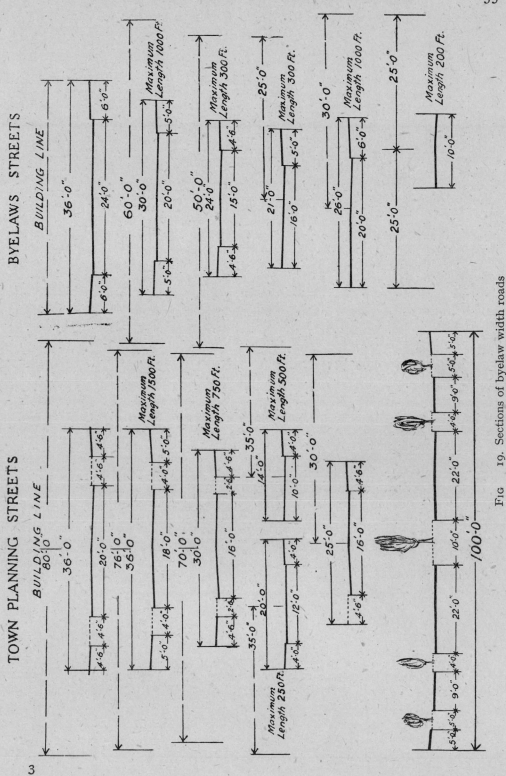

FIG 19. Sections of byelaw width roads

3

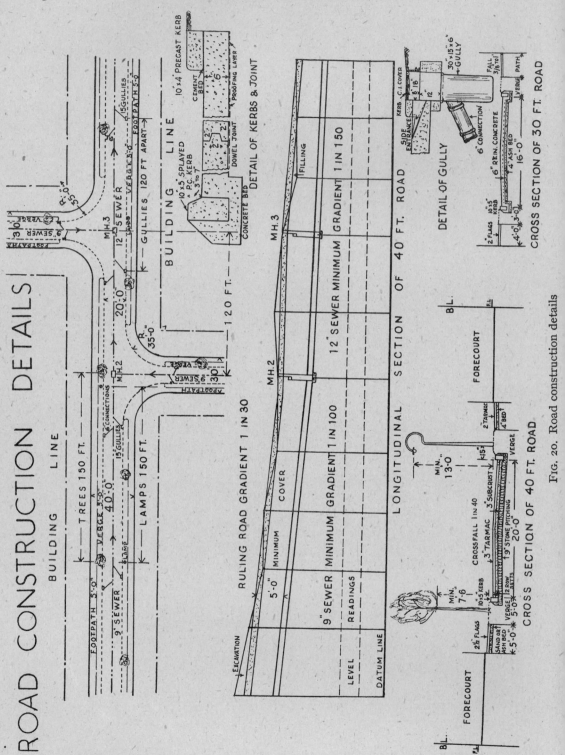

Fig. 20. Road construction details

MODEL SPECIFICATION FOR ROADS
Prepared by the Institution of Municipal Engineers, 1945

EXTRACTS RE DRAINAGE OF ROADS

Pipes. Salt-glazed-ware pipes as specified in B.S. No. 65/1937 shall be used for all diameters up to 12 in. For 15-in. diameter pipes and over, concrete pipes as specified in B.S. No. 556/1934 may be used.

Laying and Jointing Pipes. The bottoms of all trenches shall be thoroughly punned. The pipes shall be laid and bedded with the inverts true to line and levels as shown on the drawings.

Sight rails for this purpose should be erected not more than 150 ft. apart and at each change of gradient.

The barrel of the pipe shall be continuously supported on the trench bottom or concrete bed, appropriate joint holes being excavated or left for the pipe sockets.

The joints shall be filled with a ring of tarred gaskin driven home with a wooden caulking tool and then filled with cement mortar. Care should be taken that any surplus cement mortar be cleaned out of the pipes as the work proceeds. Where, in the opinion of the engineer, the nature of the ground or depth demands it,* the pipes shall be bedded on or surrounded with concrete 6 in. thick, or bedded on or haunched with concrete 6 in. thick, to the horizontal diameter of the pipes and splayed off to the face of the pipe above that level.

Testing of Drains. Such tests of the drains as the engineer may specify shall be carried out before the trenches are re-filled and before any concrete be placed in the trench or about the pipes.

The contractor shall provide for all timbering, strutting, pumping, refilling, ramming, and removal of surplus, and all filling shall be of selected excavated material in 12-in. layers each thoroughly compacted. No timber should be removed from trenches until the refilling has been brought up and sufficiently compacted to permit its removal with safety. The ends of all house connections and all junction positions are to be clearly marked by painted signboards stating the size and depth below kerb level. The open ends of all pipes are to be sealed by approved stoppers, clay jointed

---

* As a guide, the following are the present normal requirements of the Ministry of Health as regards concrete protection of glazed ware and concrete sewer-pipes :

(a) All pipes and tubes in heading or with 20 ft. or more of cover in trenches to be surrounded with at least 6 in. of concrete.

(b) Subject to (a), all pipes and tubes with over 14 ft. of cover to be bedded on and haunched with at least 6 in. of concrete to at least the horizontal diameter of the pipe or tube. Any splaying of the concrete to be above that level.

(c) Subject to (a), all pipes and tubes of 18 in. diameter and over to be bedded on and haunched with at least 6 in. of concrete to at least the horizontal diameter of the pipe or tube. Any splaying of the concrete to be above that level.

(d) Subject to (e), all pipes and tubes under 18 in. in diameter and with less than 14 ft. of cover may be laid without concrete if the joints are of the socket or collar type (but concrete tubes with O.G. joints are permissible when laid as in (a), (b), (c), or (e)).

(e) All pipes and tubes with less than 4 ft. of cover under roads, or 3 ft. not under roads to be surrounded with at least 6 in. in concrete.

in position before commencing the re-filling of trenches. The refilling of trenches shall not be proceeded with unless the drains have been tested and passed by the engineer.

Gullies. Gullies as specified below shall be set or constructed at the points shown on the contract drawing.

Gully pots shall be set on a foundation of 6 in. of concrete, and this shall be haunched about the bottom of the pot and after the concrete has set and hardened back-filling shall be carried out and thoroughly compacted.

A surround of concrete 6 in. thick shall be formed about the top of the gully pot to form a base to receive the C.I. gully grating and frame, which shall be set in cement mortar at the correct level.

Gully Pots. Gully pots shall be of first-quality salt-glazed ware from an approved source, and shall comply with the dimensions given in B.S. No. 539/1937, Table 21 (Round Street Gullies), with rodding eyes each complete with an approved stopper secured with a chain.

Gully pots for carriageways shall be 18 in. diameter by 36 in. deep unless otherwise specified.

Gully pots for footways shall be 12 in. diameter with 4 in. diameter outlet and 24 in. deep unless otherwise specified.

Alternatively, gully pots may be of pre-cast concrete of approved pattern, dimensions, and manufacture, complying with B.S. 556/1934.

Manholes. The foundations and floors of manholes shall be formed of concrete 6 in. thick and shall extend at least 6 in. beyond the outer face of the brickwork or pre-cast concrete chamber ring as the case may be. Glazed stoneware or pre-cast concrete channel pipes of appropriate diameter shall be used to form the inverts. Benchings shall be properly shaped and shall be formed of concrete and finished with a smooth surface. The manholes above the base shall be constructed either in brickwork laid in English bond or of pre-cast concrete chamber-rings, taper pieces and shaft rings of approved manufacture, as the engineer shall direct. (Fig. 30, p. 63.)

The brickwork in manholes shall be 9 in. thick, except that where the total depth of the manhole measured between the invert and the surface of the manhole cover exceeds 10 ft., the brickwork of the manhole chamber shall be 14 in. thick.

A half-brick ring arch of brickwork shall be built over all pipes of 15 in. diameter and under connecting to manholes.

In the case of pipes over 15 in. diameter, two half-brick rings shall be provided.

All joints shall be made in cement-mortar.

The internal dimensions of the manhole chambers shall in all cases conform with the contract drawings.

The space between the brickwork or concrete rings and the face of the excavation shall be carefully back-filled with selected surplus material or, if directed by the engineer, with concrete brought up to 6 in. above the soffit of the chamber.

When completed the inner face of the manhole shall be true and smooth throughout.

STREET AND DRAINAGE IRONWORK. (*a*) *Manhole Covers and Frames.* The manhole covers and frames shall be of cast iron and, except as indicated below, shall be of the heavy pattern, non-ventilating, weighing not less than (4 cwt. suggested) with a 20-in. opening and 2 ft. 6 in. square base treated with an approved protective coating, and are to be obtained from an approved maker.

In the particular case of manholes situated in the footpath or in the verge and not exceeding 5 ft. in depth to the invert, the cover and frame shall be of a light footway pattern with an opening 20 in. in diameter and total weight of $2\frac{1}{2}$ cwt.

(*b*) *Gully grates and frames* shall be of an approved pattern weighing not less than 2 cwt., and are to be obtained from an approved maker.

(*c*) *Steps irons* shall be of an approved pattern and of dimensions 14 in. × 6 in.

and either of galvanized malleable iron, approximate weight 5 lb., or of cast iron, approximate weight 10 lb., treated with an approved protective coating.

HOUSE CONNECTIONS TO FOUL AND SURFACE-WATER DRAINS. These shall be laid in the same trench as far as possible at a minimum distance apart of about 6 in., measured socket to socket. The pipes shall be fully jointed, entirely surrounded with concrete, and the open ends sealed and clearly marked, as before specified.

SURFACE-WATER SEWERS

If a separate system of sewers is used the storm-water sewer should be laid at a shallower depth than the foul sewer, with brick manholes not more than 120 yds. apart. The sewer should have a minimum cover of 4 ft. under roads and be laid to such gradients as will afford self-cleansing velocities. Surface-water sewers are not always required to be haunched in concrete unless the ground is unstable or waterlogged.

Manholes may be formed of brick or concrete, and for shallow manholes concrete slab landings are formed over the chambers ; deep manholes have arched chambers, which can allow more head room above sewer inverts. Benchings and inverts are formed of cement concrete laid to proper falls and curves. (Illustrations are given in Figs. 20 and 30 of specimen level sections of roads and sewers, and typical road surface-water manholes.

TYPES OF ROADS AND THEIR CONSTRUCTION

The foundations to be used will depend upon the nature and bearing capacity of the subsoil, and trial holes should be made along the proposed routes before deciding upon the kind of foundation to be used.

In wet or clay grounds, an underbed foundation of ashes or clinkers between 3 in. and 6 in. deep should be provided before stone pitching is laid.

For carriageways up to 20 ft. the foundations may be 6 in. to 9 in. deep of hardcore, consisting of small broken stone or slag, broken bricks, or hard clinkers, all to be well consolidated and rolled to form a close and compact foundation. For carriageways of greater width than 20 ft. the foundation should be between 9 in. and 12 in. deep, formed of handpitched stone or slag carefully placed by hand in a compact manner, and afterwards consolidated by a 10-ton roller. The top of the foundations should be so covered with small stones, broken or old macadam, well rolled in order to fill all the interstices and to give a smooth even surface to the foundations.

The surfacing should be of a non-skid type, and if tarmacadam or other bituminous surfaces are used it should be laid in two coats to a finished thickness of 3 in. and in three coats for a 4-in. thickness.

The choice of materials will depend upon local costs and supplies easily available, and should be made with due regard to future maintenance costs.

CONCRETE ROADS

In recent years more advances have been made in the use of concrete roads, more particularly for estate roads. It is important, however, to secure rigid supervision in their construction. Careful consideration must be given to the choice of aggregates and the composition of the concrete. As a rule, the concrete bottom course is made of four parts of aggregate consisting of ¼ to 1½-gauge shingle or stone, mixed with two parts of clean, sharp, washed sand and one part of cement. The concrete is laid in two courses, the bottom course between 3 in. and 5 in. thick ; and the top course, between 1 in. and 2 in. thick, is made of three parts granite chippings graded from ⅛ to ½ in., two parts of sand and one part of cement. For roads of major traffic importance mild steel reinforcement of up to 14 lb. weight per sq. yd. is incorporated in the concrete with at least 1½ in. of concrete cover over the reinforcement. The concrete is generally laid in strips about 30 ft. long and half the width of the carriageway where more than 18 ft. wide, with expansion joints formed at each end of strip. The concrete work is progressive from strip to strip, but sometimes done in alternate bays.

The concrete is laid on a layer of waterproof paper spread over an ash underbed, and expansion joints are inserted to interlock the strips of concrete. The surface of the concrete is tamped down to form a corrugated finish to the correct camber, and afterwards covered over with sand and kept damp for about two weeks to effect complete curing of the concrete. (See Fig. 21.)

THICKNESS OF CONCRETE CARRIAGEWAYS

The minimum thickness of slabs, subject to the subsoil being firm and dry, are:

    (1) for private streets and estate roads : 6 in. up to 16 ft. wide.
    (2)   ,,   ,,   ,,   ,,   ,,   ,,   7 in. ,, ,, 20 ft.   ,,
    (3) minor traffic streets and link roads   8 in. ,, ,, 24 ft.   ,,
    (4) major traffic roads carrying over
        5000 tons a day   8 in. to 12 in.

The adoption of concrete roads is increasing rapidly because of their relatively easy and quick construction, giving ready means of access to the site ; and they are better able to stand the rough wear and tear that building operations give to estate roads. (See Fig. 22, p. 42.) In the worst of weathers concrete roads are unaffected, and their maintenance is very little compared with that of other types of roads.

FIG. 21. Tamping concrete road surface

FIG. 22. A concrete road affords easy access to building sites

MINISTRY OF TRANSPORT'S MEMORANDUM No. 575 ON LAYOUT AND CONSTRUCTION OF ROADS

This Memorandum, published in October 1943, gives useful notes on layout and construction of roads based on the results of investigations made by representatives of Work on Highways (Technical) Committee of the Institution of Municipal Engineers and the County Surveyors' Society.

Recommendations are made for the adoption of certain standards of design and construction as will further public safety, promotes smooth flow of traffic, and enhances the amenities of the neighbourhood.

Here is a brief summary of the Memorandum:

(1) LAYOUT. This depends on volume and character of traffic, and normal width of a traffic lane is 10 ft. to 11 ft. No carriageway should be less than 16 ft. which links up two roads. Ample space should be made for central reservations and verges, and provision be made for future widenings to include cycle tracks and dual carriageways if these become necessary. Planting of trees and shrubs, laying of underground mains and services, and ensuring adequate space for traffic at junctions are considered essential.

(2) ROAD WIDTHS

	Effective Width
Single carriageway not exceeding 30 ft. with footpaths	60 ft.
Single carriageway not exceeding 30 ft. with footpaths and cycle tracks	80 ,,
Dual carriageway (each of two traffic lanes) with footpaths	80 ,,
Dual carriageway (each of two traffic lanes) with footpaths and cycle tracks	100 ,,

(3) CURVES. Should be laid out as segmental arcs of largest practical radius, and where less than 1000 ft. the curve should be approached at each end by a transition curve. If this is not possible the curve should be made transitional throughout.

(4) SUPER-ELEVATION. The elimination of adverse camber and the attainment of the desired super-elevation should be obtained by raising the outer above the inner channel at a uniform rate along the length of the transition, from the end of the straight to the commencement of the circular curve, where the super-elevation should reach its maximum. It is recommended that super-elevation should not exceed 1 in $14\frac{1}{2}$ for radii up to 1200 ft., and above radii of 5000 ft. the ratio can be 1 in 40 to 48. A graph illustrated in Fig. 23, p. 44, gives at a glance the super-elevation factors for various radii of road bends, and safety speed of vehicles suitable to such factors.

Ruling gradient of road should be 1 in 30 wherever possible, and drainage channels graded to minimum fall of 1 in 200.

(5) VISIBILITY. On a single carriageway a clear view for 1000 ft. at eye-level height of 3 ft. 9 in. is needed, and on dual carriageways a distance of 500 ft. will suffice.

On hilltops the road level should be well rounded off in a vertical direction. Splayed corners are preferable to circular, and the splay should be 45 degrees commencing at a distance not less than 30 ft. from the intersections of the frontage lines produced.

(6) TRAFFIC LANES. Assists orderly movement of traffic, and the carriageway should be divided into lanes by means of markings in lines or studs 4 in. to 5 in. wide set out 15 ft. apart.

(7) JUNCTIONS. Should be kept to a minimum and not less than 440 yds. apart to provide sufficient space and visibility for traffic, and provision be made for pedestrians wherever possible. Junctions can be controlled by traffic lights, roundabout

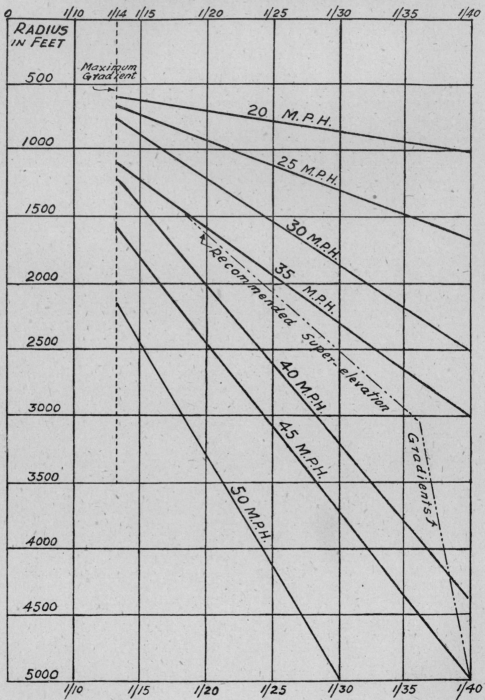

FIG. 23. Super-elevation graph

islands, and refuge islands. Several typical designs of junctions are illustrated in Figs. 24, 25, 26, and Fig. 3, p. 9.

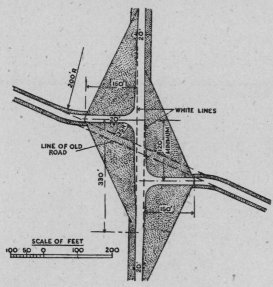

FIG. 24. Typical design of road junctions

Various notes are given on construction of carriageways, footpaths, cycle tracks, verges and drainage, and also recommendations that consideration be given to the desirability of duplicating service mains and drains on each side of carriageway, and adequate accommodation should be provided for future developments.

MODEL SPECIFICATIONS FOR ROADS

The Institution of Municipal Engineers, in conjunction with the Ministry of Health and the Ministry of Works, issued in 1945 Model Specifications* which can be regarded as

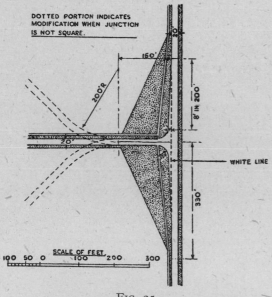

FIG. 25.

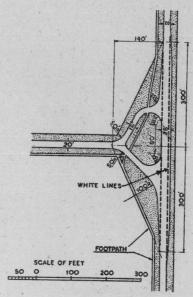

FIG. 26.

Typical designs of road junctions

* May be purchased from The Institution of Municipal Engineers, 2s. 6d. each Specification.

models for road construction, more particularly for preparation of post-war housing sites. Briefly they are as follows :

(1) Tarmacadam Roads ;
(2) Asphalt or Bitumen Roads ;
(3) Concrete Roads.

(1) *Tarmacadam Roads*

SUB-BASE. Where a sub-base is specified, the sub-base material shall be spread evenly over the formation and rolled so as to give a thickness of 6 in. on a sub-soil of soft clay or of 3 in. on a sub-soil of hard clay or other material having a good bearing value or such of these thicknesses as may be directed by the engineer.

The roller shall be the heaviest which will compact the sub-base without unduly disturbing the underlying formation. The material may be moistened, but care must be taken to ensure that water is not added in such quantity as to wet a clay sub-soil.

Any clay or other material that works up through the sub-base shall be cut out and replaced with sub-base material.

BASE COURSE. The base course for carriageway shall consist of one of the following types, as directed by the engineer :

(a) a single course of pitching 9 in. thick ;
(b) hardcore rolled in two layers each 4½ in. thick.

(a) *Pitching, Penning, or Bottoming.* The stones shall be set by hand on edge to form a close, firm pavement of uniform depth not less than 8 in. They shall be laid, with their largest end down, in parallel lines across the roadway, breaking joint as much as practicable. The rows shall subsequently be wedged tight by inserting stones in any gaps or loose place as nearly as possible for the full depth of the course until the whole is firmly bound into position. Projections of the upper part of the course shall be broken off, care being taken not to loosen the pavement. The small interstices shall be filled with stone chippings and firmly wedged. The whole surface shall be levelled up with broken stone, blinded, watered, and rolled with a roller not less than 10 tons in weight until the surface of the course is even and to the correct levels. The thickness after consolidation shall be 9 in.

(b) *Hardcore.* The hardcore shall be laid in two layers, the bottom layer being rolled, blinded, and consolidated before the upper layer is placed. The hardcore shall be placed in position by hand by means of spreader boxes or by other means approved by the engineer. The upper layer shall be packed with smaller material blinded, watered, and rolled with a roller of not less than 10 tons in weight until an even contour at the correct levels is obtained. The combined thickness of the two layers after consolidation shall be 9 in.

SURFACING FOR CARRIAGEWAY—SINGLE-COURSE TARMACADAM 3-IN. CONSOLIDATED THICKNESS. The workmanship shall be of the best of its kind and shall conform to the specification, which is as follows :

Nature of Aggregate. The aggregate, which shall be subject to the approval of the engineer, shall be either :

(a) crushed igneous rock or limestone : hard, durable, free from all foreign matter, and substantially free from dust ; or

(b) best blast-furnace or acid-steel flag, free from all deleterious matter. The weight per cu. ft. and stability of the slag shall be in accordance with the requirements of B.S. 1047 and the total sulphur content and increase in weight of the slag due to the absorption of water shall not exceed 2·75 per cent. and 4 per cent. respectively when tested in accordance with the appropriate methods in B.S. 1046.

Grading. The grading of the aggregate, including any filler, when tested in accordance with B.S. 812, Method 1, shall be within the following limits:

Sieve Size (B.S. 410)	Percentage by Weight, Passing
2 in.	100
$1\frac{1}{2}$,,	95 ± 5
1 ,,	65 ± 15
$\frac{1}{2}$,,	40 ± 10
$\frac{1}{4}$,,	20 ± 5
200 mesh	0 to 5

Elongation Index. The elongation index, determined in accordance with B.S. 812, Method 2, shall not exceed 35.

Filler. Any filler which may be added to the aggregate to comply with the above grading shall consist of igneous rock, limestone, portland cement, or suitable slag. It shall all pass 7 B.S. mesh, not less than 90 per cent. shall pass 52 B.S. mesh, and not less than 50 per cent. shall pass 200 B.S. mesh.

Binder. The binder shall be tar, which shall comply with B.S. 76, 1943 ; the type and viscosity shall be agreed between the engineer and the tarmacadam manufacturer, the range suitable being :

Type A or Type B, summer working—E.V.T. 34°–36° C., viscosity 100–140 secs. at 30° C.

Winter working, E.V.T.—27°–37° C., viscosity 30–50 secs. at 30° C.

In most cases, tars of the above-mentioned viscosity should be satisfactory for use in cold and warm weather, but it may be advisable to increase the viscosity up to 80 seconds at 35° C. (E.V.T. 38° C) for tarmacadam laid during hot weather, or reduce the viscosity to 20 seconds at 30° C. (24° C., E.V.T.) in very cold weather or for rail deliveries.

Alternatively the binder may consist of one of the following mixtures by agreement between the purchaser and the suppliers :

(*a*) Tar to B.S. 76 types A and B and asphaltic bitumen as defined in B.S. 594.
(*b*) ,, ,, B.S. 76 ,, A and B and refined lake asphalt as defined in B.S. 594.
(*c*) ,, ,, B.S. 76 ,, A and B and natural asphalt as defined in B.S. 595.

The proportions of the ingredients and the characteristics of the mixtures shall be agreed between the engineer and the supplier.

When asphalt is added to the tar, an appropriate adjustment should be made to the quantity of added filler to compensate for the amount of inert material contained in the asphalt.

Quantity of Binder. The quantity of binder used shall be such that all particles of aggregates are thoroughly coated, but there shall be no excess ; at the mixing temperature it shall be not less than 8·4 nor more than 10·5 gallons of binder per ton of dry aggregate. The temperature and the quantity of the binder shall be measured at the time of mixing.

Temperatures of Mixing. The temperature of the aggregate shall not exceed 50° C. (120° F.). The temperature to which the binder shall be heated will depend upon the nature of the aggregate and binder as well as upon the climatic conditions, but shall not exceed 105° C. (220° F.).

Prolonged heating of the binder must be avoided, as it will alter the viscosity of the tar and may seriously affect the quality of the resulting tarmacadam.

Method of Mixing. The aggregate shall be thoroughly dry and shall be heated to the temperature specified in Clause 9. The binder shall be separately heated to the appropriate temperature specified in clause 9 and the aggregate and the binder shall then be measured into the mixer and thoroughly and intimately mixed together, any filler being subsequently added and thoroughly mixed. The mixing shall be carried out in a mechanical mixer of approved type and shall be continued until every part of the aggregate is completely coated, but in no case for less than $1\frac{1}{2}$ minutes ; where filler is added, the mixing shall be continued for at least one minute after the adding of the filler.

(2) *Using Pitched or Hardcore Foundations and Rolled Asphalt or Single-Course Bitumen Surfacing*

SURFACING FOR CARRIAGEWAY

(1) Specification A—Rolled asphalt surfacing.
(2) Specification B—Single-course bitumen macadam.
(3) Specification C—Single-course bitumen gravel macadam.

The workmanship shall be the best of its kind and shall conform to either Specification A, B, or C.

SPECIFICATION A. ROLLED ASPHALT SURFACING—2-IN. CONSOLIDATED THICKNESS —TO BE LAID ON PITCHED OR HARDCORE FOUNDATION. The contractor shall provide and lay upon the prepared foundation of pitching or hardcore, rolled asphalt conforming to War Emergency British Standard 1152, 1944.

Notes for Engineer. (*a*) In respect of Clause 6 of the B.S., select from Table I the type of asphaltic cement to be used or state that you will be prepared to consider alternative quotations for rolled asphalt manufactured with any of the three types of asphaltic cement specified in Table I.

(*b*) In respect of Clause 10 of the B.S., state the type and thickness of asphalt required. A suitable selection would be single coat asphalt, coarse type, of the composition shown in Table II laid to a consolidated thickness of 2 in. The coarse aggregate shall be $\frac{3}{4}$ in. graded material and shall contain at least 20 per cent. of material passing $\frac{3}{4}$-in. mesh and retained on $\frac{1}{2}$-in. mesh.

(*c*) In respect of Clause 13 of the B.S. it is not considered that a surface application of chippings is necessary for the coarse-textured material recommended above.

SPECIFICATION B. SINGLE-COURSE BITUMEN MACADAM—3-IN. CONSOLIDATED THICKNESS, GRANITE LIMESTONE OR SLAG AGGREGATE—TO BE LAID ON PITCHED OR HARDCORE FOUNDATION. *Nature of Aggregate.* The aggregate, which shall be subject to the approval of the engineer, shall be either :

(*a*) crushed igneous rock or limestone : hard, durable, and free from all foreign matter ; or

(*b*) best blast-furnace slag, free from all deleterious matter. The weight per cubic foot and stability of the slag shall be in accordance with the requirements of B.S. 1047 and the total sulphur content and increase in weight of the slag due to the absorption of water shall not exceed 2·75 per cent. and 4 per cent. respectively when tested in accordance with the appropriate methods in B.S. 1047. Steel slag of a suitable nature may also be used subject to the approval of the engineer.

Grading. The grading of the aggregate, including filler, when tested in accordance with B.S. 812, Method 1, shall be within the following limits :

Sieve Size (B.S. 410) Square Aperture	Percentage by Weight, Passing
2 in.	100
$1\frac{1}{2}$,,	90–100
1 ,,	50–80
$\frac{1}{2}$,,	30–50
$\frac{1}{4}$,,	20–30
200 mesh	0–5

Elongation Index. The elongation index determined in accordance with B.S. 812, Method 2, shall not exceed the following limits : maximum size of aggregate $1\frac{1}{2}$ in., $1\frac{1}{4}$ in., 1 in., or $\frac{3}{4}$ in.—not more than 40 ; $\frac{1}{2}$ in. or $\frac{3}{8}$ in., not more than 45.

Filler. The filler added to the aggregate to comply with the above grading shall consist of limestone, portland cement, or other material approved by the engineer. It shall all pass 7 B.S. mesh, not less than 90 per cent. shall pass 52 B.S. mesh, and not less than 50 per cent. shall pass 200 B.S. mesh.

Binder. The binder shall be Pool Cutback Grade, Grade No. 1 or No. 1A. The grade shall be agreed between the engineer and the manufacturer, Grade 1 is suitable for winter work and Grade 1A for summer work. Note.—In cold weather the cutback bitumen may be fluxed by adding creosote oil. The amount used shall not exceed 2 per cent. by volume of the amount of binder used.

Quantity of Binder. The quantity of cutback bitumen used shall be such that all particles of aggregates are thoroughly coated, but there shall be no excess : at the mixing temperature it shall be not less than 8 nor more than 10 gallons of cutback bitumen per ton of dry aggregate.

Temperature of Materials. The aggregate shall be dry and the temperature immediately before mixing shall not exceed 70° C. or 160° F. The temperature to which the binder shall be heated will depend upon the nature of the aggregate and binder as well as upon the climatic conditions, but shall not exceed 115° C. (240° F.).

Method of Mixing. The aggregate shall be thoroughly dry and shall be heated to the appropriate temperature. The binder shall be separately heated to the appropriate temperature and the aggregate and the binder shall then be measured or weighed into the mixer and thoroughly and intimately mixed together, any filler being subsequently added and thoroughly mixed. The mixing shall be carried out in a mechanical mixer of approved type and shall be continued until every part of the aggregate is completely coated, but in no case for less than $1\frac{1}{2}$ minutes ; where filler is added, the mixing shall be continued for at least 1 minute after the addition of the filler.

Thickness. The material shall be laid to a minimum thickness of 3 in. after thorough consolidation by rolling.

Application of Grit. Immediately after final rolling and before traffic is allowed on it, the surface of the tarmacadam shall be blinded with grit not exceeding $\frac{1}{8}$ in. nominal size, which shall have been coated with a suitable matrix. The grit shall be of an approved material and the quality and quantity used shall conform to the specified requirements of the engineer.

SPECIFICATION C. SINGLE-COURSE BITUMEN MACADAM—3-IN. CONSOLIDATED THICKNESS—GRAVEL AGGREGATE TO BE LAID ON PITCHED OR HARDCORE FOUNDATION. *Coarse Aggregate.* (*a*) The aggregate shall be subject to approval by the engineer or his representative, which shall be gravel and may be composed of particles of flint, chert, quartzite, or limestone.

(*b*) Water absorption : when tested in accordance with Method 18 of B.S. 812, the water absorption shall not be greater than 2 per cent.

(*c*) Shape : the gravel particles as naturally occurring and/or as a result of crushing in a suitable type of crusher shall be mainly irregular or angular in shape. When tested in accordance with Clause 67 the flakiness index shall not exceed 30 per cent. and the roundness index shall not exceed 20 per cent.

Fine Aggregate. The fine aggregate shall consist of clean sand grit, fine crushed rock, or slag (which shall comply with the following requirements).

(*a*) The sand and grit shall not contain more than 3 per cent. by weight of silt, loam, or clay. The test shall be carried out according to Method 17 of B.S. 812.

(*b*) The fine aggregate shall not contain organic matter in sufficient quantity to show a darker colour than the standard colour when the aggregate is tested according to Method 16 of B.S. 812.

(*c*) Slag : the slag, which shall be approved by the engineer or his representative, shall be best selected blast-furnace free from all deleterious matter. The weight per cubic foot and stability of the aggregate shall be in accordance with the requirements of B.S. 1047 and the total sulphur content shall not exceed 2·75 per cent. when tested in accordance with the appropriate methods in B.S. 1047.

Filler. The filler which may be added to the aggregate to comply with the above grading shall consist of limestone, portland cement, or other materials approved by the engineer. It shall pass 7 B.S. mesh, not less than 90 per cent. shall pass 52 B.S. mesh, and not less than 50 per cent. shall pass 200 B.S. mesh.

Grading. The grading shall be such that the composition of the finished material after mixing shall fall within the following limits :

	Per cent.
Soluble bitumen	6 to 7
Aggregate passing 200 mesh B.S. sieve	2 to 4
Aggregate retained on 200 B.S. sieve, but passing 8 mesh B.S. sieve	15 to 18
Aggregate retained on number 8 mesh B.S. sieve but passing $\frac{1}{8}$-in. mesh B.S. sieve	4 to 6
Aggregate retained on $\frac{1}{8}$-in. mesh B.S. sieve but passing $\frac{3}{4}$-in. mesh	65 to 73
	100

The grading of material retained on $\frac{1}{8}$-in. sieve shall be within the following limits :

	Per cent.
Passing $\frac{3}{4}$ in., retained $\frac{1}{2}$ in.	45 to 55
Passing $\frac{1}{2}$ in., retained $\frac{1}{4}$ in.	25 to 35
Passing $\frac{1}{4}$ in., retained $\frac{1}{8}$ in.	15 to 20

Binder. The characteristics of the binder to be used shall be agreed between the engineer and the supplier of the bituminous macadam. For normal conditions a Pool grade of asphaltic bitumen, having a penetration of 180 to 220 at 25° C. (77° F.) will be suitable.

Quantity of Binder. The quantity of binder used shall be such that all particles of aggregates are thoroughly coated, but there should be no excess. The quantity used should be not less than 6 per cent. nor more than 7 per cent. by weight of the finished macadam.

Temperature of Materials. The temperature of the aggregate shall not be less than 77° C. (170° F.), nor more than 104° C. (220° F.). The temperature to which the binder shall be heated will depend upon the nature of the aggregate and binder as well as upon climatic conditions, but for the grade of bitumen recommended above should not exceed 138° C. or 280° F. Prolonged heating of the binder must be avoided, as it will alter its viscosity and may affect seriously the quality of the resulting bitumen macadam.

Method of Mixing. The aggregate shall be thoroughly dry and shall be heated to the appropriate temperature. The binder shall be separately heated to the appropriate temperature, and the aggregate and binder shall then be measured into the mixer in suitable proportions and thoroughly and intimately mixed together, any required filler being subsequently added and thoroughly mixed. The mixing shall be carried out in a mechanical mixer of approved type, and shall be continued until every part of the aggregate is completely coated, but in no case less than $1\frac{1}{2}$ minutes; where filler is added the mixing shall be continued for at least 1 minute after the adding of the filler.

Method of Determination of Flakiness Index and Roundness Index. The stone shall be tested for flakiness index according to the method described in B.S. 812, Method 2. Flaky material is illustrated in Fig. 10 of B.S. 812.

The roundness index shall be determined in a similar manner, but in this case rounded stones (using this term as defined in B.S. 812 and illustrated in Fig. 7 of that Specification) shall be separated from the screened sample, and the number shall be expressed as a percentage of the total number of stone particles examined.

Spreading and Consolidating. The bitumen macadam shall be spread to such thickness that on the completion of consolidation by rolling the thickness shall not be less than 3 in., and the surface shall conform to the level and cross-section specified within a maximum limit of $\frac{3}{8}$ in. in 10 ft. or such other prescribed limits as may be required by the engineer. Every precaution shall be taken to avoid segregation and to prevent the bitumen macadam from becoming contaminated with dust or other foreign matter, such as manure, leaves, and wood.

Joints. When laying new material abutting on freshly laid or old material, care should be taken to secure good adhesion between joints by cutting back to the full depth to a dense vertical face, the face being painted, if necessary, with other bitumen.

All manhole covers, kerbs, channels, and similar projections against which the surfacing is to abut shall be cleaned prior to the material being laid. The bitumen macadam shall be tamped around and against such projections so that after final rolling the finished surfacing shall be left flush or not exceeding $\frac{1}{4}$ in. above such projections. Manhole covers and similar fittings shall be adjusted to the correct level before the surfacing is laid.

(3) *Concrete Roads : using Mechanical Methods of compacting the Concrete*

MATERIALS

CEMENT MORTAR. Cement mortar shall consist of Portland cement and clean sharp sand, as previously specified, in the following proportions :

Where used for brickwork. 1 volume of Portland cement to 3 volumes of clean, sharp sand. *For Pipe Joints.* 3 volumes of Portland cement to 1 volume of clean, sharp sand. *For rendering.* 1 volume of Portland cement to 2 volumes of clean, sharp sand.

All mortar is to be conveyed fresh to the works as required for use. No mortar after it has set or commenced to set shall be used or remixed for use.

HARDCORE. The hardcore used shall consist of broken brick, stone, or other approved hard material, clean and free from extraneous matter.

CLINKER. The clinker used shall be approved hard well-burnt furnace clinker, free from waste-metal dust or china.

CONCRETE KERBS AND QUADRANTS. The concrete kerbs and quadrants shall comply in all respects with the following clauses of B.S. No. 340, 1936 ; Clauses, 1, 2, 3, 4, 5, 6, 7, 8, 12, 13, 14, 15, 16, 17, and 18.

The dimensions of the kerbs shall be 10 in. × 5 in. and to the section shown in Fig. 2, Plate 1 of B.S. No. 340, 1936.

MANHOLE COVERS. The manhole covers and frames shall be of cast iron and, except as indicated below, shall be of the heavy double-sealed pattern, non-ventilating, weighing not less than ($4\frac{3}{4}$ cwt. suggested) with a 20-in. opening and 2 ft. 9 in. square base coated with Dr. Angus Smith's solution, and are to be obtained from an approved maker. The frames shall be set on at least two courses of brickwork set in cement mortar and shall conform to the finished level of the surrounding surface.

In the particular case of manholes situated in the footpath or in the verge and not exceeding 5 ft. in depth to the invert, the cover and frame shall be of a light footway pattern with an opening 20 in. diameter and total weight $2\frac{1}{2}$ cwt.

GULLIES. Gullies as specified below shall be set or constructed at the points shown on the contract drawings, these points being so chosen that no carriageway gulley is required to drain an area of more than 250 sq. yds. and no footway gulley an area of more than 150 sq. yds.

The gulley pots to be used for the carriageway gullies shall be of precast concrete or stoneware, 1 ft. 6 in. diameter × 3 ft. 6 in. deep internal dimensions, with 6 in. single-seal trapped outlet and cleaning eye complete with C.I. stopper and chain. The pot shall be set on a foundation of 6 in. cement concrete. The concrete shall be haunched about the bottom of the pot, and after this has set and hardened back-filling shall be carried out and thoroughly compacted. A surround of cement concrete 6 in. thick will be formed about the top of the gulley pot to form a base to receive the cast-iron gulley grating and frame, which shall be of approved pattern and set in cement mortar at the correct level. Weight of grating and frame to be not less than $1\frac{1}{2}$ cwt.

Alternatively, at the sole discretion of the engineer, the gullies may be constructed in 9-in. brickwork set in cement mortar and built on a foundation 6 in. thick of cement concrete. The internal dimensions of the brickwork shall be 22 in. × 16 in. × 3 ft. deep and the upper edge of the trapped outlet pipe shall not be less than 18 in. nor more than 24 in. below the top surface of the gulley frame. The grating and frame shall be of an approved pattern, weight, and manufacture, and shall be set in cement mortar on a base 6 in. thick of Portland-cement concrete.

Footpath gullies where required shall be constructed in $4\frac{1}{2}$-in. brickwork in cement mortar and built on a foundation 4 in. thick of cement concrete. The internal dimensions of the brickwork shall be 15 in. × 12 in. × 18 in. deep. The outlet pipe shall be 4 in. diameter. The cast-iron grate and frame shall be of an approved pattern and manufacture and set in cement mortar.

Workmanship

CONCRETE—QUALITY A. Concrete, quality A, shall consist of 14 parts of all-in ballast or all-in crushed stone, as specified, to 1 part of cement by weight of dry materials.

CONCRETE—QUALITY B. Concrete, quality B, shall consist of 5 parts of coarse aggregate as specified to $2\frac{1}{2}$ parts of fine aggregate as specified and 1 part of cement by weight of dry materials. The size of the coarse aggregate shall be $1\frac{1}{2}$-in. nominal maximum size and conform to the grading set out in Clause 5, B.S. No. 882, 1940.

The fine aggregate shall be as specified in Clause 5, sub-clause (b), sub-clause (i) of that specification.

CONCRETE—QUALITY C. Concrete, quality C, shall consist of 14 parts of all-in ballast or all-in crushed stone, as specified, to 1 part of cement by weight of dry materials, the all-in ballast being $\frac{3}{4}$-in. nominal maximum size.

WATER–CEMENT RATIO. Great care is to be exercised in the gauging of the amount of water used in each batch of concrete so as to ensure uniformity and equality in the mixed concrete. Mechanical vibration or compaction of the concrete shall be used. The amount of water to be added to the aggregates and cement shall take into account the amount of moisture already present in the aggregates. The ratio of water to cement by weight shall not exceed 0·90 for concrete quality A and C and shall not exceed 0·60 for concrete quality B. The consistence of the concrete shall be measured in accordance with the procedure set out in Appendix M. in B.S. No. 882, 1940, and for concrete quality A, B, and C, no subsidence or slump will be permitted.

CARRIAGEWAY. (i) On a sub-soil of soft clay there shall be laid a sub-base 6 in. thick compacted of concrete, quality A—see clause 29—and a surface 6 in. compacted thickness of concrete quality B—see Clause 30.

(ii) On a sub-soil of loam, loose chalk, hard clay, or similar material, a sub-base shall consist of 4 in. compacted thickness of concrete, quality A, and a surfacing of 6 in. compacted of concrete, quality B.

(iii) On a sub-soil of hard chalk, gravel, rock or similar material a sub-base shall consist of 2 in. compacted thickness of concrete, quality C—see Clause 31—with a surfacing superimposed 6 in. thick compacted of concrete, quality B.

The carriageway shall be constructed to the dimensions, lines, and levels shown on the drawings. Immediately on the approved formation or sub-base a layer of water-proof paper as specified shall be spread, care being taken to ensure that the paper is not damaged and that the joints are lapped at least 6 in., and the paper shall be laid immediately before the concrete is deposited. Forms to support the concrete along the edges of the road shall be of steel set correctly to the lines and levels indicated on the drawings and secured in a position so as to be sufficiently rigid to obviate any movement during the process of laying and compacting the concrete. All mortar and dirt must be removed from steel forms which have been previously used, and the forms should be greased or oiled before any fresh concrete is deposited against them. The forms shall remain in position after the concrete has been placed for such length of time as the engineer may determine. Provided that the specified water–cement ratio be strictly observed and the compaction of the concrete is thorough and care be taken to avoid damage to the concrete, the steel forms may be removed on the expiration of 24 hours after the setting of the concrete.

DEPOSITING CONCRETE. As soon as possible after mixing and in no case more than 20 minutes thereafter, concrete is to be deposited from barrows, dumpers, lorries, or other method approved by the engineer, provided that the concrete be not transported over the formation to the carriageway. The concrete shall be spread so as to obtain a uniform thickness sufficient to ensure, when compacted, the thickness as specified and shown on the drawings. Mechanical spreading shall be adopted if approved machines be available. The depositing of the concrete shall be continuous between expansion joints and at no point shall compacted concrete be of less depth than that specified.

COMPACTING CONCRETE. Concrete shall be compacted with a mechanically operated vibrating beam and/or tamping beam, such beams to be capable of compacting the concrete as specified with a close-knit, uniform, sealed surface free from any depressions exceeding $\frac{1}{8}$ in. in depth. The compacting beams shall be driven either mechanically, electrically, or pneumatically, and shall be of a design approved by the engineer. Compaction of the concrete shall be completed before the initial set of the concrete has taken place.

CURING. Immediately the compaction of the concrete has been completed the concrete shall be protected from rain, sun, and wind, by placing over it a shield of canvas, hessian, waterproof paper, or cloth, or other approved material, mounted on a light frame or frames so as to avoid touching the concrete surface. Such shield shall extend for a distance of 40 ft., from the compacting machine and shall remain in position until the concrete is sufficiently hard to lay thereon a covering of coconut matting, sand, soil, or other approved material, which shall be kept damp for a period of at least 14 days. Alternatively, curing may be effected by the application of bituminous emulsion uniformly spread over the concrete, within 24 hours of its completion, at the rate of 1 gallon of emulsion to 10 sq. yds. of concrete.

LONGITUDINAL JOINTS. Where the width of the carriageway exceeds 16 ft. a longitudinal central joint should be provided, such joint to be of the butt type, painted with hot tar, bitumen, or cold bituminous emulsion. The arrises of the joint should be neatly rounded by a steel float to a radius of $\frac{3}{8}$ in. After compacting the concrete, each edge along the line of the kerb to be removed for a depth of 1 in. and a width of 18 in. to receive concrete kerbs.

TRAVERSE JOINTS. Expansion joints $\frac{3}{8}$ in. wide shall be formed at intervals of 60 ft. longitudinally and filled with approved jointing material to within $\frac{1}{2}$ in. of the finished surface. Midway between the expansion joints a dummy joint shall be formed by the insertion of a strip of wood 2 in. deep by $\frac{1}{4}$ in. thick laid on the waterproof paper so that the 2 in. face lies perpendicular to the formation. These strips shall be supported in position during concreting in such a way as to obviate any movement. The arrises of the transverse joints shall be rounded by means of a suitable tool to a radius of $\frac{3}{8}$ in. before the concrete is hardened.

KERBS. A 10 in. × 5 in. concrete kerb is to be laid on the concrete carriageway to the lines and levels shown on the drawings and is to be bedded and jointed in cement mortar and backed with concrete to the dimensions shown on the drawings, such concrete to be made with 6 parts by volume of all-in ballast or crushed stone to 1 part of cement.

CHAPTER 3

DESIGN AND CONSTRUCTION OF SEWERS

THE design and construction of sewers for estates call for careful consideration of many factors before an efficient and economical scheme can be
satisfactorily prepared.

There are, in brief, three systems of drainage, namely : combined,
partially combined and separate, and the adoption of any one system will
depend to a great extent upon the requirements of the Local Authority.
Generally speaking, the majority of the Local Authorities have the
combined system in operation ; whilst others, in order to relieve existing
combined sewers, insist upon the partially combined or separate systems
being adopted.

COMBINED SYSTEM

This is the simplest system, wherein one pipe has to take both sewage
and surface-water flow, and must of necessity be a rather large size sewer
capable of dealing with both flows. This has the disadvantage that the
large sewer will in dry weather only have in it a comparatively small
sewage flow, with a slow velocity, which may result in the silting up of the
sewer. This system also necessitates the provision of storm overflows with
low weir heights, and may be troublesome at times. Times of heavy
storms may tax the capacity of the combined sewer unless adequate
overflows can be provided.

PARTIALLY COMBINED SYSTEM

This system involves the provision of two sewers, one of which deals
with sewage and surface-water flow from back roofs and paved paths, and
the other takes only the surface water of the streets, front roofs, and
paved areas. By this system the sizes of each sewer are kept within
reasonable limits. The difficulty of this system in actual practice is
preventing any sewage-water flow getting into the storm sewers.

THE SEPARATE SYSTEM

This system, as the name implies, requires two sets of sewers, one for
sewage and the other for storm water. It means that smaller sewers
only are necessary, and storm overflows can discharge heavy flows into
watercourses. It is also cheaper to provide small dual sewers than large
combined sewers, which have to be laid deeper. A disadvantage is that
the foul sewers will have very small flows, and unless the sewers are laid
at self-cleansing gradients silting up will arise frequently unless flushed.

As the amount of sewage is so small the size of sewers is based on taking six times the sewage flow.

SEWER FLOW CALCULATIONS

It is essential to calculate with some degree of accuracy the estimated amounts of sewage and storm water sewer flows that are to be provided for on the average housing estates. The sewage flow, or the dry-weather flow, as it is termed, is based upon the local water consumption, which may vary from 25 gallons to as much as 60 gallons daily per head. On an average it may be assumed that 35 gallons per head is a fair basis to be taken ; this, expressed in cubic feet per minute, is 0·0036 cu. ft. min. per head, and this is over a period of 24 hours.

From observations in different localities it is found that half of the sewage flows off in 6 hours, therefore provision must be made to deal with twice calculated flow of 0·0036 cu. ft. min., *i.e.* 0·0072 cu. ft. min. per head.

To arrive at the population of an estate we may assume five persons per house in a zoning area of 12 houses to the acre, which gives a population of 60 persons per acre. With regard to public buildings such as churches, community halls, schools, public conveniences, the foul flow from these places may be made on the basis of five persons per lavatory.

STORMWATER DRAINAGE

The stormwater flow is based on the local rainfall statistics. On the east coast the annual rainfall varies from 22 to 30 inches, whilst on the west coast it is between 45 and 85 inches. The average rainfall for England and Wales is about 37 to 40 inches. In 1939–1940 the Ministry of Health set up a Departmental Committee on Rainfall Calculations, who recommended in the design of sewers that a rainfall intensity curve, based upon average rainfall records taken over a number of stations, should be used to arrive at the rainfall intensity in relation to the time of concentration. This curve is based upon the formula

$$R = \frac{30}{T+10}$$

where T is 5 to 20 minutes (see Fig. 27).

wherein R =rainfall in inches per hour ;

    T =time of concentration.

The factor T is the time taken for the stormwater flow from the extreme limits of the drainage area to reach the point of entry into the sewer plus a time of entry—usually 3 minutes—taken for the rain from the ground to enter the head of the sewer. In closely built-up areas the time of entry may be reduced to ½ minute.

STORMWATER CALCULATIONS

The calculations of stormwater run-off may be done by two methods. The first is the " flat rate of rainfall " method, and the other is the more complicated " time of concentration " method, which is more accurate for dealing with very large drainage areas. The former method can be adopted as being suitable for average-sized estates of say up to 500 houses. The " flat rate method " is based upon an assumed figure of rainfall in inches per hour per acre, which may vary from ¼ in. to 1 in. per hour.

RAINFALL CHARTS

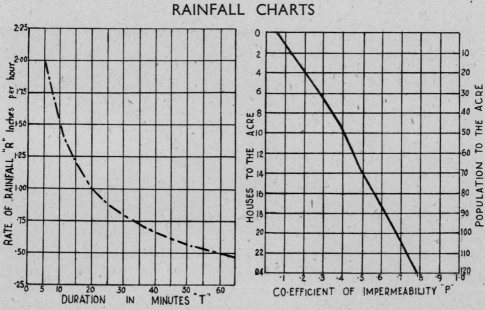

FIG. 27. Ministry of Health rainfall curve   FIG. 28. Impermeability chart

All the rainwater does not enter the sewer, except from the impermeable areas, *i.e.* the roofs and streets (and small proportions from gardens), from which all surface water is expected to discharge to the sewers. The extent of this impermeable area is governed by the total paved areas, roofs, and streets on the estate.

Fig. 28 shows an Impermeability Chart, giving impermeability factors in ratio to the number of houses and population per acre. It will be observed from the chart that the percentage of impermeability increases with greater house and population density.

It is essential wherever possible to determine accurately these percentages from actual local data and conditions, as these greatly determine the amount of surface water likely to enter the sewers.

The following Table gives average results of calculated percentages of impermeability made in respect of different types of estates.

Densely built-up areas	..	..	0·70 to 0·90 impermeability
20 houses to the acre	..	..	0·50 ,, 0·70	,,
12 ,, ,, ,, ,,	..	..	0·33 ,, 0·50	,,
8 ,, ,, ,, ,,	..	..	0·25 ,, 0·33	,,

CALCULATED DISCHARGE INTO SEWERS

(1) *Sewage or Dry-weather Flow.* Water consumption per person on an average per day = 35 gallons, which is 0·0036 cu. ft. min. It is estimated that half of this flow passes through the sewer in 6 hours, and this means that the maximum dry-weather flow is twice the average rate, *i.e.*

$$0·0036 \times 2 = 0·0072 \text{ cu. ft. min.}$$

On basis of 5 persons per house and 12 houses to the acre, this means a total dry-weather flow of :

$$0·0072 \times 60 = 0·0432. \text{ cu. ft. min. per acre.}$$

(2) *Stormwater Flow.* Assume ¾ in. rainfall per hour per acre from impermeable areas, *i.e.* roofs, paths, and roads, and ⅛ in. rainfall from permeable or garden area.

Roof area of house	=	650 sq. ft.
Paved paths and yards	=	390 ,, ,,
Area for half width of 36-ft. street	=	540 ,, ,,
Total Impermeable Area	=	1580 sq. ft.=175 sq. yds.=0·036 acre.

(3) *Total Flow per House.*

Stormwater flow = 0·036 × ¾ in. × 60·5 = 1·632 cu. ft. min.
Permeable area in garden = 100 × 30 = 1040 = 1960 sq. ft. or 0·05 acres.
Stormwater flow = 0·05 × ⅛ in. × 60·5 = 0·30 cu. ft. min.
Total stormwater flow = 1·632 + 0·30 = 1·932 cu. ft. min.

Dry-weather flow to sewers = 0·04 cu. ft. min. per house.
Stormwater flow = 1·93 ,, ,, ,, ,, ,,

Combined flow = 1·97 ,, ,, ,, ,, ,,

Thus a total flow of 1·97 cu. ft. per min. per house enters the sewers.

Partially separate flow	Dry-weather flow	= 0·04 cu. ft. min.
	Surface-water flow from roofs	= 1·09 ,, ,, ,,
	Paths and gardens	= 0·30 ,, ,, ,,
	Total	= 1·43 ,, ,, ,,

The quickest method of calculating the amount of sewage and storm-water discharging into the sewers is to estimate the amount of such discharges from an average house and garden, and to multiply the result by the number of houses on the estate.

The calculations of discharges from each house, whether drained by separate, partially separate, or combined systems, can be based on the above data for a type of house usually zoned at 12 houses to the acre.

Where a separate drainage system is adopted the sewage and stormwater flows can readily be ascertained from the foregoing calculations, and sizes of sewers can be calculated in relation to gradients of sufficient capacity to deal with these flows.

Table No. 2, p. 67, gives the capacities, gradients, and velocities of various sizes of sewers, and also the number of houses and areas served by each type of drainage system, which will be of help to sewer designers.

Drainage Areas

In order to comply with the requirements of the Public Health Act, 1936, as regards adequate drainage of new estates, it is necessary to obtain an Ordnance map of the district concerned, which should contain useful information with regard to the contours of the ground, watercourses, ditches, ponds, positions of existing roads and sewers, with spot levels also given, all of which will assist in designing a satisfactory drainage system.

The sites should be inspected and notes made regarding the levels of ground, positions of summits and hollows of roads and fields, and the positions, depths, and sizes of existing sewers and overflows.

Example of Drainage Scheme

To take a practical example, consider a drainage system for a proposed housing drainage area map such as that illustrated in Fig. 29, p. 60, on on the assumption that a combined system is to be used. From the spot levels and contours can be gauged the limits of the land that can be drained by gravitation to the line of the proposed main sewer. Having definitely fixed the limits of the whole drainage area, it can then be sub-divided into smaller drainage areas and lettered off A, B, C, etc., as shown on the map. The sub-divisions are governed by the positions of the proposed branch sewers and their connections with other sewers, which depend of course on the layout designs adopted. Having now indicated all drainage areas and approximate main lines of sewers the estimated sewage and storm flows from each area can be calculated on the basis of flow per house as explained previously.

The results are tabulated as in Table No. 3, p. 68, which also gives the sizes of sewers necessary, together with their respective capacities and velocities.

Each drainage area is separately calculated as to the amount of sewage and stormwater likely to drain to the sewers. When these subsidiary sewers are brought together into the main sewer, at the various " points of consideration " shown numbered on the drainage map, the size of this main sewer is determined by the total discharges from the areas entering the sewer at each point of consideration. Ultimately, it will be seen that at the outfall, by consideration point No. 6 the total discharges from the areas A to G requires a 30-in. diameter sewer. At its junction with the existing sewer an overflow chamber is provided to permit the volume of

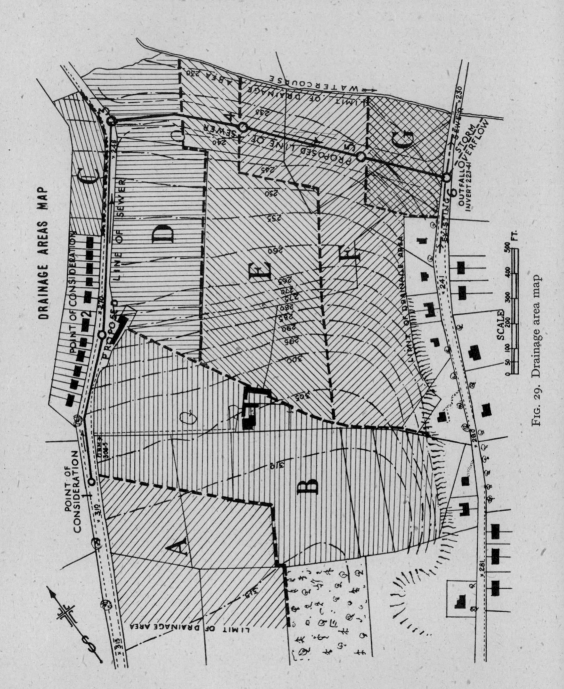

FIG. 29. Drainage area map

stormwater in excess of $6 \times$ D.W.F. to overflow and discharge into the watercourse through the overflow sewer.

" TIME OF CONCENTRATION " METHOD

This more complicated method is used for large drainage areas incorporating several building estates, as the calculations based on time of concentration result in larger size sewers being required, governed by amount of storm flow entering the sewers at various points. The time factor is the time taken for the storm flow to reach the point of discharge into the proposed sewer from the outermost limit of the drainage area, and an allowance of 3 minutes is generally added for the rainwater to enter into the sewers.

From the drainage area map the approximate distances of the tributary sewers are measured, and the times are calculated by dividing the distances by the velocities obtainable according to the probable gradients and sizes of sewers.

If the sizes of sewers give satisfactory capacities and velocities with the gradients available to take the calculated flows, then the calculations are complete ; but if not, it is necessary by a process of trial and error to amend the sizes of sewers and velocities until they are satisfactory.

The main factors for such calculations may be summarised as follows :

(1) The percentage of impermeable area is directly proportional to the stormwater discharge from it.
(2) The discharge of storm water is proportional to the rain that falls during the time it takes for the water to flow from limits of the area under consideration to the point of discharge.
(3) The maximum flow is reached when the greatest rainfall occurs in the minimum time of concentration that can be applied to the district under consideration.
(4) The total volume of stormwater received into the systems is proportional to the maximum rate of flow.

The result of these factors is expressed by the Lloyd Davies formula:

$$ Q = (60 \cdot 5 \times \frac{60}{T} \times r) \times A \times p $$

in which :

Q = discharge in cu. ft. min.

r = total rainfall in inches ; $\frac{T}{60} \times R\,p$ = percentage of impermeability.

T = Time of concentration in minutes.

A = Area in acres.

The calculations on the " time of concentration " method are tabulated in Table No. 4, p. 69, which is in respect of the same drainage area illustrated in Fig. 29. A comparison of Tables 3 and 4, pp. 68 and 69, of the two methods described will show the different results of each, but due regard must be taken of sizes of drainage areas in adopting the more suitable method.

By the " Time of Concentration " method used for large drainage areas, it will be observed that the size at the outfall end of the sewer is less than would be the case by the " Flat Rate of Rainfall " method, as the intensity of rainfall decreases with the greater distance of the flow to the sewer.

LEVEL SECTIONS OF SEWERS

When the plan of a drainage scheme for an estate is prepared, it is necessary to take longitudinal and cross-sections to indicate the levels of the ground along the lines of the proposed sewers. Levels are taken by means of the dumpy, or surveyor's level, and readings are taken on the ground at, say, 30 to 50 ft. intervals on even surfaces, and shorter intervals on uneven surfaces. Lines of sections should be taken from the head of the proposed sewer to its outlet into existing sewers or sewerage disposal works. The levels must be taken in reference to defined Ordnance bench marks, which are given on Ordnance maps ; if there is no convenient bench mark, a fixed point, such as a gate-post, step, or top of a manhole, may be used, and for which an assumed level can be stated.

The sections of levels are then plotted to a suitable scale, such as 20 ft. to 1 in. horizontally and 8 ft. to an inch vertically. The ground levels are scaled off and joined by a line, which thus gives the level of the ground, and under this line can be plotted the line or invert level of the new sewers in such positions as will give suitable self-cleansing velocities and the required depth of cover over the pipes. (See Fig. 20, p. 36.)

CONSTRUCTIONAL DETAILS

Generally, sewers for housing estates are constructed of glazed stoneware circular pipes for small diameter sewers, and for larger sewers the pipes may be of cast iron, steel tube, concrete tube, or brick culverts.

Byelaws sometimes require foul sewers to be laid on and haunched with 6 in. of concrete in bad ground, and where there is less than 3 ft. or 4 ft. of cover available under roads, or where sewers are laid under buildings, the pipes should be surrounded with 6 in. of concrete. Stormwater sewers are often permitted to be laid without a concrete bed, unless the ground is waterlogged or undermined. All pipes are jointed in cement well worked into the sockets, particularly underneath the pipes. Pipe joints are shown in Fig. 30, p. 63.

Brick or concrete manholes should be provided at every change of direction of the sewer and at no greater distance than 120 yds. on straight lengths. The chamber of the manhole should be at least 4 ft. 6 in. × 3 ft. and shaft 2 ft. 3 in. square, starting at least 4 ft. 6 in. clear above sewer invert. Flushing eyes, formed of pipes laid vertically in concrete surround at the head of the sewer from its invert to ground level, are useful to indicate the head of the sewer as well as affording access for flushing the sewer.

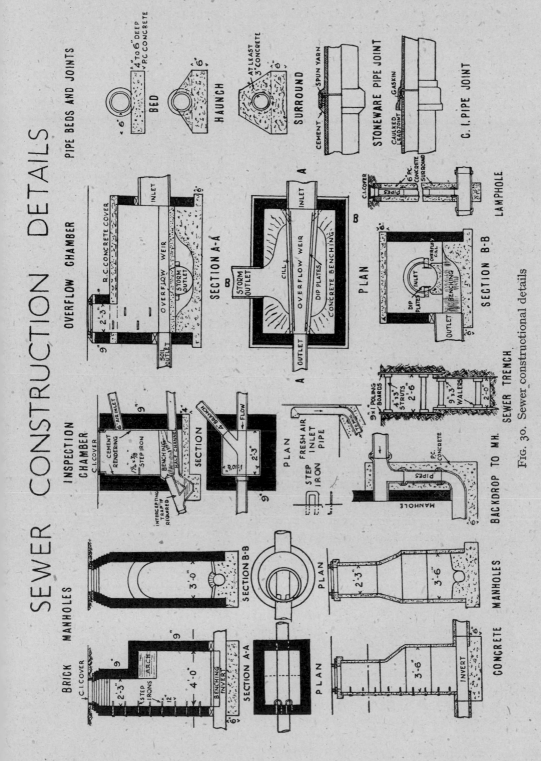

Fig. 30. Sewer constructional details

All branch sewers should join the main with bends pointing in the direction of the flow, and this can be done by cement concrete channels and benchings in the bottom of the manhole or by placing stoneware channels and junctions at the required levels. Sewer construction details are shown in Fig. 30, p. 63.

LAYING OF SEWERS

Sewers are laid in open trenches up to 15 ft. deep and in tunnels at greater depths. In loose or wet ground the trenches must be timbered, and in wet ground a bed of ashes should be laid before the concrete is laid. Sight rails for fixing the level of each pipe, according to the required gradients, are formed of horizontal boards, say, 9 in. × 2 in., fixed across the trench and supported by two upright poles. The horizontal board or "sight rail", as it is called, is accurately fixed to definite height above the sewer invert level, generally about 3 ft. or 4 ft. above ground level, and the "boning rod", which is a tee-shaped upright, is made to the exact height of sight rail above invert level.

Another sight rail is fixed at a convenient length along the sewer, and the boning rod when placed on the invert of the pipes laid in the trench should be sighted in line with two sight rails, which will show that the pipes are being laid to the correct gradients. In other words, the sight line along the tops of the sight rails and boning rod is a parallel line to the gradient line of the sewer. The levels of the sight rails should be fixed by a surveyor's level to ensure the accuracy of the sewer invert levels being obtained.

Sewer pipes are laid from the outfall towards the head, and all joints must be carefully made, and tested by either a smoke or water test. Generally, local council building inspectors carry out the test for newly laid sewers. The filling in of sewer trenches should be carried out in 12-in. layers, each well rammed down, until the whole trench is filled in and well consolidated. All house junctions put on the sewer should be indicated above ground by a wooden post on which can be marked the depth of the sewer, so that when the house connections are to be laid no difficulty should arise as to the location of the nearest junction left in the sewer.

VENTILATION OF SEWERS

In years past it was the practice to ventilate sewers through the medium of house drains, but this was checked by the use of intercepting traps. Then, gratings were put in manholes which became offensive ; and so tall ventilation shafts were erected to ventilate sewers. These shafts give both inward and outward air currents, and experiments have shown that the average downward current is only 34 ft. per minute, as compared with upward current of 162 ft. per minute.

As a result many tall ventilation shafts 6 in. in diameter have been used, and are erected either against buildings or alongside kerbs or footpaths. Their height should be at least the same as the ridges of the houses adjoining.

Storm Overflows

On an estate where a brook course exists it is customary to allow excessive storm water to overflow into it from combined sewers during times of storms, provided the amount overflowed is more than six times the amount of the foul water flow, or " dry-weather flow ", as it is often termed. This avoids excessively large sewers being provided to deal with heavy storms, which would be a very costly matter.

The Ministry of Health in the prevention of pollution of brook courses have considered that foul water is sufficiently weakly diluted to be harmless when over six times the dry-weather flow is allowed to discharge into brook courses.

It is thus often necessary in designing combined sewers to provide storm overflow chambers at suitable points which will pass off the weak foul water—*i.e.* flow in excess of six times the dry-weather flow—into a convenient brook course or river.

There are various types of storm overflows, but the latest type of overflow is effected by means of either a single-sided or double-sided overflow weir. The depth and length of the weir are calculated from the amount of flow in excess of the $6 \times$ D.W.F. that has to be diverted from the foul sewer into the overflow to the brook course.

The formula for obtaining the depth and length of an overflow weir is as follows (by the Smith and Coleman formula) :

$$\text{Length of weir} \atop \text{(in feet)} = 0.548 \text{ W V } Y_2{}^{0.13} \left(\frac{1}{Y_1} - \frac{1}{Y_2} \right)$$

where W = average width of inlet and outlet pipes in feet
     V = average velocity in channel in feet per second
    Y_2 = Incoming head in feet above weir level
    Y_1 = Outgoing head in feet above weir level.   Value of Y is taken as 0.06 ft.

An example of a storm overflow of a double-sided weir type is shown in Fig. 30, p. 63.

Small Sewage Disposal Plants

In rural areas where a public sewer is not available it will be necessary to treat the sewage from an estate by providing a self-contained sewage disposal plant. The principle of such a plant is the provision for the digestion of the sewage solids in a septic tank and for a filtration system for purifying the effluent to a sufficiently harmless nature to enable it to be discharged into a brook course without fear of polluting it. The sewage enters into a settling tank, where after a period of settlement of solids, etc., it passes to a filter tank filled with a filtering media of gravel. After filtration the effluent is more or less purified and can be drained away into a brook course.

The dimensions of the tanks will of course depend upon the number of houses they have to deal with. A basis of about 3 cu. ft. per person may be taken in calculating the sizes of the tanks. An illustration of a typical small sewage disposal plant is shown, which will deal with sewage disposal for 100 houses, and details of its construction are such as will comply with most local byelaws. (See Fig. 31.)

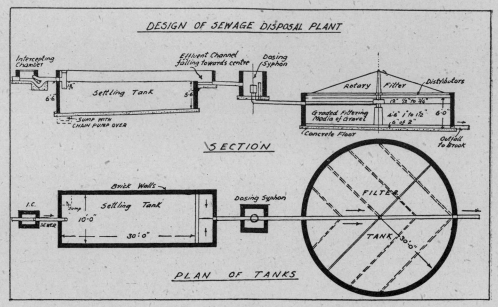

FIG. 31. Small sewage disposal plant

It should be noted, however, that under the Town Planning Acts housing development may not be permitted where it is found impracticable to drain the houses into sewers.

It is essential that where septic tanks are resorted to, they should be regularly cleaned and properly maintained, otherwise they become great sources of nuisance.

House Drainage

The drainage system should be so designed, by the grouping of sanitary arrangements in an efficient and economical manner, as to avoid long lengths of pipes, unnecessary gullies and inspection chambers.

The gradients of pipes should be at least 1 in 40 for 4-in. pipes, 1 in 60 for 6-in. pipes and 1 in 90 for 9-in. pipes; the pipes should be of stoneware, cement jointed, and should be well ventilated and not pass under buildings. Gully traps with efficient water-seals should be fixed in suitable positions to collect waste water from kitchens, bathrooms, and rainwater pipes, and for collection of water from paved areas. Inspection chambers are required at every change of direction of drains, and sizes may vary from 2 ft. × 1½ ft. up to 4½ ft. × 2½ ft. where depth is greater than 2½ ft. A chamber is essential near where the house drain connects.

TABLE 2

TABLE OF SEWER CAPACITIES, GRADIENTS, AND VELOCITIES. NUMBER OF HOUSES AND ACREAGE SERVED BY SEWERS

Basis:—Crimp and Bruges formula, $V = 124 \sqrt[3]{m^2} \sqrt{i}$; 5 persons per house at 35 galls. per head ; density 12 houses and 60 persons per acre ; combined system estimated flow per house = 1·97 cu. ft. min. ; partially separate system estimated flow per house = 1·43 cu. ft. min. ; separate system estimated 6 × D.W.F. per house = 0·08 cu. ft. min.

Diam. of Sewer in inches	Gradient: 1 in.	Self-cleansing Velocity, ft. per sec.	Discharge flowing, full, c.f.m.	No. of Houses served on Combined System (1·97 c.f.m. per house)	Acreage served on Combined System, acres	No. of Houses served on Partially Separate System (1·43 c.f.m. per house)	Acreage served on Partially Separate System, acres
6	60	4	47	23	1·92	31	2·58
9	100	4	105	52	4·33	64	5·33
12	150	4	190	95	7·83	127	10·58
15	200	4	290	145	12·08	194	16·17
18	270	4	410	205	17·08	275	22·92
21	320	4	580	270	24·17	390	32·50
24	400	4	740	370	30·83	563	46·92
27	450	4	950	475	39·58	635	52·92
30	500	4	1200	600	50·00	800	66·66
33	600	4	1400	700	58·33	930	77·50
36	660	4	1600	800	66·66	1070	89·17

TABLE 3

DRAINAGE CALCULATIONS FOR AN ESTATE BASED ON FLAT RATE OF RAINFALL OF ¾ IN. PER HOUR PER ACRE

Area Ref.	Area in acres	No. of Houses	Combined Flow. Storm = 1·96 c.f.m. Soil = 0·04 c.f.m. Per House = 2 c.f.m.	Point of Consideration	Size of Sewer, in.	Gradient	Velocity, ft. per sec.	Discharge full, c.f.m.	Remarks
A	9·14	108	216	1	12	1/100	5·00	235	Head of Main Sewer.
B	15·16	182	364						
A and B	24·30	290	580	2	18	1/120	5·75	600	In existing road.
C	1·13	13	26						
A to C	25·43	303	606	3	21	1/200	5·00	720	Change of direction.
D	8·44	100	200						
E	9·26	110	220						
A to E	43·13	513	1026	4	24	1/200	5·50	1030	In field.
F	8·47	102	204						
A to F	51·62	615	1230	5	30	1/400	4·40	1310	In field.
G	1·31	15	20						
A to G	52·93	630	1260	6	30	1/400	4·40	1310	Overflow M.H.
		Less 6 × D.W.F. = 50		6	12	1/100	5·00	235	Into existing soil sewer.
		Over 6 × D.W.F. = 1210		6	27	1/250	5·00	1220	Overflow to watercourse.

TABLE 4

DRAINAGE CALCULATIONS FOR AN ESTATE BASED ON "TIME OF CONCENTRATION" METHOD—FORMULA

$$Q = 60 \cdot 5 \times R \times A\,p$$

Area Ref. on Map	Gross Area in acres	Impermeable Area, based on 43 per cent. in acres	Storm Flow T (Length/Velocity +3 mins. entrance, mins.)	Storm Flow R $\frac{30}{T+10}$ inches	Resultant Storm Flow Q, c.f.m.	Sewage Flow, c.f.m. based on 0·5 c.f.m. (½ off in 6 hrs.)	Combined Flow, c.f.m.	Point of Consideration	Size of Sewer	Gradient	Velocity, ft. per sec.	Discharge full, c.f.m.	Remarks
A	9·14	3·93	7	1·11	274	5	279	1	15	1/150	4·6	360	Head of sewer.
B	15·16	6·51											
A and B	24·30	10·44	10	1·00	632	12	644	2	21	1/200	5	720	In road.
C	1·13	0·48											
A to C	25·43	10·92	11	0·96	640	13	653	3	21	1/200	5	720	Change of direction.
D	8·44	3·63											
E	9·26	3·98											
A to E	43·13	17·53	16	0·83	930	22	952	4	24	1/200	5·5	1030	In field.
F	8·49	3·65											
A to F	51·62	22·18	20	0·75	1005	26	1031	5	27	1/250	5	1220	In field.
G	1·31	0·56											
A to G	52·93	22·74	21	0·73	1004	27	1031	6	27	1/250	5	1220	Overflow M. H.
				Less 6 × D.W.F. = 27 × 2 = 54		27 × 2 = 54		6	12	1/100	5	235	Discharge to existing sewer.
A to G				Over 6 × D.W.F. to overflow = 977			= 977	6	27	1/250	5	1220	Overflow to watercourse.

5

to the sewer, and some local authorities insist that an intercepting trap be provided. The question of the need for such a trap has been a matter of much controversy, as it is argued that they are easily blocked up and difficult to keep clean. The Ministry of Health byelaws leave it to local authorities to decide if traps are necessary, but they are required if the drainage discharges into a cesspool.

COMBINED DRAINAGE

This method is allowed by many local authorities where a number of houses may be connected to the sewer, which is more economical than separate connections. As a rule not more than six houses should be on a combined drain, which for the first two houses can be of 4-in. diameter, and for the rest must be of at least 6-in. diameter.

Ventilation of drains is essential, and can be done by providing at least one ventilating pipe as near as possible to the building and as far as practicable from the sewer. Where an intercepting trap is used another ventilation pipe near the trap is also required.

Pre-War Building Studies, No. 26 (1947). Domestic Drainage. (His Majesty's Stationery Office. Price 6d.)

Recommendations for underground drainage for domestic houses are made in this Report which has been compiled by the Plumbing Committee of the Building Research Board of the Department of Scientific and Industrial Research on behalf of the Ministry of Works.

In making the recommendations special attention has been paid to minimising the cost of installing and maintaining drainage systems, but the need for preserving proper sanitary standards and quality of work has been kept well to the forefront. The report gives a summary of commonly occurring defects in domestic drainage which are very many but the Committee states emphatically that they do not consider current drainage practice in this country to be of a low standard generally. It is recognised that a progressive improvement has been taking place in recent years and many local authorities insist on increasingly higher standards.

The recommendations in the Report cover a wide range of subjects, including general design and layout of systems, sizes of pipes, gradients, gutters, protection of pipes, manholes, ventilators, and trapping, excavations and filling.

Reference is made to pipes made from a base of macerated compressed paper, impregnated under heat and pressure with a high melting point pitch, which have been used for drainage for some years in Canada and America. These pipes are lightweight and resistant to corrosion. They are jointed by means of driven tapered collars and it is claimed can be jointed as fast as they are lowered into the trench. Investigations are being made to manufacture and use such pipes in this country.

CHAPTER 4

SUBMISSION OF PLANS OF NEW STREETS AND LAYOUTS

THE private estate developer having decided to proceed with building development must prepare plans and sections of streets and sewers of the layout design best suited to the site and which complies in its provisional draft stage with local town-planning requirements and local byelaw regulations.

Such plans have to be submitted by him to the local planning authority or local council surveyor for formal approval, and this is necessary before any constructional work begins. An outline of the procedure involved is described later, but there may be some variations in different parts of the country, where the regulations may vary in detail.

Under Article 8 of an Interim Development Order an application cannot be refused because insufficient plans or particulars have been submitted unless within seven days of the receipt of the application the applicant has been requested to supply the particulars. Another point to note is that where the Interim Development Authority is also the Byelaw Authority, an application under byelaws must, subject to Article 8, be treated as an application under the Order : where permission is granted subject to conditions, or refusal to approve is decided on, the Authority must give their reasons in writing.

In dealing with an application for a street layout it may be necessary to give notice to adjoining owners and to consider any proposals they may wish to make before approval is given.

TOWN PLANNING APPEALS

Appeals may arise under the Town and Country Planning Act itself or under the provisions of a particular scheme. Under Section 10 of the Act any applicant who is aggrieved by refusal of the Authority to consent to his application for permission to develop, or by any conditions imposed by the Authority, may within twenty-eight days of receiving notice of the Authority's decision appeal to the Minister of Health. The Minister of Health if so requested may hold a Local Inquiry, and his decision is final and operates as though it were the decision of the Authority.

Appeals can also be made to the Minister of Health under the Model Clauses, which apply to particular planning schemes, or such appeals may be heard by a Court of Summary Jurisdiction, according to the wishes of the local authority.

The respective parties may also agree to submit appeals to an Arbitrator, agreed upon and appointed by the Minister of Health.

The Ministry of Health publish Annual Reports on Town Planning Appeals, and below is given a specimen schedule classifying appeals and comparing them with the appeals for the previous years :

		Per cent.		Per cent.
(1) Use of buildings		44	as against	50
(2) Density of buildings		9	,,	,, 12
(3) Proportion of site		1·8	,,	,, 1·6
(4) Design and external appearance of buildings ..		8	,,	,, 7·3
(5) Use of land for building including permanent and temporary restrictions		11	,,	,, 6
(6) Use of land for purposes likely to involve danger or injury to health and amenities		1	,,	,, 2
(7) Streets and building lines		12	,,	,, 9
(8) Reservation of open spaces and allotments ..		5	,,	,, 4
(9) Miscellaneous		7	,,	,, 5

Half of the appeals received proceed to Local Inquiry, the others are either withdrawn or settled by agreement.

Deposit of Plans

A local authority generally appoints a Special Plans Committee, with executive powers to consider deposited plans, who are advised by specially appointed planning officers and building surveyors. Good estate development co-ordinates the framework on a town plan. Powers are given in the Model Clauses to relax the width of streets which are not to be used for through traffic.

The byelaw widths for estate roads are often in excess of traffic needs and only entail heavier maintenance costs when taken over by the local authority. In order to obtain sound economic development many local authorities suggest layouts to prospective developers of estates which system works well in actual practice. From a contour plan of the site preliminary sketch layouts are made and agreed upon with the developer before final detail plans are submitted.

The basic principles upon which estate plans are dealt with may briefly be summarised as follows :

(1) For submission to carry out estate development under the Town and Country Planning (General Interim Development) Order, 1933, it is essential to obtain particulars relating to the use, height of buildings, proportion of plot which may be covered by building, and the building line allowed, from the Planning Authority before a formal decision can be obtained.

(2) Any proposals likely to involve any departure from the primary use or density zoning should be considered in the preliminary stages and consent to such variations obtained before preparing final plans for formal submission.

(3) The layout of estates showing the setting out of roads, plots, and the siting, and grouping of buildings must be approved before details of the buildings are submitted.

A general block plan, to a scale of not less than 1/2500 and up to date, should be prepared showing the division of the land into plots, size and shape of buildings, width of streets, and building line clearly dimensioned, and the general method of drainage to be used. As regards compliance of estate plans with local byelaws, we may take the Ministry of Health Model Clauses as a reliable standard, as these clauses are now generally adopted by many local authorities.

Ministry of Health Model Clauses

The Ministry of Health have from time to time issued provisional sets of Model clauses and amendments in respect of new streets and buildings which are to serve as a basis for formulating local byelaws.

Clause 11. Sites of new streets and widenings only allows a Local Authority to declare land reserved for a new street or widening of a street (*a*) with the consent of the persons interested, (*b*) after acquiring the land.

Clause 14 defines the number and sites of new streets to be allowed to enter existing or intended classified roads. This clause is now greatly helped by the Restriction of Ribbon Development Act, 1935.

Clause 19 refers to the diversion and stopping up of highways. This gives power to divert or stop up existing highways and footpaths affected by layouts of new estates where alternative rights of way will be provided by new roads.

Model Clauses dealing with Density. The definition of a " Building Unit " will only apply to dwelling houses, whilst flats are dealt with on population basis, *i.e.* 100 persons per acre. The erection of flats in all residential zones will be subject to the consent of the Council.

Clause 47. Preservation of Trees : this clause is intended to prevent destruction of trees when new estates are developed.

Building Byelaws

The clause with regard to buildings that chiefly concern estate developers is that dealing with space about buildings, wherein it is recommended that:

(1) There shall be provided in front of a domestic building intended to be used wholly or partly for human habitation an open space which, measured at right angles from the building to the boundary of any land or premises immediately opposite, or in the case of a building fronting on a street to the opposite side of the street, shall throughout the whole frontage of the building extend to a distance of not less than 24 ft. Provided that, if the building fronts on a street of a less width than 24 ft., the distance may be not less than the width of the street, together with one half of the difference between that width and 24 ft.

(2) Any open space provided within the curtilage of the building in pursuance of this byelaw shall be free from any erection thereon above the level of the ground, except a fence or wall not exceeding 7 ft. in height, or a portico, porch, step, or other like projection from the building, or a gate.

(3) There shall be provided in the rear of a domestic building intended to be used wholly or predominantly for human habitation an open space exclusively belonging thereto and of an extent not less than one hundred and fifty square feet.

(4) The open space shall extend throughout the entire width of the building and in the distance across the open space from the line of the rearmost wall of the building and from any projection from the building to the boundary of any lands or premises immediately in the rear of the building shall be not less in any part than :

(*a*) 15 ft., if the height of the building is not more than 25 ft.

(*b*) 20 ft., if the height of the building is more than 25 ft., but is not more than 35 ft.

(*c*) 25 ft., if the height of the building is more than 35 ft., but is not more than 50 ft.

(3) Where by reason of the exceptional shape of the site of the building the distance across the open space required by this byelaw cannot be obtained throughout the entire width of the building, it shall be sufficient if the mean distance across the open space is not less than the required minimum distance.

*Restriction of Ribbon Development Act, 1935

This Act enables local highway authorities to define the building line along classified roads and such other unclassified roads as may be decided by them with the approval of the Ministry of Transport. The building line under this Act in respect of classified roads is controlled up to 220 ft. back from the middle of such roads. With regard to unclassified roads for which standard widths have been decided upon by the local authority with the approval of the Ministry of Transport, the building line is fixed at a minimum distance back from the road equal to half the width of the standard width applicable to that road. If, for example, it is an 80-ft. standard-width road, then the building line will be set back at 40 ft. from the middle of the road. The standard widths of such roads are decided on by the highway authorities, and are shown on a map which is open for inspection to the public.

The Act also restricts the number of new streets communicating with classified roads to the very minimum sufficient for the needs of adjoining layouts. To obtain access to buildings fronting such main roads the developer must provide service roads adjoining the main roads, and their width and construction should be agreed upon with the highway authority before depositing final layouts.

Schedule of Standard Widths

(*Restriction of Ribbon Development Act,* 1935)

Section 24. Plan of " proposed road " or " road as proposed to be improved " to be approved by the Minister prior to adoption of standard widths, or provisions of Section 2 by resolution, if required to fix new " middle of the road ".

The " middle of the road " is the mid-point between the boundaries of an existing road, or, if a plan for the improvement of the road has been approved before the restrictions come into force, the mid-point of the road as proposed to be improved in accordance with the plan.

In the case of a " proposed road " the middle is the mid-point between the boundaries of the road as shown on the approved plan of the proposed road.

Section 1. Standard widths adoptable by highway authority for any road, by resolution and with Minister's approval. Unlawful to construct new means of access, building, permanent excavation and works within standard width, except with

* The Town and Country Planning Act, 1947, repeals Sections 1 to 3, 5 to 12, and parts of Sections 13, 15, 18, 19, 23, 24, and Schedules 1 to 3.

consent of highway authority. Standard widths up to 440 ft. may be adopted where additional width required for purpose of providing for embankments or cuttings (Stat. Rules and Orders, 1936, No. 161). See Circ. 454 (roads) of 24/3/36.

Compensation which is eligible for grant from Road Fund (Section 19 (2)), payable for injurious affection (Section 9), except where access denied to new roads.

SECTION 2.   Building (other than agricultural building) within 220 ft. from middle of road and new means of access unlawful without consent of highway authority.

Restrictions apply to all roads classified at 17/5/35, and to any other roads by resolution with Minister's approval.

Compensation for injurious affection as for Section 1 (Section 9), but not eligible for grant from Road Fund.

SECTION 13.   Highway authorities empowered to acquire land compulsorily, if necessary, within 220 yds. from the middle of the road, for the construction and improvement of roads, and for preventing the erection of buildings detrimental to the view from the road. Land in the neighbourhood of any road may be acquired by highway authority by agreement, where necessary, for the purpose of preserving amenities (including the purpose of preventing the erection of buildings detrimental to the view from the road). Expenditure on the acquisition of land for the construction or improvement of roads (but not for amenity) eligible for grants from the Road Fund (Development and Road Improvement Funds Act, 1909, as amended by subsequent Acts).

The Ministry of Transport has decided that certain classes of roads should be restricted under this Act ; these are as follows :

(1) Roads along which building development is taking place or is likely.
(2) Proposed road or roads to be widened approved by the Ministry.
(3) Roads serving areas which are zoned for building development in operative town-planning schemes.

Service roads have to be provided outside the boundary of the highway boundary with connections to the main road agreed upon with the highway authority. The levels of service roads need not be coincident with the highway if the ground levels make this difficult. The width of service roads may be of a minimum overall width of 25 ft. with a carriageway of 16 ft.

Standard road widths have been prescribed by the Ministry of Transport, and are in units of 20 ft. from 60 ft. to 160 ft.

Application for estate development on land within 220 ft. of the main road must be made to the highway authority as well as to the town planning authority if within a planning scheme. It may be observed here that there is some complication between the provisions of the Town Planning Acts and those of the Restriction of Ribbon Development Act requirements, especially with regard to the matter of compensation arising out of the various restrictions imposed. No compensation can be sustained for injurious affection in respect of such restrictions imposed by whatever Acts if such have been approved by the Ministries of Health and Transport and if notice of the proposals has previously been given to affected owners.

Some local authorities have their own special Acts with regard to laying down of new streets, which provide for the construction of preliminary streets before building is commenced and for final street works to be carried out upon completion of building work.

APPEALS

Under the provisions of Section 10 of the Act an applicant who is aggrieved by the decision of the interim development authority may lodge an appeal with the Minister of Health. The right of appeal undoubtedly relieves the local authority of a certain amount of responsibility, and in the case of extreme difficulty there is something to be said for refusing the application, leaving the applicant to appeal to the Minister.

The number of local appeals has increased rapidly in recent years, and in quite a number of instances they have been upheld by the Ministry of Health, and in many cases a compromise arrangement has been effected more or less satisfactorily to both parties.

PUBLIC HEALTH ACT, 1936

By sections 17 to 19 of this Act, the estate developer may be called upon by the local authority to provide larger sewers to allow satisfactory drainage of the surrounding district as a whole, and the extra cost of larger pipes thus entailed is to be borne by the local authority. The duty is imposed on the local authority to provide adequate public sewers for the drainage of areas within their district, and the onus is upon them to co-ordinate a satisfactory drainage system for different adjoining estates by arrangements with the various owners affected. Power is also given to a local authority to adopt sewers and sewage disposal plants, and application should be made by a private owner for such adoption who does not wish to be responsible for the maintenance of such sewers and disposal plants. Appeal can be made to the Ministry of Health should the local authority refuse to agree to such adoption. Under this Act it is compulsory upon a local authority to keep open for public inspection an accurate map showing (*a*) public sewers ; (*b*) sewers declared to be vested, but with the vesting not yet effective ; and (*c*) sewers in respect of which there is an agreement to declare them vested later. Foul and surface-water sewers must be differentiated. No buildings can be erected over existing sewers shown on the map without official consent.

*TOWN AND COUNTRY PLANNING ACT, 1943

This Act provided for bringing under planning control all land not already controlled by a scheme under the Town and Country Planning Act, 1932. Also it secured the more effective control of any development pending the coming into operation of planning schemes already matured or being prepared.

An interim development authority under the Act can postpone consideration of any application for development either indefinitely or during

* This Act has been repealed by Town and Country Planning Act, 1947. See Appendices, p. 153.

such period specified, unless the applicant proves to their satisfaction that immediate development can be carried out if the application were granted.

Appeal against any postponement can be made to Court, who have powers to cancel notice of postponement if they think fit. Also every application is deemed to have been *refused* at the end of 2 months unless the applicant has been notified that the application has been (*a*) determined, or (*b*) referred to the Minister for decision, or (*c*) postponed by notice of postponement.

The Submission and Approval of Building Plans

Intending estate developers may justly be perplexed as to what exactly are the powers local authorities have regarding estate and building works, in order to comply with the many Acts, Orders, Regulations, and byelaws relating to them. It is advisable to obtain a copy of the local byelaws and the town planning regulations and provisions, from which vital information may be obtained.

The private estate developer, having decided to proceed with building development, must prepare plans and sections of streets and sewers of the layout design best suited to the site, and which complies in its provisional draft stage with local town-planning requirements and byelaw regulations.

Plans have to be submitted to the local planning authority or the local council surveyor for formal approval, and this is necessary before any constructional work begins. An outline of the procedure involved was described earlier, but there may be some variations in different parts of the country, where the regulations may vary in detail.

Under the Town Planning (Interim Development) Order, 1933, and Ministry of Health Model Clauses it is provided that submitted schemes must be considered within one month of deposit, but in Section 10 of the Act it states the interim development authority " shall be deemed to have granted the application unconditionally unless within two months from the receipt thereof, or within such longer period as the applicant may agree in writing to allow, they give notice to him that they have decided to the contrary, stating their reason for so doing ". This decision of course, operates to the advantage of the developer, who is thus insured against unreasonable delay on the part of the Authority.

The Town and Country Planning Act, 1943, has cancelled this clause, and it now empowers the interim development authority to serve notice on the applicant (for the development of land) that application is postponed (Section 2), unless the applicant shows to the satisfaction of the authority that the proposed development would be carried out immediately if the application were granted. The applicant has a right of appeal to the Justices against the postponement.

Effect of Town and Country Planning Act, 1943

The Town and Country Planning (Interim Development) Act, 1943, makes several alterations and amendments in the provisions with regard to interim development.

It is now possible for an interim development authority to serve on the applicant developer a notice of postponement as already mentioned. Under Section 4 of this Act, where before a scheme comes into operation the interim development authority consider it expedient, having regard to the provisions then proposed to be included in that scheme, they may, by order made with the consent of the Minister, revoke or modify any permission for development that they may have given, to such extent, as appears to them to be necessary in that behalf.

Section 5 states that if any development of land is carried out otherwise than in accordance with the terms of the interim development order, such work carried out can be removed and pulled down (in the case of buildings), and the land reinstated, if necessary.   If, however, it is reasonably practicable to bring such works into compliance with the order, permission to do so can be granted.

*Town and Country Planning Act, 1944

It is provided under Section 41 that for the purposes of any planning scheme which comes into operation after the date of this Act, a building of any description as specified in Section 12 of the 1932 Act (*i.e.* mainly agricultural buildings) shall be treated as an existing building and the provisions of Section 5 of the 1943 Act will *not* apply.

Power is given to responsible authorities under Section 46 during the war period to grant under planning schemes their consent to develop with effect for a limited period.   Reference may also be made to Section 34–37 of this Act, which contain some important provisions as to applications for development by statutory undertakers, and as to revocation and modification of interim development permission given to such undertakers, and as to the postponement of applications for development by such undertakers.

The main provisions of this Act provide for the acquisition and development of land for planning purposes and for assessing compensation on 1939 basis of prices ; it enables authorities to acquire by a simplified and expedited procedure land in war damaged areas, together with land required for " overspill." from badly developed areas.

Drawings

The drawings for building plans should be prepared on linen tracings or prints.   If paper drawings are submitted they should be mounted on cloth.   Only in the case of steelwork or reinforced-concrete details can blue-prints be accepted, but these are generally in addition to the general building plans required.

The general plans and elevations should be drawn to a scale not less than 8 ft. to 1 in.   A block or site plan to a scale of not less than 44 ft. to 1 in. must accompany the building plans, showing thereon the site of the work proposed, and with a sufficient surrounding area shown to enable the location of the site to be readily ascertained.

* The Town and Country Planning Act, 1947, repeals Sections 1–14, 16–18, 20, 21, 31–46, 50–56, and definitions in Sect. 65 are amended.   Schedules 1–3 also repealed.

It is essential that the north point be shown on the site plan. The drainage of the proposed buildings and the existing sewers to which they are to be connected must also be clearly shown on the site plan.

For plans of extensive buildings a scale of 16 ft. to 1 in. may be accepted. A plan of each floor and sections of each storey, floor, and roof of the building are required. Upon the plans and sections should be indicated :

(a) The position, form, and dimensions of foundations, walls, roofs, and chimneys, in such detail as necessary to show compliance with byelaws.

(b) The form and dimensions of any water-closet, privy, or cesspool to be constructed in connection with the building.

(c) The level of the building site, level of lowest floor, and the adjoining street level should all be shown in relation to some known datum, preferably to Ordnance datum level.

EXEMPTED BUILDINGS

The following buildings are exempt from local byelaws :

(1) Government buildings.
(2) County or borough asylums.
(3) Prisons.
(4) Public undertakings, such as, water, gas, electricity, docks and harbours, and hospitals.

And buildings to be erected exclusively for the purpose of :

(1) Poultry house or aviary, if it is wholly detached and at a distance of 10 ft. from any other building.
(2) Greenhouse, summerhouse, coal-house, cycle or tool shed, provided there is a clearance of 10 ft. from other buildings, and that no internal form of heating apparatus is constructed within the building.

It is, however, necessary to give notice of intention to erect the above-mentioned buildings to the local authority, in order to show that they satisfy the conditions applying to exempted buildings.

With regard to small garages, *i.e.* those not exceeding 300 sq. ft. in area, it is essential if the garage is to be erected near a building that it should be constructed of incombustible or fire-resisting material.

In some districts wooden garages may be allowed if built 10 ft. or 15 ft. away from the nearest building.

Plans and particulars of such garages should be submitted.

CONSTRUCTIONAL DETAILS

The whole ground surface within a new domestic building shall have a 6-in. thick concrete foundation or be properly asphalted, unless the nature of the ground renders this unnecessary. The external walls are to be of good whole brick or stone, bonded solidly with lime mortar, cement, or cement mortar. Hollow walls must have not more than 3-in. wide cavity, and be properly drained and ventilated, and the walls to be tied together with strong galvanised iron bonding ties placed not less than 3 ft. horizontally and 18 in. vertically.

All walls are to rest on solid concrete foundation or footings of sufficient width and depth to rest on solid ground. A damp-proof course of sheet lead, asphalt, vitrified stoneware, or double course of impervious slates or blue brick bedded in cement mortar, or other suitable materials, must be laid below lowest floor timbers and not less than 6 in. above adjoining ground level.

The various thicknesses of walls for domestic buildings are governed by the height of the walls. Up to 25 ft. high, thickness of wall to be at least 8½ in. for a maximum length of 30 ft. For walls of greater length up to 35 ft. the thickness of walls shall be 13 in. for one storey and 8½ in. for the rest of its height. A similar ratio follows for walls up to a height of 100 ft. If the wall is 100 ft. high and not more than 45 ft. long, the thickness of the wall for ground storey is to be 26 in., then 22 in. for the next two storeys, 18 in. for the next three storeys, and 13 in thick for the rest of its height.

The jambs of chimneys must be at least 8½ in. wide and brick work surrounding flues to be at least 4 in. thick.

The angle of flues in chimney breasts should not be less than 45 degrees ; chimneys to be carried up to at least 3 ft. above the highest point of the adjoining roof.

The treads of staircases must comply with British Standard Specification, and be not less than 7 in. wide, with the rises not more than 8 in. in height. The hand-rail should not be less than 2 ft. 3 in. above tread.

Every habitable room should have at least one window opening directly to the external air. Rooms without a fireplace must be provided with an adequate means of ventilation by means of an air shaft or aperture.

Larders and w.c.s should have a window opening directly into the external air. The height of habitable rooms must not be less than 8 ft., but if in the roof they should be 8 ft. in height over not less than one half of the area of room measured at a height of 5 ft. above floor-level of the room.

DRAINAGE

The lowest level of a building must be at such a level as will allow effectual drainage of the building to the main drain or sewer. The roofs must be drained by sufficient gutters and connected to down-spouts, which in turn must be connected to drains so as not to cause dampness to the walls.

All drains should be of good sound stoneware, cast-iron, or concrete pipes of adequate size—not less than 4 in.—and laid properly at effective gradients : for 4-in. pipes, 1 in 40 ; 6-in. pipes, 1 in 60 ; and 9 in. pipes, 1 in 90 at least.

Drains passing under buildings must be of cast iron, or other pipes surrounded with 6 in. of concrete, with access chambers at each change of direction. At least one ventilating pipe must be provided at the head of the drain against the building, and the pipe must be at least 3 in. internal diameter. Where no public sewer is available, sanction must be obtained for constructing septic tanks. Such tanks must be of sufficient dimensions to deal adequately with sewage discharging to them, and be at least 50 ft. away from the nearest building and 60 ft. away from any wells or from any springs used as drinking water.

Inspection chambers are necessary at every change of direction, and in no case should chambers be more than 100 yds. apart.

It is not desirable for more than four houses to be connected to a 4-in. drain, and where possible each house should have a separate connection to the sewer. Where this is not possible, however, a combined drainage order must be applied for, permitting several houses to be drained to a combined drain connected to the sewer.

A connection between a drain and a private or public sewer shall be so made that the drain shall join the sewer obliquely in the direction of the flow of the sewer.

MISCELLANEOUS

When submitting plans it is necessary to give written notice to the local council clerk, or surveyor, giving particulars with regard to:

(a) The nature of proposed building and whether it is to be used partly or wholly as a dwelling-house.
(b) Materials to be used.
(c) Method of drainage.
(d) Means of water supply.
(e) Plans of every floor and roof together with sections of each.
(f) Block plan of building.
(g) Key plan of district.

Before building is commenced, twenty-four hours' notice must be given to the local surveyor, and inspection of drains and foundations should be made before such work is covered over. Notice of completion of work must be given in writing to the surveyor not less than seven days before it is occupied. The schedules attached to local byelaws as to requirements of dead loading, superimposed loading, permissible pressures on walls, and crushing strength of materials should be carefully read.

PUBLIC HEALTH ACT, 1936, AND BUILDING BYELAWS

The Public Health Act, 1936, consolidated with amendments the previous Acts under which building byelaws were made. Section 61 of this Act gives the scope of building byelaws by which Local Authorities are empowered to make byelaws for the regulation of :

(a) Construction of buildings and materials to be used.
(b) Space about buildings, lighting, ventilation, and dimensions of buildings intended for human habitation.

(c) Height of buildings and chimneys.
(d) Sanitary conveniences and drainage.
(e) Ashpits and water supplies.
(f) Private sewers—connections between drains and sewers.

Power is given under Section 53 to enable plans for buildings to be constructed of short-lived materials to be approved only for limited periods or even to be rejected by local authorities, although such plans may conform with the byelaws.

Owing to the constant changes in building materials and methods, it is necessary to revise byelaws to keep pace with the changes.   Guidance is given by The British Standards Institution, The Institute of Plumbers, and The Building Research Department in preparation of specifications and practice to conform with the latest byelaws.

It was the intention of the Ministry of Health to standardise, as far as possible, the building byelaws throughout the country, and it is expected that all local authorities will have revised their byelaws on the lines of the model clauses issued by the Ministry of Health.

New clauses are recommended in respect of building materials, specifications for which may be required to be in accordance with British Standard Specification and those of the Institute of Plumbers and the Building Research Board.

A local authority has no power to reject plans which are in accordance with the byelaws, and notice of approval or disapproval must be given within one month, but where meetings are only held once monthly and plans are deposited less than three days before such meeting, then the prescribed period is five weeks.

A local council may relax any byelaws only with the approval of the Ministry of Health, and then due notice must be given.   A rejection notice must state the defects or byelaw or sections of the Act which have been contravened.   An approval notice expires after three years if work has not been commenced.

OTHER PUBLIC HEALTH ACT, 1936, REQUIREMENTS

Building over Sewer.   Under Section 25 buildings cannot be erected over a sewer without the consent of a local authority before commencement of building.

Section 37 states that satisfactory drainage must be provided before building is undertaken.

Drainage must be into a public sewer if there is one within 100 ft. of such building, and if sewer is a greater distance away, then the drain may enter an approved type cesspool.

Where the local authority thinks fit a combined drain can take a combination of buildings into a public sewer, and the costs of construction and maintaining the combined drain are to be borne by affected owners.

Closet Accommodation.   Building plans must show sufficient and satisfactory closet accommodation, and can be insisted upon where water supplies and sewers are available (Sections 43 and 60).

Water Supply. Under Section 137 new houses must not be occupied without sufficient water supply, as certified by local authority as being sufficient for domestic purposes. Under the Water Supply Act, 1945, a proper piped water supply is now necessary otherwise building plans may be rejected on this account.

Section 37 of the Water Act, 1945, is of particular importance in relation to new housing development ; it imposes a specific obligation on water undertakers to lay mains in advance of development, subject to the receipt of a prescribed guarantee and, also, where applicable, of a deposit by way of security as provided in this Section ; a deposit is not required where the prospective developer is a local authority.

Section 29 also affects new houses ; in general, it requires the local authority to reject plans of new houses unless the public piped water supply is to be laid on to each house ; an appeal lies to the justices on the question of reasonableness.

This section amends section 137 of the Public Health Act, 1936.

CHAPTER 5

PRIVATE STREET WORKS PROCEDURE

PRIVATELY developed estates often have the streets constructed in preliminary formation and are not finally completed until they are fully built up.

In the case of small estates the streets are sometimes left for years in their preliminary construction, with the result that they get into a very bad state and are even dangerous for pedestrians to use. The owners of houses adjoining such streets in consequence have to pay heavy street work charges ; therefore it is advisable to get newly made streets taken over by local highway authorities as public highways as soon as building is completed.

There are primarily two public enactments by which private streets can be taken over by highway authorities as public highways and maintained at the expense of local ratepayers. The first is the Public Health Act, 1875, Sections 150, 151, and 152, and the other is the Private Street Works Act, 1892. Some local authorities have their own Private Acts for dealing with the adoption of streets, among which are Surrey County Council, Birmingham, and Baildon Urban District Council.

THE PUBLIC HEALTH ACT, 1875, SECTIONS 150–152

These sections give power to a local authority to enforce the repair and making good of private streets by owners of premises fronting, adjoining, or abutting upon such streets. When such streets are made good they are formerly adopted.

Briefly, here is the order of procedure under this Act.

(1) Resolution of a local authority to notify affected owners of the necessity to carry out necessary street works.

(2) Plans, sections, and estimates have to be prepared by the surveyor, which must be deposited in the offices of a local authority for public inspection.

(3) Notice to be given to respective owners or occupiers fronting the street.

(4) If such notice is not complied with, the local authority may execute the work themselves, and may recover in a summary manner the expenses of such work.

(5) The surveyor to apportion the expenses incurred according to the frontages of the respective owners.

(6) Notice of the amount settled by the surveyor to be due from the owner to be served upon the owners.

84

The same proceedings may be taken and the same powers may be exercised in respect of any street or road of which a part is, or may be, a public footpath, or repairable by the inhabitants at large, as fully as if the whole of such street or road was a highway not repairable by the inhabitants at large.

As a rule notices served under Section 150 are not complied with, and the local authority themselves do the work. When the works are completed and the actual cost is known, the surveyor must make an apportionment, as expenses under Section 150 are recoverable from the owners in default according to the individual frontages and in such proportion as is determined by the surveyor.

Any dispute with regard to the apportionment is determined by arbitration, and objection must be notified within three months by written notice to a local authority. By Section 81 of the Public Health Act, 1925, a local authority can contribute the whole or a portion of the expenses of the private street works executed under Section 150 of the Public Health Act, 1875.

There are certain exemptions from apportionment costs which include: Crown properties, and the incumbent or minister of any church, chapel, or place of worship, which by law is exempt from poor rate. A church-yard or burial ground attached to a church is also exempted.

The trustees of chapels are *not* exempted under this Act.

When all street works are completed the local authority may take over the street as a public highway by public declaration (see Section 152 of the Public Health Act, 1875), provided that within one month a majority of owners do not object. Under the 1890 Acts, where adopted, Section 41 is substituted for Section 152 of the Public Health Act, 1875, and the local authority may take over the street if only part of the street works have been carried out, provided that if within one month no objection has been made by a majority of owners or *value* of such owners.

Procedure for Recovery of Expenses

The following are the ways by which a local authority may, under Section 150 of the Public Health Act, 1875, recover expenses of a completed street works:

(1) Expenses may be recovered summarily from owners in default together with interest (at rate fixed under Section 257 of the Public Health Act, 1875, as amended by the Public Health Acts, 1925, Section 77).

(2) A local authority may declare payment of expenses by instalments within a period of thirty years.

(3) Amounts under £50 may be obtained through the County Court (under section 261, Public Health Act, 1875).

6

(4) The local authority may declare the expenses as private improvement expenses (Section 150) and make a private improvement rate upon occupiers of sufficient amount to pay the expenses together with interest (Section 213 of the Public Health Act, 1875).

(5) By Section 257 of the Public Health Act, 1875, expenses are a charge on the premises even though they become unoccupied during the period in which they are liable to a private improvement rate (Section 213).

A local authority must wait three months before attempting to enforce payment.

Appeal may be made to the Ministry of Health by affected owners within twenty-one days of demand notice. In any legal proceedings for recovery of expenses the Court has no jurisdiction to consider the extent of the liability or the necessity for the works.

The omission to follow strictly the terms of a local authority's notice as to the work to be done and materials to be used does not prevent a local authority recovering from the owner his proportion of the expenses incurred.

PRIVATE STREET WORKS ACT, 1892

This Act is in force in those districts in which it has been adopted by the local authorities. It, of course, supersedes the Public Health Act, 1875. The procedure under this Act may be summarised as follows:

(1) *The First Resolution.* Under Section 6 it is provided that the local authority may from time to time resolve to undertake private street works, *i.e.* to sewer, level, pave, metal, flag, channel, or make good, or to provide proper means of lighting, such street or part of a street. The expenses incurred for such works shall be apportioned on the premises fronting, adjoining, or abutting on such street or part of a street.

Where Section 35, of the Public Health Act, 1925, has been adopted, in all rural districts the local authority may by their resolution decide to vary the relative width of the carriageway and footway of such street, but the expenses incurred by such variation will not be apportioned to the frontagers.

(2) *Preparation of Plans, etc., by the Surveyor.* When the first resolution has been passed the surveyor has to prepare a specification, plans, and sections, for such streets as are referred to in the resolution, together with an estimate of probable expenses of the work. He must also prepare a provisional apportionment of the estimated expenses upon the premises liable to be charged.

The local authority may, however, if they think just, resolve that in settling the apportionment regard shall be had to the following considerations :

(a) The greater or less degree of benefit to be derived by any premises from such works.

(*b*) The amount and value of any work already done by owners or occupiers of any such premises.

(*c*) They may include other premises which, though not fronting such streets, have access thereto through a court or passage, and may fix the sum or proportion to be charged against any such premises accordingly.

(3) *The Second Resolution.* The local authority must approve of the surveyor's plans and sections, estimate, and provisional apportionment with or without modifications. This resolution must be publicly advertised once in each of two successive weeks in the local newspaper and also be publicly posted in or near the street to which it relates once at least in each of three successive weeks.

Copies of the resolution shall be served upon the owners of premises shown as liable to be charged within seven days after the date of the first resolution. The notice to the owner is a condition precedent to liability of the owner. If no notice is served the owner is not liable ; also notice served upon the " reputed owner " is not sufficient.

(4) *Deposit of Plans, etc.* For one month from the first publication of the second resolution, the approved specification, plans, and sections, estimate, and provisional apportionment shall be kept deposited in offices of a local authority and shall be open for inspection.

(5) *Objection to Works.* During the month the owner of premises may by written notice served upon a local authority object to the proposals on any of the following grounds:

(*a*) That an alleged street or part of a street is not, or does not form part of, a street within the meaning of the Act.

(*b*) That a street or part is in whole or in part a highway repairable by the inhabitants at large.

(*c*) That there has been some material informality, defect, or error in respect of resolution, notice, plans, sections, or estimates.

(*d*) That the proposed works are insufficient or unreasonable or that the estimate is excessive.

(*e*) That any premises ought to be excluded from or included in the provisional apportionment.

(*f*) That the provisional apportionment is incorrect in respect of some matter to be specified, *i.e.* in respect of degree of benefit or the value of work already done by the owners.

(6) *Hearing of Objections.* At the end of one month a local authority may apply to a Court of Summary Jurisdiction to appoint a time to hear and determine any objections received.

(7) *Execution of the Works.* Having disposed of the objections the work may be executed. By Section II the local authority is empowered from time to time to amend the specification, plans, sections, and provisional apportionments ; but if such amendment increases the estimate,

then the whole procedure must be gone through again. This is not necessary if the estimate is not increased.

(8) *Final Apportionment.* The surveyor upon completion of the works
is to make a final apportionment of the actual expenses in the same manner
as the provisional apportionment, and notice of such final apportionment
must be served upon the owners.

(9) *Objections to the Final Apportionment.* Within one month owners
may by written notice to a local authority object to the final apportionment on the following grounds :

(a) That the actual expenses have without sufficient reason exceeded
the estimated expenses by more than 15 per cent.

(b) That the final apportionment has not been made in accordance with
this Section.

(c) That there has been an unreasonable departure from the specification, plans, and sections.

These objections may be considered in the same manner as those of the
provisional apportionment. Expenses can be recovered summarily or
by action, under Section 14.

ADOPTION OF STREET

A local authority can declare the street upon completion of the works
to be a public highway (Section 19), or owners may make application if
the works are completed to satisfaction of a local authority and shall
within three months declare such a street to be a public highway. By
Section 16, the incumbent or minister or trustee of any church, chapel, or
place of worship, and any churchyard, or burial ground attached thereto,
shall be exempt from expenses.

In making a comparison between the two Acts it will be seen that there
is no way under the 1875 Act of questioning the liability of the owners
until after the street works have been completed.

Under the 1892 Act all objections are considered and disposed of *before*
street works are undertaken, and also it is left to the discretion of local
justices to consider the reasonableness of the proposed works, whereas
under the 1875 Act this is a matter left to the local authority.

There are, however, several objections to either of these Acts from the
frontagers' point of view, such as what will be their probable share of the
costs of the street works and their ability to meet such costs. Also as it
may be several years before streets are adopted, the frontagers feel
aggrieved at paying rates for public services in respect of street cleansing,
repairs, etc., which they do not have, and then suddenly be called upon to
pay for street works.

ADOPTION OF ESTATE ROADS UNDER SECTION 146 OF PUBLIC HEALTH ACT, 1875

When the developer of an estate wishes to have the roads taken over by
the local highway authority on completion, an agreement is entered in
accordance with the above section, the principal points being as follows:

FIG. 32. An example of a builder's road

FIG. 33. A concrete estate road

(1) The estate developer shall construct roads in accordance with the local highway authority's standard specification for private street works under the supervision of the surveyor.

(2) The local highway authority will adopt the roads as highways repairable by the inhabitants at large when fully built upon, and when they have been maintained to the satisfaction of the surveyor for a period of six months after completion. Both these conditions must be fulfilled before adoption.

(3) The estate developer will repay to the local highway authority the cost of the employment of a Clerk of Works to act under the control of the surveyor, this employee being appointed and paid by the local highway authority.

(4) The estate developer will pay for any testing of materials ordered by the surveyor.

The last two clauses ensure that the local highway authority is not called upon to bear, out of revenue, charges which under section 150 of the Public Health Act, 1875, would form part of a private street works loan. When these conditions are fulfilled, the roads are formally adopted by resolution in accordance with Section 152 of the Public Health Act, 1875.

" BUILDER'S " ROADS

A landowner may construct roads on an estate for the purpose of producing frontage land to be sold in building plots. There being no co-ordinated scheme for sewer and service connections, it will be necessary to open up such roads at any time and places required.

A " builder's " road must be constructed in accordance with the local council's byelaws, and comply with Regulations of Sections 146 or 150 of the Public Health Act, 1875.

Here is a typical specification of a " builder's " road generally used :

Carriageway. 6 in. of good clean gravel, flint, or granite, laid on a foundation of 9 in. of hardcore with a crossfall not less than $\frac{3}{4}$ in. nor more than $\frac{1}{2}$ in. to 1 ft. (See Fig. 32, p. 89.)

Channelling. Not less than three courses of setts of granite or other suitable material, properly grouted with cement grout and laid upon a bed of 6 in. of concrete.

Kerbing. Dressed kerb of granite or other suitable material, 10 in. × 5 in. or 12 in. × 6 in. on 6 in. of concrete.

Footways. 4-in. binding noggin or 6 in. of slag, clinker, or hardcore laid to a crossfall of $\frac{1}{2}$ in. to 1 ft. Under Section 150 of Public Health Act, 1875, it is necessary for a local authority to supervise the construction of "builder's" roads and also its statutory making up.

Concrete Roads. Carriageway constructed of two-course reinforced concrete 6 in. thick laid on bed of 3 in. of ashes and provided with expansion joints. (See Fig. 33.)

In all cases plans, specifications, estimates, and serving of notices, etc., have to be done by the local authority under Section 150.

In contrast with this, under Section 146 of the Public Health Act, 1875, the local authority is relieved of all this work, except supervision and issuing of final notices of adoption. The negotiations are with only one party instead of individual frontagers, and consequently they are considerably simplified and accelerated.

The procedure under this Section also affords considerable benefit to the estate developer, since he thus obtains a well made road which facilitates transport and building operations, and then the houses being completed, forms an excellent selling factor.

Again, the purchaser of limited means finds difficulty in meeting road charges demands under Section 150. The effect of Section 146 is to spread these charges over a term of years, corresponding to the terms of house mortgage repayments, instead of a limited period allowed by local authorities.

PRIVATE ACTS

Several local authorities have had special Acts passed to ensure street works being satisfactorily carried out or financially provided for before any buildings are erected in such streets. Surrey County Council had an Act passed in 1931 imposing the condition that before a building is let, sold, or occupied a sufficient and properly constructed means of communication must be provided.

An Act of special interest is the Baildon Urban District Council Act, 1935, in which the Council has the power to require an estate developer to give security for the payment of any expenses likely to be incurred by the Council in executing private street works prior to development taking place.

A right of appeal against the Council's decision may be had in Court of Summary Jurisdiction. It is stated that this simple but effective Act has prevented financially unsound estate developers from jeopardising housing development generally.

New street works and sewers should be properly constructed and finally completed as and when building development takes place and in accordance with a reasonable specification and standards required by the Local Authority.

A specimen private street works plan and section is shown in Fig. 34.

SPECIFICATIONS FOR PRIVATE STREET WORKS

The Institution of Municipal Engineers in 1932–1933 prepared for the Ministry of Health a Specification for private street works, which highway authorities might accept as a reasonable standard under normal conditions, which is given below.

STANDARD SPECIFICATION FOR PRIVATE STREET WORKS

The following specification is regarded as a standard of reasonable requirements in normal circumstances and under urban conditions. In some circumstances a lighter or heavier specification may be justified.

It should be understood that other equally suitable materials may be admitted where their use would not increase the cost ; and the use of suitable local materials should be encouraged.

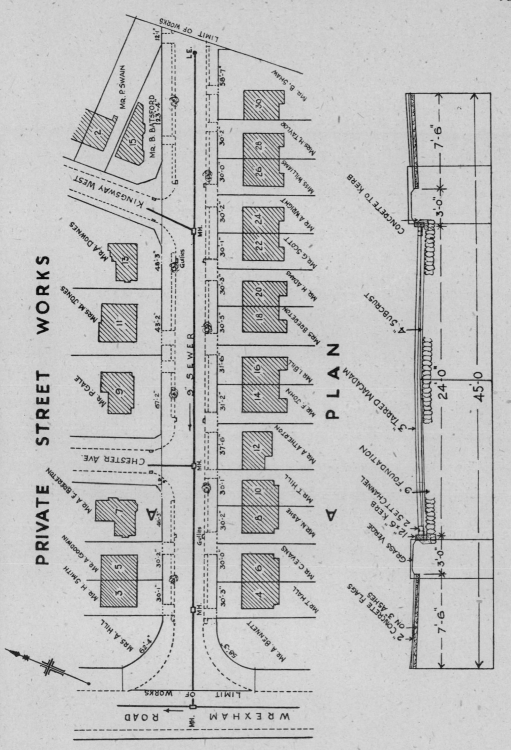

CROSS SECTION A-A

Fig. 34. A specimen private street works plan

A. CARRIAGEWAYS

Tar or Bituminous Macadam

(1) Foundation.

9 in. finished thickness of suitable stone, hard-core, old bricks, chalk, slag, or other equally satisfactory material, based on 3 in. of ashes when the subsoil is clay or marl.

(2) Surfacing.

3 in. to 4 in. finished thickness of tar or bituminous macadam.

(3) Channels.

Where considered necessary a single row of setts or channel stones laid on concrete.

Concrete

The thickness should be 6 in. and the proportion should be 1 part of cement to 4 parts of stone or gravel and 2 parts of sand (1 : 4 : 2). Where rendered necessary by subsoil conditions the concrete should be based on a 3-in. thickness of ashes. The aggregate to be used should depend largely on what suitable material is available. Where necessary in the opinion of the engineer, reinforcement should be used. The concrete should be consolidated by tamping or other means to correct camber and levels. Expansion joints should be provided where necessary.

B. KERBS.

To be of granite, gritstone, whinstone, Blue Pennant, hard sandstone, pre-cast concrete, or other suitable material. Size 12 in. × 6 in. if laid on edge or 12 in. × 8 in. if laid flat. Kerbs of smaller section should be laid on concrete. Where rendered necessary by subsoil or other conditions, the kerbs should be concreted in.

C. FOOTWAYS

(1) Foundation : 4 in. ashes, broken bricks or other suitable material.

(2) Surfacing. Such portion as is paved should be of concrete flagging not less than 2 in. thick.

TOWN AND COUNTRY PLANNING ACT, 1947, PART IV, SECTION 48.
CONSTRUCTION AND IMPROVEMENT OF PRIVATE STREETS

(1) The provisions of the above section shall apply to any land defined by a development plan as the site of a proposed road, or as land required for the widening of any existing road which is of less than byelaw width, being land which is designated by the plan as land to which this section applies.

(2) Where any land is so defined and designated as aforesaid, the appropriate council may at any time declare the land to be a private street, and thereinbefore the land shall be deemed to have been dedicated to the public and to be a private street.

(3) In relation to which land which is deemed to be a private street, the provisions of the Private Street Works Act, 1892, or sections 150–151 Public Health Act, 1875, shall apply, subject to such exceptions, adaptations and modifications as may be presented by regulations made under this Act, as if the land were a street to which these provisions respectively apply.

(4) Such regulations provide that

    (a) the amount of expenses incurred for private street works shall not exceed the amount as would be charged if carried out to comply with byelaws or such requirements of the local highway authority prior to declaration of such streets as highways repairable by the inhabitants at large ;

    (b) no expenses for street works shall be recoverable against agricultural land or buildings ;

    (c) no expenses be recoverable in respect of any land unless and until access is provided and used from such land to the street.

CHAPTER 6

TYPES OF HOUSES AND PRACTICAL ASPECTS OF DESIGN

SINCE 1919 the great advances made in municipal housing, garden city, and estate development have brought about a great improvement of housing conditions in this country.

In 1918 a Special Committee under the Chairmanship of Sir J. Tudor-Walters thoroughly investigated housing construction, and issued a comprehensive Report * as to types of houses and accommodation required by the working classes.

The Report stated the need for parlour houses and provision of a large living-room to relieve congestion in the kitchen or scullery, and the provision of separate bathrooms was also stressed.

The Committee recommended these minimum standards for various rooms:

Non-parlour House				Floor Area in sq. ft.
Living-room	..	..	.. ..	180
Scullery ..	..	..	.. ..	80
Larder ..	..	..	.. ..	24
Bedroom No. 1 ..	..	..	.. ..	150
,, ,, 2 ..	..	..	.. ..	100
,, ,, 3 ..	..	..	.. ..	65

Parlour House				
Parlour ..	..	..	.. ..	120
Living-room	..	..	.. ..	180
Scullery ..	..	..	.. ..	80
Larder ..	..	..	.. ..	24
Bedroom No. 1 ..	..	..	.. ..	160
,, ,, 2 ..	..	..	.. ..	120
,, ,, 3 ..	..	..	.. ..	110

See illustrations in Fig. 35, p. 96.

PLANNING THE INTERIOR

Economy in Planning. Simple, straightforward plans will usually prove the most economical, without out-building and back projections except in specific cases. This is especially so in the case of non-parlour cottages.

Flues should be grouped into as few chimney-stacks as possible.

* Report published by His Majesty's Stationery Office.

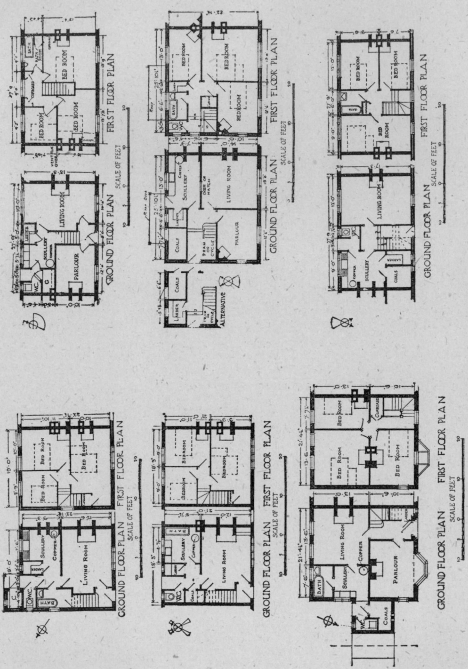

Fig. 35. Plans of houses mentioned in Tudor-Walters' Report, 1918

Ornament to the exterior of the cottage is both unnecessary and costly. Therefore effect should be gained by good proportion in mass and openings and well considered use of materials. Local materials and knowledge should be exploited to the full.

Roof design should be simple and eaves run in an unbroken line just above first-floor window heads. The introduction of dormers increases the cost, though it may reduce the cube of the building. In a row of houses on sloping sites, to avoid expensive and ugly steps in the roof a low type of house could be used at the high end of the row and a special three-storey house could be introduced (for larger families) at the other end at very little extra cost. Flat roofs become a design problem as a result of the introduction of concrete.

End houses offer planning opportunities, such as easy lighting and ventilation for the staircase or larder, variety of position for the front door, etc. Paragraphs 152 to 158 of the Report, fully illustrated, go into details of planning possibilities under varied circumstances.

The parlour should be provided whenever possible, and not at the expense of the necessary accommodation and area of the living-room and scullery. In all housing schemes a large proportion of houses having parlours should be included.

In the two-bedroomed house, a room could be provided on the ground floor for duty as parlour or third bedroom.

The parlour should never be less than 120 sq. ft. A west aspect is most suitable, though north-west would do where the living-room has a south-east frontage. There should be direct access to it from the front entrance lobby. It need not have more than one door, and this should not open directly across the window or the fire.

The living-room should not be less than 180 sq. ft., rectangular rather than square in plan, and preferably with a south-east aspect. There should be as few doors as possible, and these should be grouped on one side or as near a corner as possible, and away from fireplace and window areas. If any cooking is done in the living-room, then there should be a door communicating with the scullery.

Cooking, washing-up, etc., should be eliminated from the living-room and delegated to the scullery. The difficulty of two fires can be overcome by the use of a gas fire in the scullery and an open fire complete with hob in the living-room ; or there can be a combined living-room fire and kitchen range—the fire in the former room, the oven and hot-plate in the kitchen.

The living-room fireplace should be on a wall at right angles to the window, and preferably on one side of the short walls of the room.

Where a cooking-range is in the living-room, the boiler for heating water should be placed at the back of the range ; where there is a cooking-range-cum-grate in the living-room and a gas cooker in the scullery, the boiler should be at the back of the living-room grate ; where, however, the cooking-range is in the scullery, the boiler should be at the back of it in the scullery.

The Scullery. The minimum desirable size for the scullery is 80 sq. ft.

There should be ample space for sink, with adjacent draining-board ; table or wide shelf ; plate racks ; a copper (if there is no separate wash-house) complete with steam outlet hood and ventilator ; a simple grate or slow-combustion stove for drying clothes ; gas cooker if possible ; an additional cooking-range if possible ; a bread-baking oven in certain districts ; space for wash tubs, mangle or wringer ; ample cupboards and shelves.

The many doors necessary in a scullery should be planned carefully, so as not to encroach upon the limited floor area.

A back lobby is always useful for storing pails, tubs, cycles, etc.

The window should face the garden, not another scullery window or a blank wall, and provide plenty of light and air.   The sill should be 3 ft. 6 in. above floor level to clear sink and taps.

The Bath.   In every house with the water laid on there should be a bath. It should not be placed in the scullery where that room is used for cooking. As an expedient it could be adjacent to the scullery, so that the water can be heated in the copper ; or the copper could be in the bathroom and the room used as a wash-house when necessary.

Bathroom and scullery should be adjacent or over one another, so as to concentrate all plumbing and drainage as far as possible at one part of the house.   A desirable size for the bathroom is 8 ft. × 5 ft. minimum.

There should be a lavatory basin in the bathroom.

Baths in sculleries should be fitted with table-tops as covers.

The W.C.   The w.c. should not be altogether out of doors or too exposed to frost ; it should not be entered directly from any other room or from a lobby devoid of light and ventilation.   If possible it should not be combined with the bathroom, but if upstairs placed next to it.   In rural districts a w.c. on the ground is to be preferred.

Larder.   A north or north-east aspect is desirable, or a position on a cold side of the house ; otherwise a shutter or small pent roof should be provided.   The windows and ventilators should be fitted with flyproof gauze or perforated zinc.   The room should not be adjacent to a chimney-breast, w.c. gully, drainage, or dustbin.   It should be at least 12–16 sq. ft. in houses in urban areas and 24 sq. ft. in rural areas.

Coal Store.   This should have an area of at least 15 sq. ft.   The store should not be entered from the scullery, but from an outside lobby or passage.

Staircase and Landing.   Stairs should not be less than 3 ft. wide ; 6 ft. should be the minimum width for staircase returning on itself.   Winders should be avoided.   The staircase should start if possible from the entrance lobby.   There should always be direct light and ventilation to staircase and landing.

Bedrooms.   The minimum total area for three bedrooms in a non-parlour type of house should be 315 sq. ft. (150, 100, and 65 sq. ft.) ; and in a parlour type house, 390 sq. ft. (160, 120, and 110 sq. ft.).   All bedrooms should have direct access to the landing.

At least two of the bedrooms should be fitted with fireplaces ; and efficient ventilation should be supplied in the third bedroom not so fitted. Wardrobe cupboards should be provided.

Back Gardens. It is found less expensive and more convenient to provide access to the back garden of each house from the one front road (back roads are unsuitable and costly) by means of a side path in each case with semi-detached houses and the end houses of groups, and by means of an open archway through the ground-floor storey for intermediate houses, giving access by a joint path to two gardens behind.

Ministry of Health Housing Standards

The average size of house, as recommended by the Ministry of Health in the years 1919 to 1922, was the general type of parlour house having a maximum floor area of both storeys of about 1100 sq. ft. and a headroom of 8 ft. In 1922 to 1932 this maximum floor space was reduced to 950 sq. ft. In the 1936 Housing Act minimum floor area was as low as 620 sq. ft. and the minimum size of a parlour house was about 860 sq. ft.

Standard of Accommodation Laid Down for British Housing Under the Housing Acts of 1935 and 1936

A new standard of accommodation was laid down under the above Acts. It refers to the number of persons sleeping in any one house. The permitted number is determined in accordance with one or other of the following Tables, *whichever is the less* :

Where the dwelling-house consists of :

TABLE A

1 room	..	..	..	2 persons
2 rooms	..	..	..	3 ,,
3 ,,	..	..	..	5 ,,
4 ,,	..	..	..	$7\frac{1}{2}$,,
5 ,, or more	..	..	..	10 ,,

with an additional 2 in respect of each room in excess of 5.

The aggregate number obtained by reckoning for each room a number of persons as follows :

TABLE B

Where the floor area of a room is :

110 sq. ft. or more	..	..	..	2 persons
90–110 sq. ft.	..	..	..	$1\frac{1}{2}$,,
70– 90 ,, ,,	..	..	..	1 ,,
50– 70 ,, ,,	..	..	..	$\frac{1}{2}$,,
Under 50 sq. ft.	..	..	..	Nil.

In Table A no regard is to be had to any room which either has a floor area of less than 50 sq. ft. or is " of a type not normally used in the locality either as a living-room or bedroom ". The child of under 1 year does not count ; the child of between one and ten years old counts as half a person. This standard is not a bedroom standard.

" Suitable alternative accommodation " is defined as meaning a dwelling-house in which the family concerned can live without causing it to be overcrowded. The local authority must certify the house to be suitable to the needs of the occupier and his family as regards security of tenure and proximity to place of work and otherwise, and to be suitable in relation to his means.

PUBLIC OPINION

Recently sought opinions from people all over the country have shown the following requirements are mostly desired :

(1) Houses at a cost within their financial means. A basis these days is that rent should not be more than one-fourth of a man's income.

(2) The house should be in a pleasant and suitable locality as will not impose excessive transport costs to their work.

(3) That there must be suitable amenities within easy reach, such as, playing-fields, children's playgrounds, shops, social amenities, and schools, etc.

(4) Each house to have front and back gardens with adequate privacy. Back doors not to be overlooked by adjoining houses, and separate front gates are preferred to communal gates.

(5) The rooms should be planned to allowed maximum sunshine in every room. Draughty passages, doors, and windows to be avoided.

(6) French windows in living-room facing the garden. The position of doors and windows so placed as will prevent overlooking those of adjacent houses.

(7) Separate w.c., wash-house, and storehouse to be supplied.

COMPARATIVE STANDARDS OF ACCOMMODATION

Four-room Dwelling	Swedish Standard, sq. ft.	L.C.C. Standard, sq. ft.	Tudor-Walters' Standard for a non-parlour house, sq. ft.	
Living-room	215	160		180
First bedroom ..	129	120		150
Second bedroom ..	107·5	110		100
Third bedroom ..	75·5	110		65
Kitchen	97	75		80
Bathroom and W.C.	43	76	Bath	40
Entrance hall ..	64·5	—	Larder	12–16
Cupboards	32	—	Coal store	15
Overall area	807	755	(Say)	860–900

This Table sets out comparative standards of dwelling space as provided by the Sweden, L.C.C., and Tudor-Walters' Standards.

POINTS IN DESIGN

The sanitary accommodation should be so arranged that the w.c. is detached from the bathroom and easily accessible without crossing any rooms to reach them. The general design of new houses should allow rooms of sufficient size to permit of comfortable habitation. The living-room should be at least 180 sq. ft. and the parlour not less than 120 sq. ft. The scullery and kitchenette must be sufficient to hold a deep sink and long draining board, cooker, wash boiler, store cupboard, and small table, and a minimum area of 90 sq. ft. is essential.

With regard to the bedrooms, two of these should be sufficiently large for them to accommodate a bed 4 ft. 6 in. × 6 ft. 6 in. or two beds each 3 ft. × 6 ft. 6 in. The third bedroom should hold a bed 4 ft. × 6 ft., area not less than 80 sq. ft., and properly ventilated. All bedrooms should be supplied with built-in wardrobes or cupboards.

Bathrooms are better placed on the first floor and should be fitted with bath, wash basin, and linen cupboard, with the hot and cold water cisterns easily available contained therein. A separate w.c. is desirable.

The larder should be commodious with ample shelves, and facing north.

The height of all rooms should be at least 8 ft.

The Model Building Byelaws issued by the Ministry of Health are a standard that should be observed as the fundamentals for the construction and design of houses, and the requirements of the Housing Act, 1936, will also greatly influence future planning.

All outside drainage pipes, *i.e.* soil pipes, rainwater pipes, etc., should be arranged where possible at the rear of the house as they rather mar the appearance of the front elevations.

Partitions on each floor should as far as possible be over each other, thus adding to the strength and stability of the building.

Private Building Enterprise

The position with regard to private building enterprise is different from council housing because the clients are consulted by the architect or the builder, and careful consideration is given to the client's special requirements as to cost, choice of site, design, aspects, and features of construction required.

On the other hand, if speculative building is undertaken, then it becomes necessary on the part of the builder to erect houses attractively designed as will readily sell to prospective clients.

The primary requirements in effective house planning are :

(1) Careful arrangements of the rooms to avoid unnecessary passageways, convenience of access to each room, their aspects and judicious placing of windows and doors.

(2) As much light as possible is desirable in all rooms except the larder, so that the house should have a south-westerly aspect where possible.

In these days many people prefer one large living-room to having two small rooms. The problem of obtaining privacy in a large room can be met by having a folding partition within it, and this arrangement is becoming increasingly popular.

The bedroom should be planned around the bed, and fireplace so placed as it can be seen by the occupant of the bed. The demand is increasing for the provision of running-water basins in bedrooms and well fitted tiled bathrooms, even in the smallest houses.

Bathrooms are best placed over the kitchen so that the water cistern in the bathroom can be readily and easily heated.

The general structural planning of an average house that proves most efficient and economical is the rectangular plan without projections, and this gives economy in roof construction as well. A pitched roof over an irregular plan is both difficult and expensive, and a flat roof may have to be used to reduce costs. The judicious use of materials for elevation effects is important in house designs, as this is first of all what attracts the prospective purchaser. Brick, tile, and cement manufacturers vie with each other for variety in design and colour of their respective materials.

There is also, now, much variety in slates that give pleasing colour effects in roofs. Brick facings and cement work of varying tints and different types of slates and tiles on roofs can also be used to present a varied and harmonious elevation.

PREFABRICATED HOUSES

Other forms of house construction have been considered by the Government, the need being to erect such types of houses in the shortest time and with the minimum of skilled labour.

The question of man-hours, materials, and costs has been investigated, and experimental houses of different types erected to ascertain the most suitable to solve the post-war housing problems. Such materials as concrete, foamed slag, light-weight concrete called " no-fines ", steel frames and brick or concrete panels, all steel walls, and timber houses are all tried out under a controller of experimental building. (See Fig. 36 of an early-type of a temporary house.)

A Report of an Inter-departmental Committee on House Construction, under the Chairmanship of Sir G. Burt, set up to consider various house-building methods and materials to be used as an alternative to standard types, was published in April 1944.

This report was divided in three parts :

> Part 1 : Basic Technical Considerations.
> Part 2 : Alternative Forms of Construction.
> Part 3 : Notes on Materials.

A survey was made of all methods of house construction over recent years and selection of most satisfactory methods have been recommended.

Various types of walling systems have been considered and briefly assessed below.

Pre-cast or concrete in situ walls are good alternatives, but to be successful depend on careful control of materials and workmanship.

Timber construction is recommended, though limited by liability to fire risks and scarcity of supplies.

Steel Frame Construction opens up prospects of new methods of floor, roof, and walling construction, and should be further experimented upon.

Part 1 contains discussions and suggestions for guidance of designs giving data regarding strength and stability, thermal and sound installations.

Part 2 describes alternative forms of construction, such as concrete houses, framed or solid timber houses, steel framed houses, and metal-clad houses. (See illustrations in Figs. 37–44, pp. 105–108.)

Part 3 gives a review of some alternative materials which should be tried out whilst normal materials are still in short supply.

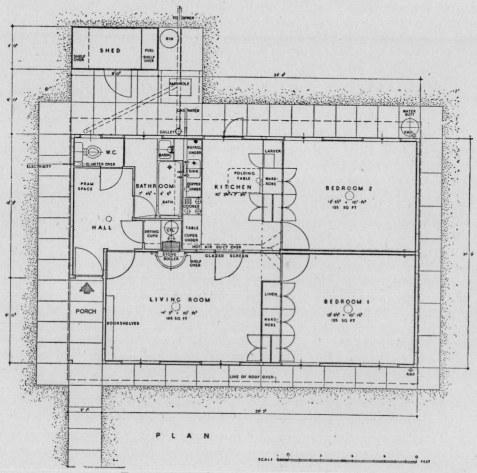

FIG. 36. Early type of a prefabricated house

Experiments are being made by the Ministry of Health for the development of new forms of construction and use of alternative materials.

Standardised types of steel casement windows, metal baths, water heaters, and cisterns are to be produced, which should secure efficiency and economy. As far as it is known, it is intended that prefabricated houses will only be provided by Government and local authorities on specially prepared sites ; but to meet fully the great housing shortage there is little doubt that private enterprise will be encouraged to build new houses in large numbers at opportune times.

7

Experimental steel houses have been constructed in Birmingham, which if successful and if reasonable in cost may be more generally adopted.

FLATS

In built-up areas where open land is both scarce and costly and in industrial areas where clearance areas are available, resort is made to flat building in order to increase building density, so as to get as many dwelling units as possible on the land available.

There are mainly three types of flats :

(1) Balcony type
(2) Corridor type
(3) Direct-access type

The Balcony Type is the cheapest form of flats. The open-access balcony generally is on the north side, and serves a large number of units ; the objection to them is that many rooms look out on to the balcony of another flat, and can be overlooked by people using the balcony.

The Corridor Type consists of flats grouped on either side of an inside corridor, and on this plan a large number of flats can be built. The rooms are generally long and narrow so as to get external lighting, and the corridor had to be lighted either artificially or by borrowed lights from the flats.

The Direct Access Type of flat is the best type of flat. Access to the flats is obtained from a common entrance hall. Such flats, however, should not be more than four storeys high, as they then require expensive lifts.

The average flat dwelling contains an entrance lobby from which are approached a living-room ; one, two, or three bedrooms ; a kitchen ; a bathroom and water closet. The areas of rooms vary between 100 and 160 sq. ft. each.

Flats, however, are not liked by many people, who prefer individual houses with gardens, where privacy is assured.

ACCOMMODATION STANDARDS

One-room Dwelling	Swedish Standards (Flats), sq. ft.	L.C.C. Standards (Flats), sq. ft.
Bed-sitting room	165	55
Kitchen and dining alcove	105	
Bathroom and W.C. ..	27	37
Entrance hall	40	—
Cupboards, etc.	—	—
Overall Area ..	365	230

The Table given shows comparative accommodation standards for flats in Sweden and those of L.C.C.

FIG. 37. The Duo-slab house in construction

FIG. 38. The Boot Pier and Panel continuous cavity house

7*

FIG. 39. The Winged Pier and Panel house in construction

FIG. 40. Typical light steel frame construction

FIG. 41. The Crane house in construction

FIG. 42. The Thorncliffe house in construction

Fig. 44. Jointing of sheets in the Weir house

Fig. 43. Light steel frame

SECOND HOUSE CONSTRUCTION REPORT, 1946 *

This is the Second Report of the Inter-departmental Committee which was formed to advise Ministers on materials, methods of construction, and in particular on experimental work in connection with house building carried out by the Ministry of Works.

This Report describes and comments on prototypes of eight methods of construction as follows :

(1) *Braithwaite Unit Frames* (steel frame with cladding of brick or asbestos cement sheeting).

(2) *Keyhouse Unibuilt* (steel frame to which are clipped asbestos cement trays).

(3) *Glasgow Corporation Foamed-Slag Flats* (walls of storey-height foamed-slag concrete units).

(4) *Birmingham Corporation Steel-Framed House* (steel frame with cavity wall of brick and foamed-slag concrete slabs).

(5) *Airey New Duo-Slab House* (precast concrete posts and panels).

(6) *Howard Steel-framed House* (steel frame with foamed-slag concrete and asbestos-cement walls).

(7) *Boot Beaucrete Concrete Houses* (concrete frame, cavity walls of concrete).

(8) *B.I.S.F. Steel-Framed Houses* (Types A and C) (steel frame, cavity walls of brick and breeze or foamed-slag blocks).

All types are considered suitable for a 60-year loan provided (in certain cases) certain conditions are fulfilled.   Attached to the Report are three appendices dealing with :

(*a*) protection of steel against corrosion ;

(*b*) internal condensation in houses whose roofs and walls are of composite construction ; and

(*c*) fire hazard.

Illustrations are given in Figs. 37–44 of various types of construction.

HOUSING MANUAL, 1944 †

This manual summarises, as far as the housing field is concerned, the work of the Central Housing Advisory Committee of the Ministry of Health and the work of the Study, Standard, and Codes of Practice Committees of the Ministry of Works.

The manual itself was supplemented in due course by a volume entitled " Housing Manual, 1944 ; Technical Appendices".

The manual is in nine sections:

(I) HOUSING AND SITE PLANNING. The importance of the relation of the house to the site, to places of recreation, and to shopping and educational facilities is stressed and the co-operation of the various authorities and interests to this end is urged.

* House Construction. Post-war Building Studies No. 23. Second Report. Published by His Majesty's Stationery Office, June, 1946 (price 1*s*. 6*d*.).

† Issued jointly by the Ministry of Health and the Ministry of Works and published by His Majesty's Stationery Office (price 2*s*.).

The manual makes a new and welcome approach to density zoning in terms of persons rather than houses per acre. This less rigid approach to density is, of course, a prerequisite to a balanced housing scheme incorporating variegated types of dwellings.

(II) THE HOUSE AND ITS SURROUNDINGS. The manual emphasises the importance of avoiding monotony in layout and of ensuring easy access to transport and shopping centres and a safe road to schools and playing-fields. Monotony can be avoided by skilful grouping, linking features, and judicious planning. The relationship of road to function is recommended, *e.g.* a 13-ft. wide carriageway for a cul-de-sac or quadrangle. See Figs. 45, 46 (Figs. 6 and 7 in manual). Attention is also drawn to the relationship between siting and daylighting standards, and an angle of obstruction, at ground-floor sill level, of not more than 18 degrees is recommended.

(III) THE THREE-BEDROOM HOUSE. Since the three-bedroom type is likely to predominate in the post-war transitional period, room sizes and planning arrangements for this type are examined in detail. Three main plan types are distinguished as the kitchen/living-room house, the working/kitchen house, and the dining/kitchen house. Plan areas aggregate 850–900 sq. ft., in comparison with pre-war standard of 760 sq. ft. (See Figs. 47–55, pp. 114–117.)

In addition to the general plan arrangements, the manual stresses the need for built-in cupboards, direct lighting and ventilation to stairs, adequate pram space, and fuel storage space. Also improved heating installations.

It should be noted that the Dudley Committee's Report on the planning of the three-bedroom house presents both problem and solution with greater clarity than does this manual.

(IV) SPECIAL OCCUPANTS. *Rural Workers.* Over and above the accommodation provided in the urban equivalent, the rural house needs more storage space for food and implements. Protective tree planting on exposed sites is also desirable.

Small and Large Households. In the two-bedroomed house the second bedroom should be of double-bedroom size. As an emergency measure, the division of a three-bedroom house into two flats, each accommodating a family, may be considered.

Houses for larger families should be mixed in with other types.

Old People and Single Persons. The needs of old and single persons should be considered, and special type of dwellings provided. Circumstances will dictate whether hostels, houses, or flats, with or without communal facilities, are the more suitable.

(V) FLATS. Room sizes to be the same as for houses, plus ground-floor stores for prams, bicycles, and the like. Also provision for the open-air drying of clothes. Lifts for flats over three storeys in height are recommended. (See Figs. 56–60, pp. 118, 119.)

(VI) EFFICIENCY IN BUILDING. The manual comes out strongly on the side of standardisation and mass production as the principal methods of reducing building costs. Performance standards have already been

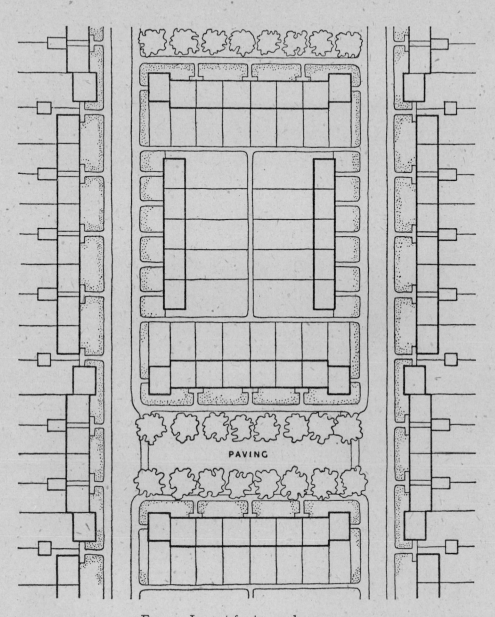

PAVING

FIG. 45. Layout for terrace houses

8

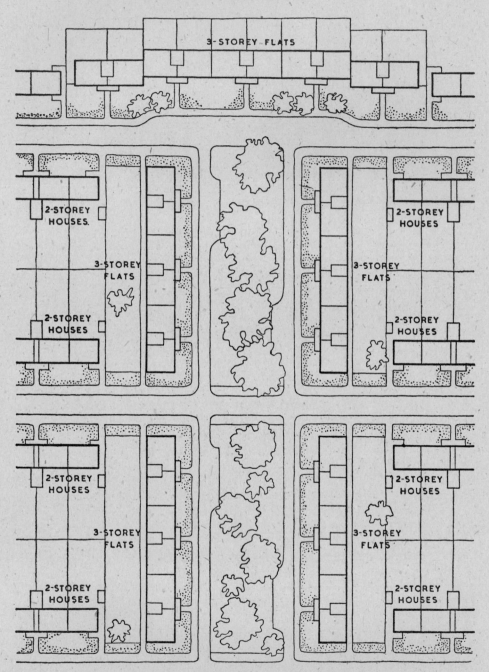

FIG. 46. Layout for houses and flats—old trees retained

laid down in the Burt Committee's Report.   Standards for materials and components have been and are being prepared by the British Standards Institution ; and standards specifying the manner in which standard materials should be used have been and are being prepared in the form of British Standards Codes of Practice.

(VII) NEW MATERIALS AND METHODS.   The brick house fails to fulfil certain performance standards and fills others to a point beyond all normal needs.   Furthermore, as a result of the war the resources of the building industry may be insufficient, both as regards material and labour, to meet the country's housing needs.   Alternative methods of house construction have therefore been carefully studied, and the manual sub-divides alternative methods into three main categories—the steel framed, light-weight concrete, and no-fines concrete houses.

(VIII) THE HEAT INSTALLATION (FUELS AND APPLIANCES).   The heat services of a house include room heating, cooking, hot water, and clothes washing.   The manual sets out six representative combinations of gas, solid fuel, and electrical appliances, and emphasises the need for studying heat services in relation to economy in the use of the nation's fuel resources.   Diagrams of typical hot-water installations are shown.

Cooking.   Attention is directed towards the merits of the partially or fully insulated self-setting solid fuel cooker.

Room Heating.   A wider use of smokeless fuel grates and of openable slow-combustion stoves is urged.   The possibility of using air—warmed by convector fires or stoves—to heat other rooms should be considered.

Water Heating.   The prime requisite of a sound hot-water system is a short and direct primary circuit.

Clothes Washing.   A wash-boiler should be provided in all houses.

Solid Fuel Storage.   There should be adequate space for the storage of two types of solid fuel, and fuel stores should be 12–24 ft. in area, with under-cover access and facilities for easy delivery.

(IX) SERVICES AND EQUIPMENT.   *Electricity and Gas.*   Ring mains and all-purpose socket outlets are recommended, with a general average of 12–14 electric points per house.   On the gas side, the manual emphasises the convenience of using pokers for lighting solid fuel fires.   As regards meters, the manual stresses the need for proper location, and a British Standards Specification is to be produced on meter-space requirements.

Plumbing.   The cold water main and storage system should always be protected against frost.   Tanks or cylinders should be of the same materials as the pipes, and pipe-work layout should be considered as an integral part of the house and combine economy with neatness.   In other words—plan for plumbing.

Kitchen and Equipment.   Kitchen fittings can be conveniently divided into two categories—fittings requiring a service (gas, electricity, water, waste pipes, etc.) for their operation and fittings used for storage.   The manual illustrates many combinations of the sink unit, both for food preparation and for laundry work.   Illustrations of typical storage fittings are also included.   Here again reference should be made to the Dudley Report.

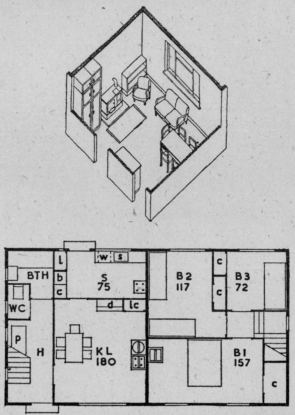

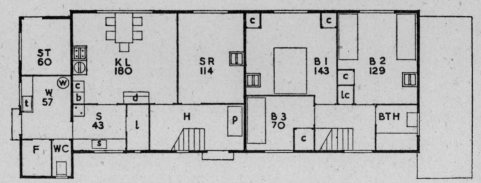

FIG. 47. An arrangement with a downstairs bathroom, such as was used in the inter-war period.   For household of 5 : 798 sq. ft.   Frontage 19′ 0″ ; depth 21′ 0″

FIG. 48. A large house with a separate sitting-room and downstairs w.c., suitable for a north aspect.   For household of 5 : 900 sq. ft.   Frontage 23′ 8″ ; depth 19′ 0″

COOKING

KEY TO HEAT APPLIANCES   Principal   Auxiliary

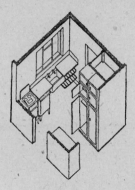

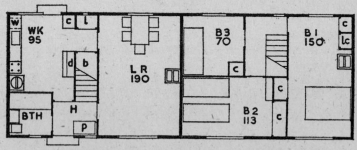

FIG. 49. A small house with a living-room running through from front to back, useful for grouping in terraces. For household of 5 : 800 sq. ft. Frontage 23′ 10″ ; depth 16′ 9″

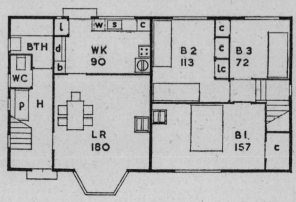

FIG. 50. In this arrangement a general plan similar to that shown in Fig. 47 has been adapted to fulfill the requirements of the working kitchen type. For this, little more space is needed. For household of 5 : 814 sq. ft. Frontage 19′ 0″ ; depth 21′ 0″

ROOM HEATING

WATER HEATING

Room heating only

With cooking

With room heating

With cooking and room heating

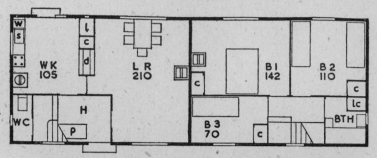

FIG. 51. Compare with Fig. 49. The wider part of the living-room provides a dining space. For household of 5: 850 sq. ft. Frontage 24′ 3″; depth 17′ 6″

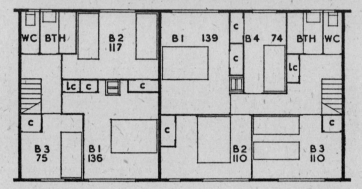

FIG. 52. The first floors of a pair of terrace houses with bedrooms over the central passage. On left, three bedrooms for household of 5; on right, four bedrooms for household of 7

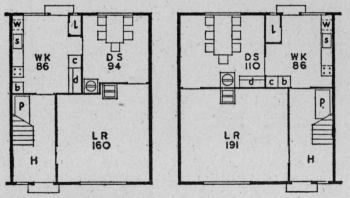

FIG. 53. The two ground floors (see Fig. 52). If the dining space is provided with doors as shown it may be used as a separate room. On left, 870 sq. ft; on right, 1075 sq. ft. Frontages 18′ 11″ and 21′ 3″; depth 23′ 0″

COOKING

KEY TO HEAT APPLIANCES   ☐ Principal   ☐ Auxiliary

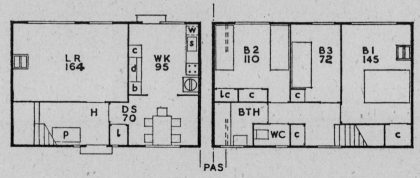

FIG. 54. In these terrace houses the upper floor party wall comes over the centre of the passage. For household of 5 ; 897 sq. ft. Frontage 25′ 3½″ ; depth 17′ 0″

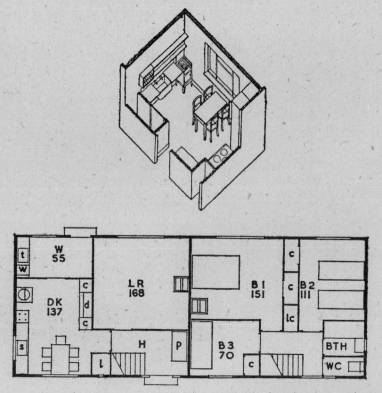

FIG. 55. An arrangement suitable for a house fronting approximately east. The living-room is at the back and the kitchen at the front. For household of 5 : 900 sq. ft. Frontage 23′ 8″ ; depth 19′ 0″

ROOM HEATING   WATER HEATING

Room heating only   With cooking   With room heating   With cooking and room heating

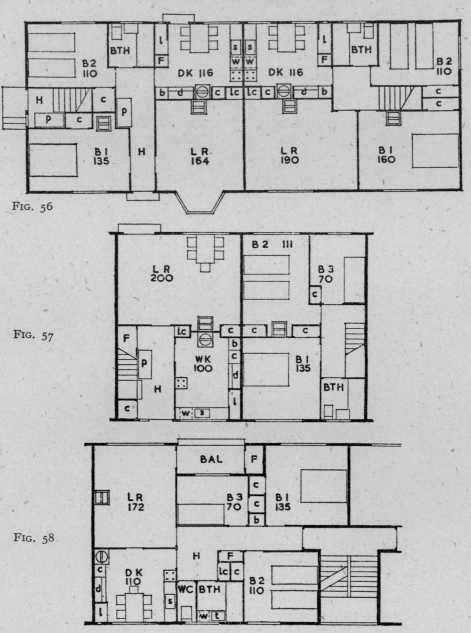

FIG. 56. A two-storey block. For household of 4: ground floor: 712 sq. ft; upper floor: 700 sq. ft. Frontage 29′ 9″; depth 23′ 6″. FIG. 57. Two-storey maisonette in a multi-storey block. For household of 5: 868 sq. ft. Frontage 17′ 0″: depth 25′ 6″. FIG. 58. In a three-storey block. For household of 5: 786 sq. ft. Depth 25′ 0″

COOKING

KEY TO HEAT APPLIANCES · · · Principal · · Auxiliary

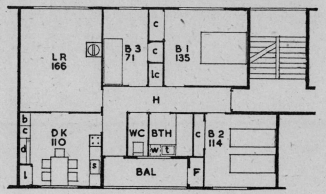

FIG. 59. For household of 5 : 788 sq. ft.   Depth 25′ 3″

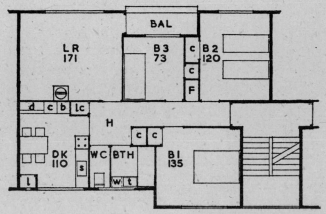

FIG. 60. For household of 5 : 792 sq. ft.   Depth 24′ 4½″

ROOM HEATING   WATER HEATING

Room heating   With cooking   With room   With cooking
only   heating   and room heating

The remainder of the Report is devoted to :

(1) Typical housing layouts :

(2) Photographs of recent housing carried out before and during the war. The photographs each illustrate some principle of siting, grouping, or design to which it is desired to call attention.

(3) Type plan embodying in varying degrees the general recommendations of the manual and especially the standards recommended in Sections III and IX.

Plans include :

(1) Two-storey houses, four to seven persons, 800 to 900 sq. ft., adjustable to various methods of living and orientation, rural as well as urban. Terrace and semi-detached types are included. (See Figs. 47–60, pp. 114–119.)

(2) Single and two-storey old persons' dwellings, suitable for two or three persons and 420 to 490 sq. ft. in area.

(3) Two and three-storey walk-up flats (including maisonette combinations) and multi-storey flats, suitable for two to five persons and 430 to 870 sq. ft. in area. (See Figs. 56–60, pp. 118, 119.)

(4) Emergency dwellings (Duplex type).

(5) Type plans showing adaptability of M.O.W. service units and cupboard units evolved for Portal emergency factory-made bungalows.

APPENDICES

(A) Space standards from densities down to cupboards.

(B) Structural standards—summation of loads, wind pressures, etc., to be allowed for in house design and standards to be achieved in respect of resistance to moisture penetration, thermal insulation, sound insulation, fire resistance, durability and ease of maintenance, and resistance to vermin infestation.

HOUSING MANUAL, 1944 : TECHNICAL APPENDICES *

This is a volume uniform with the " Housing Manual, 1944", containing nine Technical Appendices from C to L, which are as follows :

C Materials and construction.
D Light-weight concrete in cavity walls.
E The scientific use of timber.
F Cooking and heating.
G Flues.
H Notes for specification.
J Private sewers.
K Small sewage disposal works.
L British Standard Codes of Practice and British Standards.

The scientific principles governing the use of materials and their structural performance are dealt with fully in the light of latest information

* Issued by His Majesty's Stationery Office in 1945 ; price 1s. 6d. nett.

and practical knowledge. Additional specification notes are given in Section H in respect of aggregates, asbestos, asphalt (Mastic) ballast, bricks, cement, concrete, felt, glass, lime mortars, paint, plastering, slates, tiles, steel, timber, drainage pipes and chambers, floors, stairs, roofs, sanitary fittings, electrical work, and various internal fittings. The manual contains illustrations of cavity walls ; construction of ground floors, and flat roofs ; private sewers ; standard components of copings, lintels, windows, doors, and metal furnishings.

Appendix H gives notes for specifications for such materials as aggregates, asbestos, bricks, cement, concrete, mortars, paints, plastering, tiling and timber. The following extract on Drainage is given below :

Pipes

To be " British Standard Pipe " salt-glazed or salt-glazed glass enamelled fireclay with all necessary bends, junctions, channels, fittings, etc.

Laying. (*a*) Pipes to be laid in straight runs and to even gradients, all pipes being laid on even and solid foundations for the full length of each pipe. Where necessary pipes to be laid on concrete 12 inches wider than diameter of the pipe and 6 inches thick.

(*b*) Joints to be made of rope yarn and cement mortar 1 : 1, finished with fillet worked round and trowelled smooth.

Manholes and Inspection Chambers

To be of sufficient size to allow for inspection and for cleaning by rodding. To be built of brickwork or precaste concrete to conform to B.S.

Foundations to be built on 6-in. thick concrete.

The internal face of brick chambers to be built of bricks of low porosity and low sulphate content.

Step irons to be built in at 12-inch intervals and to conform to B.S. 1130.

Invert channels and bends to be half-round channel pipes to B.S. 539.

Covers to be cast iron to B.S. 497 or reinforced concrete.

CHAPTER 7

FURTHER HOUSE DESIGNS IN RURAL AND URBAN DISTRICTS

In 1943 the Minister of Health in conjunction with the Minister of Agriculture announced a scheme for the building of 3000 houses for agricultural workers.

The erection and management of the houses under the Housing Acts would be undertaken by the Rural District Councils, and sites have been chosen by them in consultation with County War Agricultural Committees.

Such schemes were under the supervision of the Senior Regional Architects of the Ministry of Health and Regional Planning Officers of the Ministry of Town and Country Planning.

These houses were erected in accordance with layouts, plans, specifications, and contracts approved by the Ministry of Health.

The plans were produced by Ministry of Health Central Housing Advisory Committee on Design, and they comprise both parlour and non-parlour types, all with three bedrooms.

The contracts for some of these houses came to over £1000, although it was decided to charge rents from 9s. to 13s. a week exclusive of rates. The ordinary agricultural subsidy under Housing (Financial Provisions) Act, 1938 of £10 per house for forty years, with minimum rate contribution of £1 from the Rural District Council and £1 from the County would be granted. Also, a lump sum of £150 per house on completion would be paid by the Ministry of Agriculture.

MANUAL ON RURAL HOUSING—1938.*

The following summarises some of the recommendations contained in this manual which was issued by the Ministry of Health in connection with Housing (Financial Provisions) Act, 1938.

Siting

(1) New houses should be placed in or close to existing villages. If not, then provision should be made for open spaces for recreation and a site for a community centre or new school.

(2) Placing of roads and buildings should be determined by the contours of the land.

(3) Cross-roads should only be introduced sparingly, and acute angles avoided. Culs-de-sac are recommended, or " village greens ".

(4) Houses placed diagonally across corners do not look well unless specially adapted to that position.

* Published by His Majesty's Stationery Office; price 1s. 6d. nett.

(5) Great care should be devoted to grouping of buildings, attention being paid to the natural irregularities of the site. The use of some long blocks of houses instead of the favoured semi-detached blocks is of great value in grouping.

The Buildings

(1) Where traditional styles of cottage building with local materials prevail, incongruous forms and inharmonious colours should not be introduced. It should be noted that the old cottages derive their pleasing effects from simplicity, appropriateness of materials used, good proportion, and variety in a few of the details.

(2) Roofs of new buildings should not be far removed in form or colour from existing roofs. Hips and ridges should harmonise, not contrast.

(3) Colour washing for walls not only has a weather-proofing effect, but also hides any incongruous material, bringing the building into harmony with its surroundings. Hard, smooth bricks should be avoided. Pointing should be in good lime mortar or lime-cement mortar, with the joints struck off flush, rather than in smooth cement mortar.

(4) Great care should be taken over the proportions of buildings. The long rectangular plan with low eaves is preferable to the short square type with proportionately high eaves.

(5) Side and back walls should be faced with the same material as the fronts of the cottages. A treatment to be avoided in short blocks is an upper storey of plaster or rough-cast and a lower storey of brick.

(6) The monotony of general uniformity can be relieved at no great cost by an occasional touch of emphasis and variety, such as a carefully placed feature to mark the centre of a group, the termination of a street vista, or the turning of a corner.

Accommodation and Planning

(1) Approximate areas for bedrooms and living-rooms constituting desirable standards of accommodation are recommended as shown below:

Persons (Adult or Child)	Bedroom				Living-room	Parlour
	1	2	3	4		
4	150	120	—	—	140–160	—
5	150	100	70–80	—	180	—
6	150	120	100	—	200	—
7	150	120	100	70–80	220 or 180	100
8	150	120	120	100	180	100
9	150	130	120	100	180	100

(2) Where more than four bedrooms are required, a large house should be planned in association with a small one, so that at some future date

the combined dwelling-house may be altered to two normal family houses.

(3) Recommendations regarding design of living-rooms and bedrooms are, in the main, a repetition of those contained in the Tudor-Walters Report.

(4) In the scullery space should be allowed for sink and drainage boards under or adjacent to window ; a copper not too near the sink ; a mangle if in general use ; and all the necessary utensils.

(5) The practice of the locality must be considered before determining whether cooking should take place in the scullery or living-room. The former is to be preferred.

(6) The bathroom should preferably be planned downstairs.

(7) The larder should be on the north or east side, well lit, and ventilated from outside area. There should be a ventilating brick, besides a small hygienic window. The size of the larder depends upon other storage space in the dwelling and on the proximity of shops or market. At least one shelf should be of slate or concrete.

(8) A good sized fuel store is essential, and a shed for cycles, garden tools, and produce, etc.

(9) The w.c. (dependent on adequate water supply) should be accessible under cover, but not direct from living-room or scullery. An earth closet must be properly ventilated and entered from outside the dwelling.

Plans and Elevations

(1) Local authorities should entrust the planning of housing schemes to experienced persons. The advice of persons experienced in architectural design, particularly in rural housing, should be secured.

(2) The limits of the type plans provided in the Housing Manual should be recognised—their unsuitability to all sites, etc. (Figs. 61 and 62.)

Reconditioning

(1) For a building "to be fit for habitation " it must be free from serious dampness, satisfactorily lighted and ventilated, properly drained and provided with adequate sanitary conveniences, and in good general repair. If existing houses to be reconditioned are so small that additions are unsatisfactory, the better alternative is to convert two inadequate dwellings into one.

(2) Subject to authorised relaxations of local byelaws, a too rigid adherence to generally desirable standards of size and height should not be required in this class of work, *e.g.* a lower ceiling level, less window area in relation to floor space, separate access to each bedroom, etc.

(3) Competent advice in matters of reconditioning is available from panels of architects set up by the Council for the Preservation of Rural England and by the R.I.B.A.

PLANNING OF FUTURE HOMES

The Report of the Scottish Housing Advisory Committee, published by His Majesty's Stationery Office (3s.) in 1944, is a very good, detailed

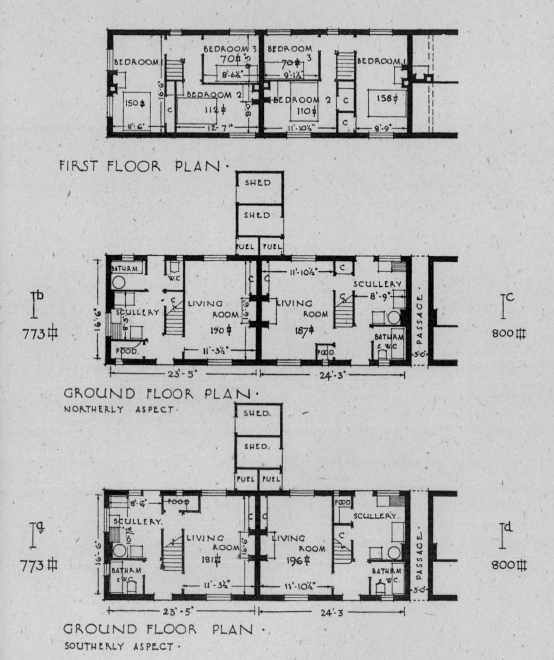

FIRST FLOOR PLAN.

GROUND FLOOR PLAN.
NORTHERLY ASPECT.

GROUND FLOOR PLAN.
SOUTHERLY ASPECT.

FIG. 61. Types of plans in Rural Housing Manual

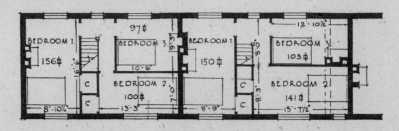

FIRST FLOOR PLAN·

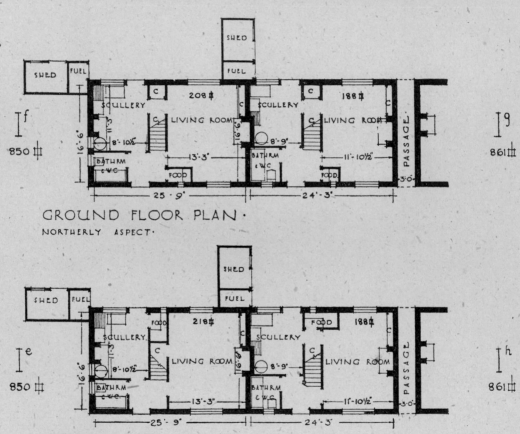

GROUND FLOOR PLAN·
NORTHERLY ASPECT·

GROUND FLOOR PLAN·
SOUTHERLY ASPECT·

FIG. 62. Types of plans in Rural Housing Manual

Report, prepared under the chairmanship of Mr. Joseph Westwood. It gives a full report on the design, planning, and furnishing of new houses; the main points are here outlined.

SCOPE OF THE REPORT. *The Problem.* 500,000 houses as fast as possible.

Type of House. The consumer survey carried out by the Committee, reveals an overwhelming preference for the two-storey house as the

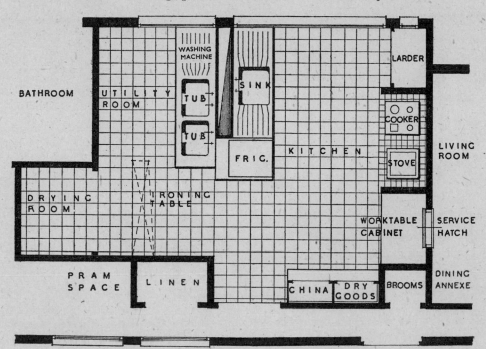

FIG. 63. Plan of kitchen and utility room

standard post-war family type. It is, however, realised that flats—two to three storeys without lifts, and six to ten storeys with automatic lifts—serve a definite purpose in the re-development of central areas. Also, in addition to family houses there is a need for special types of dwelling for single persons of either sex and for ageing persons.

Space for Living. The standards laid down in the Housing (Scotland) Act, 1935, are lower than those laid down in the English Housing Act of 1936, because under the Scottish Act the living-room is treated as a sleeping apartment. It is recommended that for post-war Scottish housing the English standards should be accepted, and that no bedroom should be of less area than 120 sq. ft. (two-persons).

As regards living-rooms, it is suggested that a greater proportion of parlour-type houses be built and that in the non-parlour type a separate dining annexe—tacked on to the living-room or kitchen—be provided (see Fig. 64).

9

In the working quarters a minimum area of 130 sq. ft. is recommended for the kitchen (80 sq. ft. kitchen and 50 sq. ft. dining annexe), and where possible a separate utility room for clothes washing—40 sq. ft. in area (see Fig. 63).

These recommendations have the effect of raising the three-bedroom non-parlour type house to an area of just over 1100 sq. ft. This compares favourably with the English pre-war standard of 750–800 sq. ft. and the anticipated post-war English standard of 850–950 sq. ft.

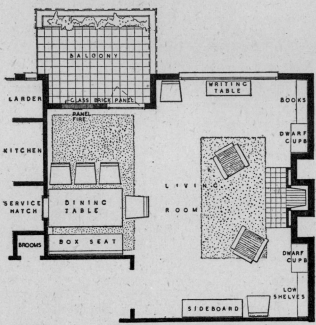

FIG. 64. Plan of living-room with dining annexe

Lastly it is pointed out that in the inter-war period the bulk of housing in Scotland was of the two-bedroom type. Continuation of this policy may be restrictive to size of family and consequently population. It is stressed that in the post-war period there will be a strong temptation to yield to the acute demand of the small family unit, created by wartime marriages. This pressure should be resisted and the long-term policy should be based upon the three-bedroom family house.

Planning the House. All habitable rooms should be entered from a lobby and not from each other. All rooms, and particularly bedrooms, should be planned in relation to the furnishings. In the three-bedroom house the w.c. may be in the bathroom but in larger houses, where the w.c. should be separate, a wash-basin should be provided in the w.c. compartment. Model plans are illustrated in Figs. 65–86, pp. 129–140.

Lastly, attention is drawn to the inevitable rash of tawdry huts which will occur unless proper care is taken that outbuildings for bicycles and garden tools, etc., are provided as an integral part of the house.

Services, Fittings, and Standard Equipment. All new houses should have a piped water-supply and main drainage. The cold of the Scottish winter and the unsightliness of external plumbing are cogent arguments for the adoption of internal plumbing. It is also recommended that greater attention be given to the use of more efficient methods of space heating, and it is suggested that only one bedroom and a living-room require a coal fireplace. The Committee draw attention to the economies

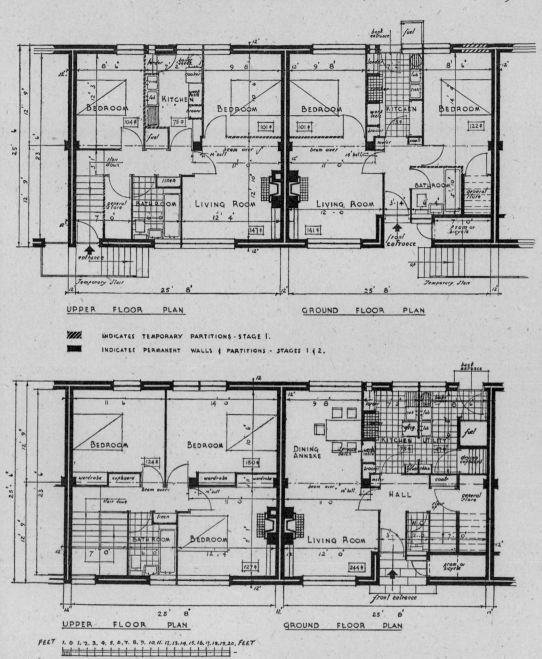

FIG. 65. The Duplex house plans

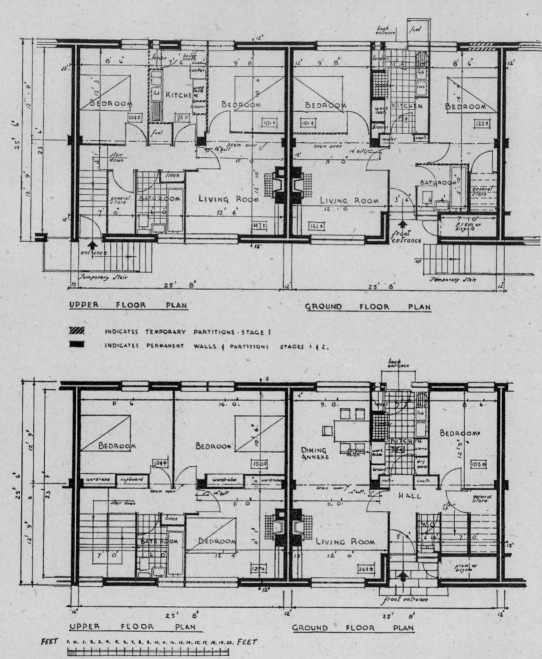

UPPER FLOOR PLAN   GROUND FLOOR PLAN

▨ INDICATES TEMPORARY PARTITIONS · STAGE I

▬ INDICATES PERMANENT WALLS & PARTITIONS STAGES I & 2.

UPPER FLOOR PLAN   GROUND FLOOR PLAN

FEET

FIG. 66. The Duplex house plans

which may result if heat and hot water are supplied from a central source on the district model.

As regards refuse disposal, the Garchey system is recommended for flats and standard bins for two-storey cottages and flatted houses.

Equipping the House. The Committee have gone into quite exceptional detail as to the fittings to be provided. It is rightly emphasised that storage accommodation for the myriad belongings of a family is of the utmost importance, not only in the kitchen but also in the living-room and bedrooms as well. This section of the Report is worthy of the closest study, since the recommendations for standard equipment are precise and detailed.

Standards of Construction. For traditional building methods the urgent need in Scotland is the production of a good-quality facing brick. As well as brickwork, alternative methods—cellular concrete, timber, steel—will be necessary to supplement housing output. At the same time it is clear that no combination of site-built techniques can be relied upon to provide houses at the rate required. The Committee therefore stress the importance of prefabrication and urge that experimental work be pressed forward now.

Design, Layout, and Amenities. The principle of neighbouring units and community layout should be adopted for all post-war housing, and attention should be given to separation of housing from industry and from through traffic. It is recommended that architects should be employed to ensure that houses are not only well built but of good appearance, and it is also pointed out that : " Good design effects economies in construction and its success lies in the use of simple compositions and in the careful proportioning of the essential elements of the housing structure."

The Committee also point out that well-designed paths, fences, and street furniture, judicious tree planting, and the proper treatment of corner sites is essential to good housing.

Supply of Furniture by Local Authorities. Under the Housing (Scotland) Act, 1925, local authorities have powers to provide items of furniture, such as beds, bedding, tables, chairs, chests-of-drawers, and floor coverings. It is recommended that more local authorities should make use of these powers. Additional household items, such as, rugs, carpets, suites of furniture, etc., should be dealt with by an extension of the Utility furniture scheme, and appliances such as vacuum cleaners, space heaters, etc., should be supplied by the power undertaking. The terms under which tenants may acquire both essential and additional household items are to be subject to the approval of the Department of Health for Scotland.

Housing Management. Full advantage cannot be taken of the general raising of standards proposed by the Committee, both as regards area and equipment, unless tenants are trained to respect and utilise these increased amenities.

The appointment of women housing managers, as well as the closest liaison with women's organisations, is therefore recommended.

Immediate Post-War Problems. In order to take off the razor edge of demand in the immediate post-war period, and yet not interfere unduly with the long-term programme, special types of dwellings are suggested:

(1) Temporary houses of limited life.
(2) Duplex houses, designed initially to accommodate two families and capable of being converted or upper-graded later to accommodate single families.
(3) Houses built by traditional or alternative methods, but as regards area of pre-war size.
(Type plans for Duplex and short-term houses are shown in an appendix to the Report.) See Figs. 65 and 66 of Duplex House, pp. 129, 130, and Figs. 67–73 and 75, pp. 133–136 for short-time plans.

THE PLANS. Only long-term plans have been selected for comment, since the short-term plans and the " Duplex " plan inevitably suffer from compromise.

Flats, and Flatted Houses. In general the plans for flatted houses and flats have three major defects (see Figs. 76–86, pp. 136–140):

(1) Long, poorly lit corridors, where there are more than two bedrooms.
(2) Poor heat services.
(3) Aspect confusion.

Corridors. In all fairness, the Committee's recommendations that in flats all rooms must be separately accessed, makes it difficult to avoid long corridors. Possible planning solutions which would eliminate the long corridor are:

(1) the use of the living-room to give access to a lobby off which bedrooms and bathroom are accessed.
(2) the provision of a second living-room—strongly recommended by the Committee—so that one living-room could be used for access and the other for privacy.

RURAL HOUSING REPORT, 1944 *

The report sets out six main objectives for the post-war period:

(1) A concentration of effort to restart rural housing activities after the last war on the widest scale then practicable.

(2) The acceleration of the rate of progress to the maximum extent as labour and materials become available.

(3) A fair allocation of labour and materials between town and country so that the rural population does not suffer.

(4) A planned programme to bring rural housing conditions up to the highest possible level in a given period of years.

(5) The raising of housing standards in backward districts up to the best attained by progressive authorities.

(6) A financial basis for new house building in rural areas which will make it possible to give the agricultural worker as good a house as the worker in other industries.

* Issued by the Ministry of Health and published by His Majesty's Stationery Office ; price 1s.

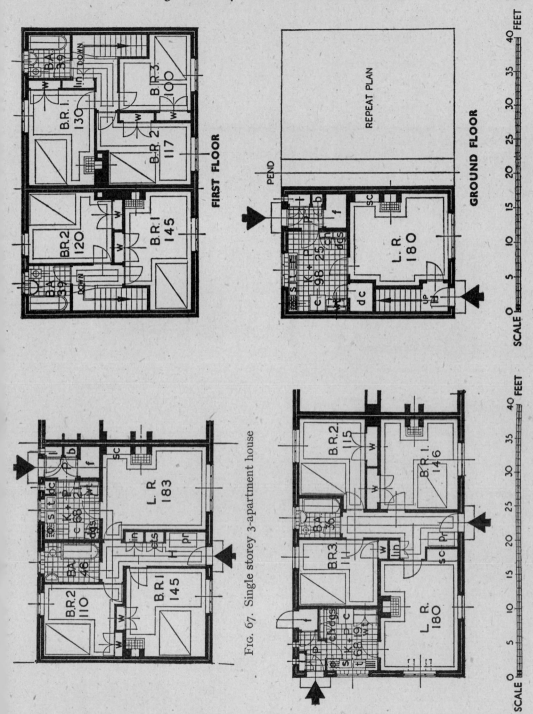

FIG. 67. Single storey 3-apartment house

FIG. 68. Single storey 4-apartment house

FIG. 69. 3- and 4-apartment houses

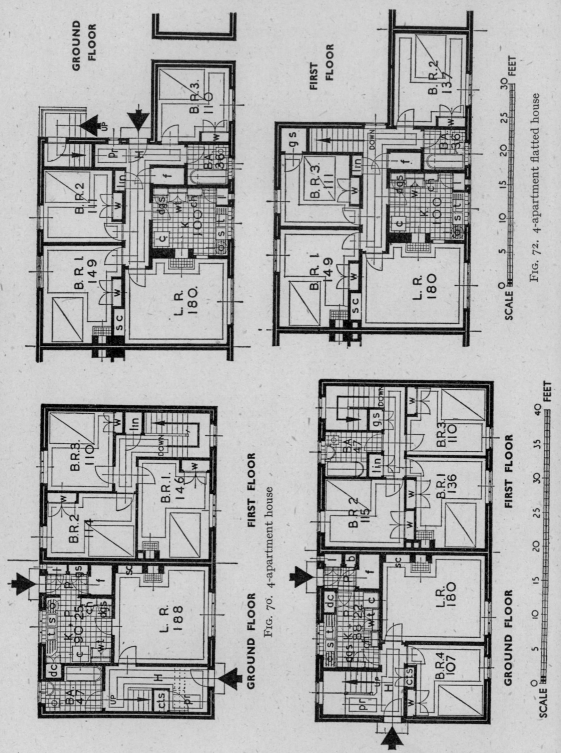

Fig. 70. 4-apartment house

Fig. 72. 4-apartment flatted house

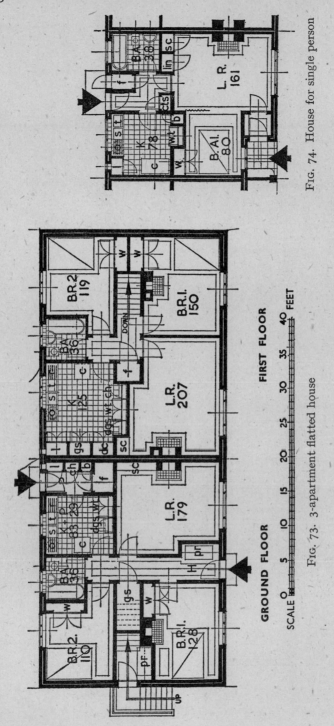

FIG. 74. House for single person

FIG. 73. 3-apartment flatted house

GROUND FLOOR   FIRST FLOOR

SCALE 0 5 10 15 20 25 30 35 40 FEET

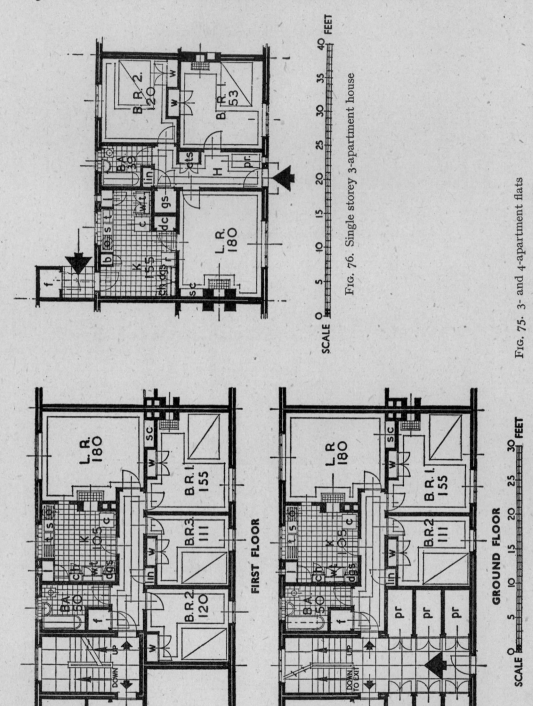

SCALE 0 5 10 15 20 25 30 35 40 FEET

FIG. 76. Single storey 3-apartment house

FIRST FLOOR

GROUND FLOOR

SCALE 0 5 10 15 20 25 30 FEET

FIG. 75. 3- and 4-apartment flats

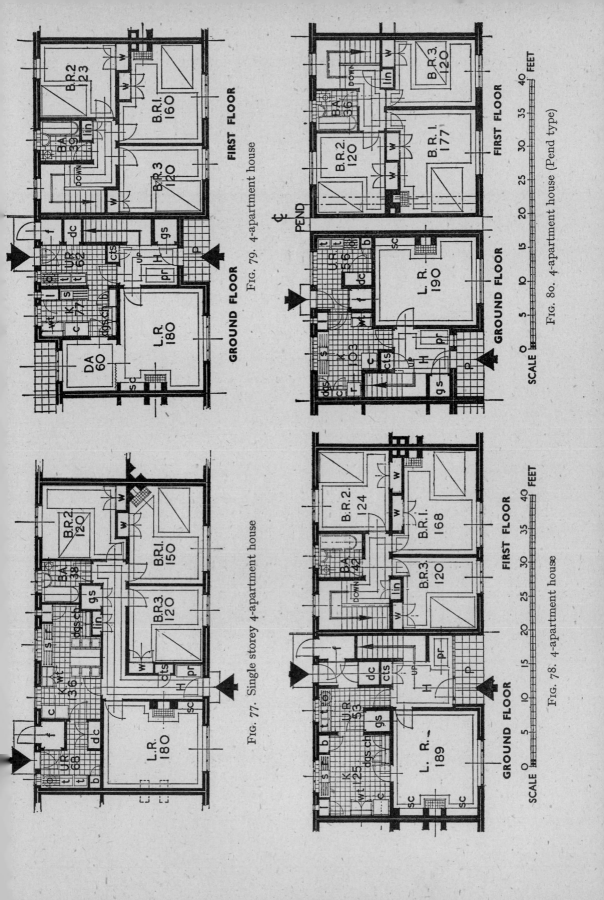

FIRST FLOOR

B.R.2
123

B.R.1
160

BA
39

lin

DOWN

B.R.3
120

w

dc

gs

cts

UP

pr

H

P

UR
62

K
77

s

t

t

l

c

wt

f

dgs.ch

DA
60

sc

L.R.
180

GROUND FLOOR

FIG. 79. 4-apartment house

FIRST FLOOR

B.R.3
120

BA
36

lin

w

DOWN

B.R.2
120

w

B.R.1
177

w

Ø PEND

PEND

t

t

b

sc

UR
56

dc

w

L.R.
190

dgs
c

c

r

f

s

K
103

c

cts

UP

H

gs

pr

P

GROUND FLOOR

SCALE 0 5 10 15 20 25 30 35 40 FEET

FIG. 80. 4-apartment house (Pend type)

B.R.2
120

w

w

BA
38

gs

lin

B.R.1
150

dgs.ch

B.R.3
120

w

cts

pr

H

sc

K
36

wt

s

f

c

UR
68

t

t

b

dc

f

L.R.
180

FIG. 77. Single storey 4-apartment house

B.R.2
124

BA
42

lin

w

DOWN

B.R.3
120

w

B.R.1
168

w

f

dc

cts

UP

H

pr

P

UR
53

b

t

t

s

th

gs

dgs.ch

K
125

wt

s

f

l

c

L.R.
189

sc

sc

FIRST FLOOR

GROUND FLOOR

SCALE 0 5 10 15 20 25 30 35 40 FEET

FIG. 78. 4-apartment house

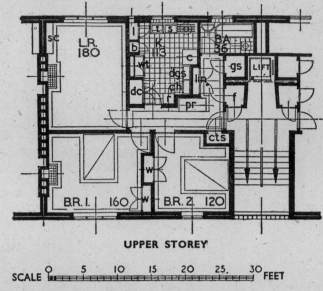

UPPER STOREY

SCALE 0 5 10 15 20 25. 30 FEET

FIG. 81. 3-apartment house

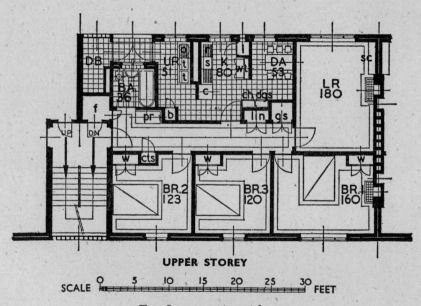

UPPER STOREY

SCALE 0 5 10 15 20 25 30 FEET

FIG. 82. 4-apartment house

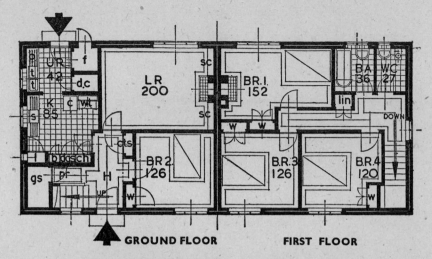

FIG. 83. 5-apartment house

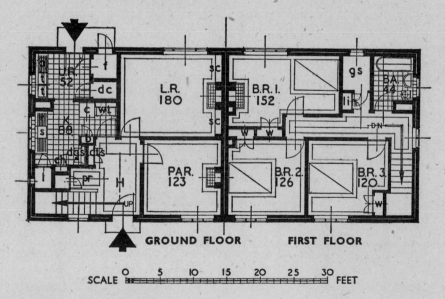

FIG. 84. 5-apartment house (parlour type)

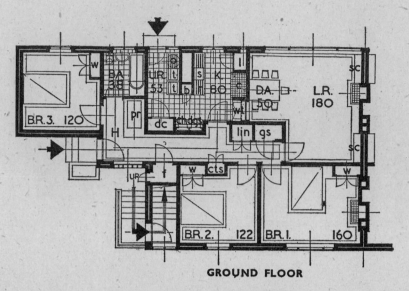

GROUND FLOOR

FIG. 85. 4-apartment flatted house

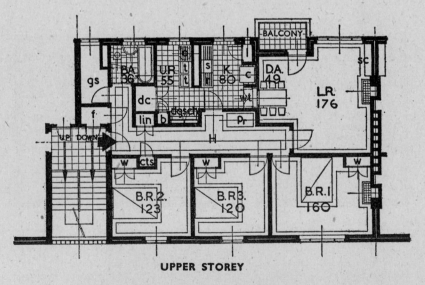

UPPER STOREY

FIG. 86. 4-apartment flat

The Committee's recommendations include the following :

Better Administration. All Rural District Councils to review their housing staff and organisation.

More stimulation of activity by the Ministry of Health, with use of publicity to stimulate a housing conscience in backward areas.

Joint committees, representing the County and Rural Councils, with co-opted representatives of organisations concerned with housing, to be set up in each county, to frame a common policy for improving housing conditions.

National Survey of Rural Housing Conditions. A thorough and comprehensive survey to be carried out as soon as possible in every rural district in England and Wales.

Every working-class house to be classified in one of the following categories:

(1) Fit for habitation, or with only minor defects.
(2) Requiring structural alteration or repair.
(3) Requiring reconditioning.
(4) Requiring demolition or replacement.

Planned Long-term Programme. On completion of the survey, each Rural Council to draw up a long-term programme of repair, reconditioning and provision of new houses ; this programme to be carried out within a period fixed by the Ministry of Health.

Financial Assistance. On the basis of a minimum agricultural wage of 65*s.* a week, the Committee considers that the rents of new houses built by local authorities for agricultural workers should not exceed 7*s.* 6*d.* to 8*s.* a week, plus rates.

The Report therefore recommends a special Exchequer subsidy of such amount as is needed to bridge the gap between the tenant's rent and the economic rent ; this subsidy to continue without reduction for five years, and to be also payable for houses built for agricultural workers by private enterprise.

In addition, a special Exchequer subsidy should be given to exceptionally poor rural districts ; this subsidy is mainly intended to meet conditions in Wales.

The reconditioning grant under the Housing (Rural Workers) Acts should be increased at once in view of the rise of building costs.

Rise in Building Costs. In making their recommendations, the Committee have assumed that post-war policy will aim at raising the general standard of living ; the financial situation will allow a continuation of subsidies ; and the minimum wage for agricultural workers will not be reduced below the present level relative to other industries. (Para. 15.)

In considering housing finance (pp. 43–50) the Committee have assumed that the cost of post-war building will ultimately reach stability at 30 per cent. above the 1939 level.* The Report says :

* S. R. & O. 1946, No. 1163, states the amount of 30 per cent. has been increased to 60 per cent. over 1939 values, in respect of compensation claims.

" One of the most disturbing features of the present position is the extent to which the rise in building costs has out-stripped the rise in the general cost of living. . . . Building costs as illustrated by the cost of the war-time agricultural cottages are on average nearly double the 1939 level. Unless building costs can be brought into line with the general cost of living, it will be impossible to carry out a post-war housing programme on the scale contemplated. We cannot agree that the problem should be met by a reduction in the size and standard of the type of house to be built. . . . We are accordingly accepting the present cost-of-living index figure of 30 per cent. above the pre-war figure as the level at which stability will be reached. How this is to be done is not for us to say, but unless it is done we do not believe that a satisfactory housing programme can be carried out."

Reviewing rural housing between the two wars, the Report says that while 871,000 new houses were built, progress was slower in the rural districts than in the towns. The chief reason was that " the various subsidies provided by the Government for new houses did not, until the end of the inter-war period, make sufficient allowance for the low rent-paying capacity of the agricultural worker". By 1939, with the help of the Housing Act of the preceding year, the stage was set for much more rapid progress ; but this great forward movement was halted by the war. (Pp. 6 to 12.)

" *Fair Share* " *for Rural Areas.* The Committee believe that the proposed Joint County Committees " will have a very marked effect in raising the level of rural housing, and particularly in improving conditions in the black spots " ; but recommend that " if any authority, having been given proper assistance, financial and advisory, fails to carry out its housing duties, there should be no hesitation to use the default powers of the County Council or the Ministry". (Paras. 121 to 123.)

Other recommendations include :

Women's Point of View. " Rural District Councils should ensure that there are on their Housing Committees women qualified to speak from the point of view of working housewives." (Para. 108.)

Simpler Procedure. " A simpler procedure should be devised for consultation with other interests concerned in the acquisition of sites. The local planning authority should be made responsible for co-ordinating those interests, and the housing authority should be under no obligation to consult any other body once the approval of the local planning authority and of the Ministry of Health has been obtained." (Para. 161.)

Public Services. " There should be a maximum extension to rural areas of public services, *e.g.* electricity, gas, water and sewage disposal." (Para. 162.)

Ugly Houses. " The Minister of Health shall require rural housing authorities to employ a qualified architect for new housing schemes unless satisfied that there are special circumstances making it desirable to waive this requirement in a particular case." (Paras. 99 and 164.)

The Small Builder. " The small builder in rural areas should be encouraged to resume his activities to the fullest possible extent after the war." (Para. 105.)

Special Problems in Wales. The Report devotes a special chapter (pp. 50 to 55) to Welsh rural housing problems.

CHAPTER 8

FINANCE AND ADMINISTRATION OF ESTATES

ESTATE development on a sound financial basis is a matter beset with many difficulties, and careful consideration of numerous factors, such as capital outlay, selling prices, and rentals, must be made before embarking on a large estate scheme.

Land and building costs vary from district to district, but a fair average can be estimated. It is difficult to assess rate charges, as these vary so much, and the amount of assessment placed on property differs widely.

Rateable value is arrived at by a calculation of gross value, *i.e.* reasonable rent less an allowance for repairs. In 1943 the average local rate was about 11s. in the £, as against 12s. 6d. in the £ in 1929 and is still rising according to statistics.*

These are important factors to take into consideration by large estate developers in deciding what type of district they will choose for development.

There are different opinions on the effect of subsidies on building costs. Some contend subsidies are a waste of money and tend rather to increase prices to the advantage of the builder. Others say the granting or withholding of subsidies only has an effect on building prices in proportion to the changes in demand for building subsequent upon the grant or its abolition. If there is sufficient building labour available the subsidy should prevent increasing costs.

METHODS OF BUILDING FINANCE

Estate developers and builders require finance to develop estates, and also prospective tenants require loans to purchase houses.

There are various methods by which necessary money is obtained:

(1) *By Private Loans.* Solicitors make private loans to their clients by the use of trust moneys on which a more remunerative return is desired. Security for such loans is, of course, essential, and the terms depend upon the personal integrity of the borrower. The average loan is two-thirds of property value, and rate of interest about 5 per cent. Legal charges are about 1½ per cent. of loan.

(2) *Joint Stock Banks.* Advances on houses are made by banks, if the managers are satisfied with the state of the client's balance sheet, and payment does not extend as a rule beyond 6 or 7 years. About two-

* Statistical survey, "Rates and Rateable Values in England and Wales 1945–46" published by His Majesty's Stationery Office for the Ministry of Health; price 1s.

thirds of the valuation is loaned and capital repayments are made half-yearly in addition to interest payments. The terms are made according to the client's financial standing with the manager and subject to satisfactory securities being offered.

(3) *Building Societies.* These societies do the majority of loans for building, and as a result of increasing demands for houses since 1919 it is estimated that they have supplied two-thirds of the total cost of housing. They advance loans on freehold or leasehold properties, and on estates where there is only land for security. The usual advance is up to three-quarters of valuation of collateral security offered. Repayments are made on an instalment system or on an annuity system, whereby fixed amounts are payable at regular intervals. Alternatively, repayments decrease as the principal is reduced, and the period of loan is spread from five to twenty-five years, but it is optional for the borrower to repay the loan off at any time.

The builders can also by collaboration with building societies raise the balance of money over the amount raised by the societies to help clients who cannot pay the cash deposit of 10 per cent. required, as this arrangement facilitates the sale of houses.

(4) *Local Council Loans.* The Housing Act of 1925 empowered the local authority to guarantee the repayment of advances made by building societies to their members.

Loans not exceeding £800 per house for up to 90 per cent. of the security value above 70 per cent. normally made are advanced. The loan must not exceed 50 per cent. of value of work done, and this includes site value.

The 1933 Housing Act gave greater encouragement to private building enterprise in the erection of cheaper houses at lower rentals. Local authority loans are repaid in regular instalments up to a period of twenty years, and interest rates are sometimes less than those of building societies.

(5) *Loans by Insurance Companies.* Mortgage advances are made by combined life assurance and house purchase policy; repayment is provided for in an endowment on borrower's life, the term of which is limited to twenty or thirty years.

(6) *Public Utility Societies*, which include Housing Associations, undertake loans for houses, and are empowered under the Public Health Act, 1936, Section 188. They do not trade for profit, and capital required can be raised by issue of shares, debentures, and loan stock. Local authorities and county councils have powers to take shares and loan grants. Many friendly and co-operative societies offer mortgage openings to their members within limits of their finances. Many make advances for construction or improvement of houses to any local authority, railway, or harbour company, housing association, or any society established for providing houses for the working classes.

(7) *Public Works Loan Commissioners.* Various Government Housing Acts since 1919 have done much to provide houses, and it may be of interest briefly to recall the history of each Act.

Housing Acts, 1919

The Housing Act, 1919, better known as the Addison Act, made it the duty of the local authority to build working-class houses, and the cost exceeding the penny rate was borne by the Government.

The State also agreed to pay public utility societies and housing trusts a percentage of the annual interest payments on approved capital expenditure. These grants proved very expensive, as building costs were very high ; and little economy was shown, as the bigger proportion of the costs were paid by the Government.

The money was raised on a long term of forty years and carried a high interest. The subsidy paid to public society housing was as much as 50 per cent. of interest and redemption charges, but oddly enough they did not make extensive use of these grants.

A further Housing Act in 1919 was designed to stimulate private enterprise, and sums of £130 to £260 were paid for each house provided it complied with type and size specified. About 25 per cent. of houses then provided were built by private enterprise.

Housing Acts, 1923 and 1924

The 1923 Act, known as the Chamberlain Act, undertook to provide a definite and limited contribution of £6 per house for a period of twenty years, and local authorities were authorised to advance money to private builders up to 90 per cent. of maximum cost of £1200 a house.

This Act did more to help private enterprise and provided more economical design and size of houses ; as the floor areas were reduced to 950 sq. ft. The result of this Act caused private enterprise to build five times more houses than local authorities.

The Wheatley Act of 1924 increased the subsidy to £9 a year for forty years, and that houses were not to be sold but to be rented at lowest rentals, so that the annual charge on the rates did not exceed £3 15s. per house. The area of these houses was further reduced—to 760 sq. ft.

The subsidies were revised by later Housing Acts in 1929, 1930, and 1933, and were subject to periodic revisions every third year afterwards.

Housing Acts, 1935, 1936, 1938

The 1935 Act laid down standards of overcrowding, and surveys made by local authorities revealed that nearly 4 per cent. of dwellings inspected were overcrowded. It was found that 5 per cent. of council houses as compared with 3·7 per cent. of private houses were overcrowded.

The Housing Act, 1936, purports to be a consolidating measure, although a number of previous enactments and provisions were left outstanding. The Act deals with clearance areas and their re-development, and acquisition of land also outside clearance areas required for housing accommodation of displaced people. The Act imposes the duty on local authorities to provide working-class houses under their management. It also provides for relaxation of byelaws in respect of laying out new streets, and erection of new buildings, subject to the approval of the Ministry of Health.

The Housing (Financial Provisions Act), 1938, provided for Exchequer contribution of £5 10s. per house per annum, payable for forty years, and increased to £6 10s. in urban and rural areas.

A subsidy of £10 was made for houses provided for slum clearance and abatement of overcrowding, more particularly in rural districts.

HOUSING (FINANCIAL AND MISCELLANEOUS PROVISIONS) ACT, 1946

Contributions under the Act

The main purpose of the Act is to fix the Exchequer subsidies and rate contributions for houses provided by Local Authorities in England and Wales in the immediate post-war period.

Sections 1 to 4 fix the standard annual Exchequer subsidies in respect of houses completed by Local Authorities after 18th April, 1946, and Sections 5 to 8 fix the contributions for those houses from the Local Authority and from the County Council. These contributions from the Exchequer and the rates will be payable annually for 60 years in place of 40 years as under the previous legislation.

In the normal case the annual Exchequer contribution, called the " general standard amount ", will be £16 10s. per house and the Annual Rate Fund contribution £5 10s., representing a total capital subsidy of £594 per house. This compares with contributions of £5 10s. from the Exchequer and £2 15s. from the rates (subsidy capital value of £187 10s.) which were paid under the 1938 Act in the period immediately before the War.

In the case of houses provided by a County District Council for the agricultural population of their district, the annual Exchequer contribution, called the " special standard amount ", will be £25 10s., and the Annual Rate Fund contribution £1 10s. with a contribution of £1 10s. from the County Council. Subject to any conditions which may be laid down by the Treasury, the Minister of Health may also agree to apply these special subsidy rates to all houses, whether for agricultural workers or not, built in county districts with a population of low-rent-paying capacity and where housing puts undue burden on the rates.

Where blocks of flats are provided on sites, the cost of which as developed with roads and sewers, etc., exceeds £1500 per acre (see Section 4 (1) and Part I of the First Schedule), the annual Exchequer contributions and the Annual Rate Fund contributions will be determined by reference to a graduated scale set out in Part II of the First Schedule ; commencing at £28 10s. per flat from the Exchequer and a contribution by the Local Authority of £9 10s. Where lifts are provided in blocks of flats of at least four storeys, additional assistance will be given by the Exchequer at the rate of £7 per flat per annum and the Local Authority will be required to contribute £3 10s. per flat per annum from the rates (see Part III of the First Schedule). Subsidies at the same rate as for flats will be paid for houses built on expensive sites as part of a mixed development of flats and houses.

Section 6 provides for additional Exchequer and Rate Fund assistance where the cost of a house is substantially increased by the necessity for providing protection against subsidence ; and Section 7 allows the Minister to give additional assistance (with a corresponding reduction in the Local Authority's contribution) in highly rated areas. Sections 9 to 11 apply the subsidy provisions in retrospect, to certain houses completed during the War, by Local Authorities and Housing Associations ; and Section 12 relates to contributions in respect of temporary housing accommodation provided in certain war buildings (e.g. Government hostels).

Provisions as to Contributions under other Acts

Section 13 raises to £15 per annum for 40 years the maximum Exchequer assistance payable in respect of each house provided for members of the agricultural population by persons other than the Local Authority under arrangements made after the passing of the new Act ; under the Housing (Financial Provisions) Act, 1938, the maximum Exchequer assistance was £10 per annum.   Aid will only be available if the house is either owner-occupied or is let to a member of the agricultural population at a rent not exceeding such rent as it would have been appropriate for the Council to charge if the house had been provided by them.

Section 14 makes it a condition of the receipt by a private owner of certain housing subsidies from the Exchequer or a Local Authority that the house should be available as a dwelling fit for habitation ; except where the house is for the time being un-inhabitable for reasons beyond the owner's control (*e.g.* war damage).

Section 15 deals with cases where subsidised houses owned by Housing Associations or provided by private persons for members of the agricultural population become vested in a Local Authority.

Review of Contributions

The aforementioned subsidies payable under the Act will apply to all houses completed by Local Authorities before 30th June, 1947, but Section 16 provides for a review to begin in December 1946, as a result of which the Minister of Health may submit to Parliament in the form of a draft Order any new proposals for reducing the subsidies, or the period for which they will be payable, for houses completed after June 1947.   The Order can only be made after an affirmative resolution by the House of Commons.

Non-traditional Houses

Where a Local Authority uses non-traditional methods of contruction approved by the Minister of Health, and the costs are substantially greater than those for traditional construction, the Exchequer may make a grant towards meeting the excess ; such extra grants applying only to houses included in approved proposals submitted by the 31st December, 1947.   (Section 17.)

Housing Associations

Section 18 provides for the setting up, in pursuance of arrangements made by the Minister, of one or more Housing Associations which will both construct houses for Local Authorities and provide houses which the associations will themselves own and manage.

Housing (Financial Provisions) (Scotland) Act, 1946

This complementary Act for Scotland, which received the Royal Assent on 6th June increases the subsidies payable to Local Authorities and to the Scottish Special Housing Association for houses built for the working classes generally, and to Local Authorities and others for houses provided for agricultural workers.

The new Exchequer and rate contributions are not the same as for England and Wales, and those who require details will no doubt consult the terms of the Act itself.

Private Enterprise Subsidy

Important recommendations are contained in a Report called " Private Enterprise Housing ", submitted by the Ministry of Health, Central

Housing Advisory Committee, in July 1944.   It was prepared by a Committee under the chairmanship of Sir Felix Pole.

Evidence was taken from large numbers of bodies and persons representative of different sides of the building industry, from the National Federation of Housing Associations, the Building Societies' Association, and other bodies.

The Sub-Committee set up a special Panel to consider best how to control the standard of construction of houses built by private enterprise.

The Committee concluded that " given favourable conditions " the housing needs of a large section of the people of this country can be met without assistance from public funds.

The conditions required include cheap money, a plentiful supply of labour and materials, building costs in close relationship with the cost of living, and stability of values.

The Report says that " if private enterprise is to maintain its position in the post-war period it must produce a large number of houses for letting ".

The participation of the building societies and other similar bodies is essential if this is to be achieved.

The Committee recommends that private enterprise should be encouraged to participate, although necessarily on a limited scale, in the short-term building programme, in order that building organisations may be brought to a state of readiness for the long-term programme.

Priority should be given to houses intended for letting, and large luxury types be not permitted until urgent housing needs are met.

The Committee also make the following recommendations :

(1) When private enterprise is meeting the same needs as local authorities, it should be eligible for the same Exchequer subsidy.

(2) The quantity of subsidy to private enterprise must be subject to some measure of control of selling prices or rents and of standards of size and construction.

(3) A subsidy to private enterprise to be effective must be simple and readily understood.

(4) The raising of the limit of value of houses for which advances may be made under the Small Dwellings Acquisition Acts and Housing Act.

(5) The simplification of the procedure for obtaining decisions on housing proposals by private builders.

(6) The granting of a Statutory Right of Appeal to the Minister of Health against local authorities' requirements in the matter of private street works.

(7) Permission to building societies to accept collateral security from persons to whom advances are made with a guarantee by the Minister of Health and the local authority.

REDUCING BUILDING COSTS

The factors that go to make up costs of a house are (1) cost of land, (2) cost of roads and sewers, (3) interest charges, (4) cost of building materials, (5) labour rates, (6) methods of production and administration.

The cost of land is said to be fixed to the 1939 ceiling level. The Uthwatt proposals advised the setting up of a central planning authority to ensure the best use of the land, that compensation be based on 1939 values, and development transferred from private owners to the State. With regard to subject of betterment, it was recommended a scheme for a periodic levy on increase in annual site values, ascertained by the machinery used for rating purposes, and that 75 per cent. of the increase levy should be paid by the person actually realising the increased value.

With regard to costs of materials and labour the Uthwatt Report advocated a stricter Government control, and that maximum rates should be fixed so as not to cause excessive profits ; as to production, that greater use be made of standardised units and alternative materials made available on mass production lines—achieved by closer co-operation of the Ministry of Works, the Board of Trade, and the Supply Departments under the direction of a central planning and reconstruction authority with full powers to control labour costs. Methods of administration should be dealt with by competent organisations to ensure the best use of labour and materials, and full use made of proper machinery to avoid disputes, unsatisfactory working conditions, and ensure smooth co-operation of employers and employees.

RAISING OF LOANS

Suggestions for raising money for housing include : that public housing loans be made at interest rates as low as $1\frac{1}{2}$ per cent. ; and that loans be made by local authorities from money loaned free of interest by the Government. The latter suggestion is only another form of subsidy, and may only tend towards wasteful expenditure.

Building societies, it is announced, are contemplating ways and means of utilising their finances to the best advantage of public interests by helping to a greater extent to finance purchase of houses by owners and occupiers, and also by letting houses on terms settled by the Government to local authorities to ensure economic rents.

GARDEN CITY DEVELOPMENT

The Garden City movement was initiated by the late Sir Ebenezer Howard in a book he wrote entitled " Tomorrow ", which was written at the close of the nineteenth century.*   In this book he stressed the need for a gradual decentralisation of both population and industry from overcrowded cities into new self-contained towns which he named " Garden Cities ".

His definition of a garden city, which was adopted by the Garden Cities and Town Planning Association, is as follows:

* A new edition of this book entitled " Garden Cities of To-morrow " was published in 1946 by Chapman & Hall, Ltd., price 6s. net.

" A garden city is a town designed for healthy living and industry ; of a size that makes possible a full measure of social life, but not larger, surrounded by a rural belt ; the whole of the land being in public ownership or held in trust for the community."

There have been a good number of garden cities developed, including First Garden City, Ltd. (Letchworth), Welwyn Garden City, Ltd., Bournville Village Trust, and Port Sunlight Estate.

The money for these garden cities has been obtained by the following methods :

(1) Issue of ordinary shares, with a dividend limited to such a rate as the Treasury may from time to time fix, and various classes of debenture, stock, and development bonds—which have now, as the result of reorganisation, taken the form of 6 per cent. debenture stock, and 7 per cent. cumulative income stock.

(2) Loans from Public Works Loan Board under the Housing and Town Planning Acts, these being secured as a first mortgage on the land and water undertaking.

(3) Temporary advances from bankers.

It should be pointed out that the Public Works Loan Board Act, under the general powers given them by the Public Works Loan Act of 1875, requires the Board to have regard to the security offered and gives them discretion as to the amount which they may lend under any special power given under any Act of Parliament. It is of great importance to bear this in mind in considering the question of whether the Public Works Loan Board is the best machinery which can be devised if Parliament wishes to further the establishment of garden cities.

In granting loans the Public Works Loan Board exercise their general powers under the 1875 Act, but are limited by the Treasury Regulations as to making loans to authorised associations establishing garden cities.

The Board has therefore :

(1) to be satisfied with the security ;

(2) to exercise their discretion as to whether, and as to how much, they should lend ;

(3) to make loans on such terms as were provided for in the Treasury Regulations.

The Regulations issued by the Treasury provided, *inter alia*, that:

(1) The loan should not exceed three-quarters of the value at any time of the security (*i.e.* in the case of Welwyn Garden City, the estate and the water undertaking).

(2) The loan should not exceed an amount equal to the sum raised from other sources.

(3) The loan should be advanced for the purpose of development approved by the Ministry of Health.

It is in the very essence of the garden city from the economic point of view that development should be reasonably rapid ; only in this way can the amount of interest placed to capital be prevented from accumulating too rapidly in the early days. It is therefore desirable, wherever possible, to direct industry and population to the new garden cities, as opposed to sporadic and haphazard development on the outskirts of the large towns.

TOWN AND COUNTRY PLANNING ACT, 1947

Finances and Local Authorities.

Sections 93–96 refer to Exchequer grants which subject to regulations may be paid to local authorities as follows :

(*a*) Expenditure incurred on the acquisition and clearing of land for redevelopment of war-damaged areas, obsolete development or bad layout, derelict land (this replaces on a more generous basis the grant provisions of the 1944 Act).

(*b*) Expenditure on payment of compensation under Parts III and VIII of the Act. Also on loss involved in the acquisition and clearing of land for which grant is not payable under the scheme for comprehensive redevelopment (Sect. 94). The scale of grants will be settled by Regulations and will be permitted for 60 years at varying rates which can be up to 90 per cent. of the annual costs for war-damaged areas, and up to 80 per cent. for other redevelopment areas.

Grants are also made to planning authorities towards compensation they have to pay to owners under a development plan by reasons of restrictions placed on future development.

CHAPTER 9

LEGAL REGULATIONS AFFECTING ESTATE DEVELOPMENT

Planning Acts

HOUSING, TOWN PLANNING ACT, 1909

This Act provided legislation to enable different areas of a locality to be developed in accordance with a scheme which would take account of their peculiar requirements. It meant repeal of certain byelaws to suit development under planning schemes prepared by local authorities. A planning scheme could be undertaken without the need of the Ministry of Health's approval, except for land affected outside the local authority's own area. Only undeveloped land could be planned, as built-up areas were excluded from the provisions of the Act.

Anyone aggrieved by the town planning scheme could appeal to the Ministry of Health, and compensation might be claimed for injurious consequences.

TOWN PLANNING ACT, 1919

This Act remedies certain difficulties in the 1909 Act. It empowers the Ministry of Health to issue an Order for building development to proceed without waiting for the whole scheme to be approved. The Act gives powers to the local authority to control development, limit density of buildings, and prescribe height, character, and type of buildings to be erected. Compulsory powers of purchase of land are also given in this Act. Clause 46 of the Act makes it compulsory on all local authorities with over 20,000 population to prepare a town planning scheme by 1923.

MINISTRY OF HEALTH MODEL CLAUSES, 1923

There are special provisions issued by the Ministry of Health in 1923 which deal with technical matters affecting acquisition of land, control of building, and repeal of byelaws. They state exact lengths and widths of new streets and road widenings, and allocation of certain lands for various purposes.

TOWN AND COUNTRY PLANNING ACT, 1925

This is the first Act devoted exclusively to town planning and consolidated previous legislation, and empowers any Local Authority to prepare and enforce schemes in accordance with the Act. It enables a local authority to acquire land by agreement or compulsion, or to claim betterment, and to check contraventions of the scheme. The Local Government Act, 1929, extended powers of county councils to prepare and administer town planning schemes and to be represented on joint town planning committees.

TOWN AND COUNTRY PLANNING ACT, 1932*

This Act conferred the force of law upon certain regulations by Ministry of Health under the Act. The most important of these are: Ministry of Health (Town and Country Planning) Regulations, 1933, and Town and Country Planning (General Interim Development) Order, 1933. Provisions for compensation and betterment are included in the 1932 Act, but the effect is the same, as compensation is frequently paid, but betterment seldom collected.

MODEL CLAUSES, 1938

The Ministry of Health issued a further set of these Clauses in 1938. They deal with such subjects as new streets, widenings, submission of development schemes, relaxation of byelaws for non-through traffic streets in residential areas, diversion and stopping up of highways, zoning, open spaces, adjustment of boundaries, and general amenities of estates.

TOWN AND COUNTRY PLANNING ACT, 1944, AS AMENDED BY TOWN AND COUNTRY PLANNING ACT, 1947

This Act makes provision for the acquisition and development of land for planning purposes ; for amending the law relating to Town and Country Planning ; for assessing by reference to certain rates of compensation payable in connection with the acquisition of land for public purposes, and as to the date of interest thereon ; and for purposes connected with the matters aforesaid. It does not operate in Scotland or Northern Ireland.

The Town and Country Planning Act, 1947, repealed Sections 1 to 14, 16 to 18, 21, 31 to 46, 50 to 56 of the 1944 Act and amended parts of other sections.

The Sections unrepealed or amended are as follows :

Section 15. The provisions of this section are becoming common form in Acts authorising compulsory acquisition of land by local authorities and the sections similar to Housing Act, 1936, S. 47. It provides, in effect, that where land acquired under this Act comprises premises in respect of which an old on-licence is in force, the purchasing authority may contribute to the compensation payable on refusal or renewal of licence under the Licensing (Consolidation) Act, 1910, and credit the sum to the expenses of purchase.

Section 17. Gives powers to local authorities to dispose or appropriate land held by them for the purposes of Part IV of 1947 Act.

Section 20. Local planning authorities are empowered to carry out development of land held by them.

Section 22. Authorisation of development of land acquired for planning notwithstanding interference with easements, etc.

Section 23. Power given to extinguish highways over land acquired for development.

Section 24. This deals with extinguishment of private ways and rights as to apparatus over or in land to be developed.

* This Act has been repealed by the Town and Country Planning Act, 1947.

Section 25.   As above as applies to statutory undertakers by serving of notices.

Section 26.   Orders can be made to extend or modify powers and duties of statutory undertakers for land to be developed.

Section 27.   This applies in reverse to Section 26, *i.e.* for the relief from obligations resting upon statutory undertakers.

Section 28.   Authorises use and development of consecrated land and burial grounds notwithstanding restrictions.

Section 29.   Similar to above in respect of open spaces, commons, etc.

Section 30.   Provides for displacements from land required for development *i.e.* residential accommodation for persons who reside on land to be appropriated under the Planning Acts.

Section 47.   Makes provisions for loans to be made to local authorities for the purposes of the 1947 Act.

Section 49.   This deals with the execution of works below high mark, as required under Planning Acts.

Section 63.   Deals with regulations and procedure for making same.

Section 64.   Relates to powers of official arbitrators in connection with references made to them under this Act.

Section 65.   Gives interpretations of expressions used in the Act.

Schedules 1, 2, and 3 are repeated by the 1947 Act.

Fourth Schedule

Assessment of compensation to Statutory Undertakers.

Fifth Schedule

Modifications of Land Clauses Acts and Acquisition of Land (Assessment of Compensation) Act, 1919, for purpose of Part I and by a development plan under the Town and Country Planning Act, 1947.

Sixth Schedule

Procedure for completion of compulsory purchase under orders providing for expedited completion, as amended by the Acquisition of Land (Authorisation Procedure) Act, 1946.

Seventh Schedule

Provisions as to operation in certain special cases of ruins.   57 (1) as to assessment of compensation.

Eighth Schedule

Ascertainment of compensation for purchase of land valued under War Damage Act, 1943.

THE TOWN AND COUNTRY PLANNING ACT, 1947

Introduction

The main purposes of this Act are : first, the improvement of planning machinery and the enlargement of the powers of local authorities to carry out positive planning ; secondly, the remedying of what is the greatest deterrent to town planning, the obligation for local authorities to pay compensation in respect of refusal of permission to develop, without in practice their being able to recover betterment.

Under this Act it is decided to transfer the existing planning functions to the county councils, the county boroughs remaining planning authorities.

This reduces the number of planning authorities from 1441 to 145, which is about 10 per cent. of their former number.

The powers which are conferred upon the new authorities are (i) to make plans in respect of their area, and (ii) to deal with applications for consent. The actual carrying out of the plan, the housing functions, the local roads, and so on, remain with the district councils as before. They are required to conform to the plan which will have been prepared by the county council. The Act provides for full consultation with the district councils in the course of the preparation of the plan, and it provides also for the district councils to have an opportunity to express their views when the plan has been prepared and is ready for submission to the Minister, so that the district councils will be consulted in every stage ; and they will be able to make representations to the Minister if they are not in agreement with the plan which has been finally submitted.

The county councils will be expected to employ an adequate staff to enable them to prepare the plan. They will be required to make a survey of their area before the plan is actually prepared, so that they will be fully acquainted with all the circumstances and conditions of their area ; and the plan will be based upon the most careful survey which is possible in the circumstances. Under the existing law, there is no obligation on any local authority to prepare a plan. Since 1943, they had been under an obligation to consider applications for development and to adjudicate upon them, but, curiously enough, although they have been under that obligation they are under no obligation to have a plan. Since only about 5 per cent. of the country was actually subject to final plans at the outbreak of war, and since less than half the country had even made provisional schemes, it will be seen that the consideration of applications for development over the greater part of the country at the present time is a somewhat haphazard affair. The Minister is to co-ordinate the different plans of the different authorities so as to make them fit into one another.

Under the Act, there will be an obligation on all planning athorities to submit their plans within three years from the appointed date ; and, since the number of plans so submitted will be relatively small, it will be possible for the Minister to examine those plans and to see that they fit in with one another, to see that they fit into a national pattern, to see that industry is broadly located in the right places, to see that the national road pattern is right, and so on. In this way it will be possible to avoid the veil of the special or distressed areas from which we suffered in the inter-war years, and to see that the country as a whole is properly balanced as regards industrial location and as regards its general economic and social life.

One of the main criticisms of the machinery of the Act of 1932 was that planning was made static, that once a plan was made and approved it had the effect of law, and could be varied even in a minor degree only by another scheme, which had to go through the same process ; and since it takes something like four to five years to get a scheme through, the great difficulty and complexity of modifying any scheme which has been approved will be realised. Under the Act there will be an automatic review of the plans every five years, and it will be open to local authorities to review their plan more often if they so desire ; and the procedure will be very much more simple than it has been in the past.   In that way, it will be possible for local planning authorities to take account of changed circumstances, of any new contingencies which may arise, and to modify their plan, after of course giving proper notice to everybody concerned, and possibly after a local public inquiry.

Powers are conferred upon local planning authorities in this Act to enable them to acquire any land which may be necessary for the carrying out of positive development—that is, for the carrying out of their plan— and also actually to carry out the development themselves if it is desirable that they should do so.   It will be for the Minister to decide whether it is desirable that the local authorities should carry out positive development, but subject to that consent they will be in a position to do so, if they think it essential for the purpose of carrying out their plan.

The Act provides that the local planning authority shall designate in the plan the land that it will require to purchase compulsorily within the next ten years.   When this land is designated, it will be open to persons interested to appear at a local public inquiry and to object to the designation ; and the Minister will in due course, having heard the views of the local authority and the objectors, either confirm the designation or otherwise as the case may be ; and where land is subject to designation it will be prima facie upon the local authority to acquire that land.

The advantage of the designation procedure is that it gives to the owner of land notice that his land may be subject to compulsory purchase within a limited period.   Land which is designated as being subject to compulsory purchase will undoubtedly be less saleable than land which is not designated.

Compensation for Loss of Development Rights

The business of the Central Land Board will be two-fold ; to deal with compensation, and to assess the development charge.   The Act proposes that as from the appointed day all development rights in land shall be subject to a permanent restriction.   With the exceptions which are set out in the Third Schedule to the Act, no one will be allowed to develop land (" development " is defined in Clause 10), without obtaining consent from the Central Land Board and paying such development charge as will be agreed.   A sum of £300,000,000 should be made available as an ex gratia payment.   Those who consider that they have a claim for compensation must make their claim to the Central Land Board.   The basis of the claim will be the actual development value which is the subject of restriction.

The actual development value is defined in the Act as the difference between the restricted and the unrestricted value of the particular unit of land which is the subject of a claim.   The unrestricted value is the value of the land in the market in the condition in which it is on the appointed day, but the values will be the values as on 7th January, 1947.   The restricted value is the value of the land if it is restricted to its existing use, also valued on the same basis.   If it is agricultural land, the restricted value will be its value as agricultural land and for no other purpose.   The difference between the two is the " development value " and it is that which will form the subject of the claim.

The vast bulk of land in this country, both in area and in value, has little or no development value. Very large areas of land are agricultural land where development is most improbable ; and, even if some development were to take place, land in the area is so plentiful that the mere fact that that land could be developed adds little or nothing to its value. Again, there will be a great deal of land in built-up areas where its use is stabilised, which is really incapable of any other more profitable use.

In respect of substantial areas of the country, however, there will be claims for compensation, and those claims will be dealt with on the basis of the regulations which will be made by the Treasury. The administration of the fund will be with the Central Land Board, and there is a provision in the Act that relatively small claims should be ignored, on the lines of the treatment of small claims under the War Damage Act.

Applications for Consent to Develop

As regards the development charge, there will be, as a condition of approval to develop land—either to build or to change the existing user—a requirement that there shall be a certificate from the Central Land Board that a development charge has been paid in respect of the application to develop.

Development Charge

The Act does not provide what is to be the amount of the development charge, except to impose a maximum. The basis of the development charge is the increased value of the land as a result of the giving of the consent. The Act provides that the Central Land Board may charge not more than 100 per cent. of the increased value. It will be the duty of the Central Land Board to get the maximum development charge which they can justifiably extract, and, on the other hand, not to impose such a charge as will impede development.

Outline of the Act

The following more important extracts are taken from the explanatory Memorandum on this Act published by His Majesty's Stationery Office in November 1947.

1. OBJECT AND SCOPE

Objects of the Act

1. The objects of the Act are briefly as follows :
(a) To set up a Central Land Board (Sections 2 and 3) ;
(b) To introduce a new planning system including new powers to control outdoor advertisements (Parts II and III) ;
(c) To confer on Ministers, local authorities and statutory undertakers wider powers of compulsory acquisition in order to make land available for necessary development (Part IV) ;
(d) To provide a new basis of compensation for compulsory acquisition instead of the 1939 standard prescribed in the Town and Country Planning Act, 1944 (Part V) ;

(*e*) To provide for payments (aggregating £300,000,000) in respect of depreciation in value of freehold and leasehold interests in land caused by the Act and the corresponding Scottish Act (Part VI) ;

(*f*) To secure the collection of development charges where the grant of permission to develop land results in an increase in value (Part VII);

(*g*) To provide Exchequer grants to assist Local Authorities in the acquisition and clearing of land (Part IX).

The principal effect of the Act will be to remove the compensation-betterment difficulties which have obstructed planning in the past.

2. THE CENTRAL LAND BOARD

5. The functions of the Central Land Board are to deal with claims on the £300,000,000 (Part VI of the Act) and to collect development charges (Part VII). The Board also has certain powers for the acquisition of land (see paragraph 39 below). The provisions of the Act setting up the Board came into effect on Royal Assent.

3. THE NEW PLANNING SYSTEM

7. The new planning system replaces that based on the Town and Country Planning Acts of 1932, 1943, and 1944. All these Acts are repealed, except parts of the 1944 Act which, as amended, are set out in the eleventh Schedule of the present Act.

Local Planning Authorities (Section 4)

8. The local planning authorities under the Act are the councils of counties and county boroughs instead of, as under previous Acts, the councils of county boroughs and county districts. (For the position in London see paragraph 96 below). Where desirable, the Minister can by order establish a joint board, covering the areas, or parts of the areas, of two or more local planning authorities, and the Board then becomes the local planning authority for the combined area. Unless all the constituent authorities agree to the setting up of the Board, the Minister is required to hold a local inquiry first and the order is subject to negative resolution of Parliament.

9. Of the powers conferred later in the Act, some are given to local planning authorities, some to county district councils, and some to both. There is also provision for consultation with county district councils and for delegation to them (see paragraphs 13 and 27 below). The allocation of functions among the different authorities, both in London and in the provinces, is fully set out in Appendix A.

10. A local planning authority can delegate their functions to a planning committee, and the committee can in turn delegate to sub-committees of which there may be several covering different parts of the area. A planning committee need include only a bare majority of members of the authority, and a sub-committee only a combined majority of members of the authority and of county district councils, so that there is ample scope for co-option. In addition, two or more local planning authorities can set up a Joint Advisory Committee, and here too only a bare majority of the members need be members of the appointing authorities. (First Schedule, Parts II and III.)

Development Plans (Sections (5–11)

11. Section 5 imposes on every local planning authority the obligation of carrying out a survey and preparing a development plan for their area. The survey will involve a physical, economic, and sociological analysis of the potentialities and future requirements of the area, dealing, for example, with natural resources, distribution of industry, communications, housing requirements, the community structure. It will provide the evidence on which the proposals in the plan are based.

12. The plan, which will consist of a series of maps and documents, must be submitted to the Minister within three years of the appointed day (although the period may be extended in particular cases). As initially submitted it will usually be in the nature of an "outline plan", and will show, for example, major road improvements, the land to be reserved for agriculture, the part of a town destined for comprehensive redevelopment and the direction in which a town may expand. It will also show broadly the stages by which development is to be carried out, and it may designate as subject to compulsory acquisition the land needed in the first stages (see paragraphs 32 and 33 below). The local planning authority can at any time submit proposals for alterations or additions to the plan, so that it can be brought up to date whenever necessary, or so that details can be filled in over a part of the area when development is about to take place. Every five years the authority are required to carry out a fresh survey and review the plan (Section 6).

13. The local planning authority are obliged to consult county district councils before preparing their plan or submitting alterations, and before the plan is submitted to the Minister they must consider representations made by those councils (Section 10 (1)).

14. Regulations under Section 10 (2) will prescribe the form and content of development plans and the procedure for their submission to the Minister. The Regulations may provide among other things:

(a) for advertisement of the plan before submission ;
(b) for consideration of objections and representations ;
(c) for local inquiries or other hearings ;
(d) for the approved plan being available for public inspection and for copies being placed on sale.

Control of Development (Sections 12–18)

15. The Act, unlike previous planning Acts, provides expressly that permission is required for all development. This requirement applies equally before and after a plan is approved. Development is defined as " the carrying out of building, engineering, mining, or other operations in, on, over or under land, or the making of any material change in the use of any buildings or other land". There are various exemptions, in particular for certain works of maintenance and for the use of land for all branches of agriculture and forestry. In addition, the Minister may by order specify classes of use, and a change from one use to another within the same class would not be development. (Section 12.)

16. The machinery of control closely resembles the machinery for interim development control under the previous Acts. In particular,

11

there is the same flexible system of relaxing control by means of a development order, which may grant block permission for certain classes of development, but which may also enable the Minister or the local planning authority to direct that the permission shall not apply in particular cases or particular areas (Section 13). For development not permitted by a development order, permission has to be obtained from the local planning authority (or from the authority to which the powers of control may have been delegated—see paragraph 27 below). The applicant has a right of appeal to the Minister if the authority refuse permission or grant permission subject to conditions, or if they fail to give a decision within a specified period (Section 16). There is power, as in the 1943 Act, for the Minister to call applications in, *i.e.*, to direct the local planning authority to refer them to him for decision (Section 15). (For control of development to be carried out by local authorities and statutory undertakers see paragraph 28 below.)

17. New features include the following:

(a) An application for permission to erect or extend a factory, if the new building or the extension is to have a floor area of more than 5,000 square feet, may require to be accompanied by a certificate from the Board of Trade that the proposal accords with national policy on the distribution of industry (Section 14 (4)).

(b) While the local planning authority will normally be guided by the development plan in dealing with applications, they may be authorised to depart from the plan either by the development order or by direction of the Minister (Section 14 (3) (b)).

(c) The local planning authority are required to keep a register, open to public inspection, of their decisions on applications for permission (Section 14 (5)).

(d) Anyone who wishes to ascertain whether operations which he proposes to carry out constitute development, or whether they are covered by a block permission in a Development Order, can apply to the local planning authority for a determination (Section 17).

18. The control of development along certain roads (which is at present administered separately by the highway authority under the Restriction of Ribbon Development Acts 1935 and 1943) is merged in planning control, so that a developer no longer has to obtain permission from the highway authority as well as from the authority responsible for planning control. The relevant parts of the Restriction of Ribbon Development Acts are repealed.

Compensation for Refusal of Permission (Sections 19 and 20)

19. In general, no compensation is payable for refusal of permission. An exception to this rule is where the development for which permission is refused is in certain special classes listed in Part II of the Third Schedule. The reason for providing for compensation in these cases is that in the calculation of " existing use value " for the purposes of Parts V and VI (see paragraphs 48 and 54 below) it is assumed that planning permission for development of these classes will be granted.

20. If land has become incapable of reasonably beneficial use in its

existing state and permission to develop is refused (or is granted subject to conditions which prevent it being made capable of reasonably beneficial use), the owner can serve on the county borough or county district council a purchase notice requiring them to buy the land. The notice is transmitted to the Minister, and, if he is satisfied that the land is in fact incapable of reasonably beneficial use, he confirms the notice and the Local Authority are then required to buy the land at a price equal to the full " existing use value " (see paragraph 48 below).

Revocation, etc., of Permission (Sections 21 and 22)

21. The local planning authority can, by order confirmed by the Minister, revoke or modify a permission. The power may be used only before the building or other operations have been completed or the change of use has taken place. Compensation is payable, under certain conditions, for abortive expenditure and other consequential loss.

Enforcement of Control (Sections 23 and 24)

22. If development is carried out without permission, the local planning authority can, within four years of the development being carried out, serve an enforcement notice requiring the removal of the building or the discontinuance of the use. No compensation is payable. The recipient of a notice can appeal to a court against the notice ; he can also apply to the authority for ex post facto planning permission (Section 18 (1)), and, if this is refused, he can appeal to the Minister. Similar enforcement action can be taken to secure compliance with conditions attached to a permission.

Miscellaneous Powers of Control (Sections 26–30 and 33)

23. Section 26 enables a local planning authority to make an order requiring the removal or alteration of a building or works (which includes any structure or erection, waste materials, refuse and other matters deposited on land) or the discontinuance of a use. The order has to be confirmed by the Minister and compensation is payable. This power is to be distinguished from the enforcement power mentioned in the previous paragraph. It is intended for use against development which was carried out before planning control was in operation and which conflicts with planning requirements. It can also be used against development which was undertaken with permission but has since, in changed circumstances, come to conflict with current requirements.

24. Sections 28, 29, and 30 reproduce, with minor changes, the provisions in previous Acts for preservation of trees and woodlands and for the preservation and listing of buildings of special architectural or historic interest. Preservation orders made under previous Acts are preserved in force (see Appendix B). Building preservation orders may be made either by the local planning authority or by a county district council. (In addition, under Section 41, these authorities can acquire compulsorily a building subject to a preservation order if it is not being properly maintained and a new power is given to the Minister of Works to acquire compulsorily in similar circumstances.) Section 33, which is based on a provision included in many planning schemes under previous law, enables

the local planning authority to require a garden, bare site or other open land to be put in proper condition if it has become an eyesore.

Control of Advertisements (*Sections* 31–32)

25. The Act provides a compehensive system for controlling outdoor advertisements. Such control as has hitherto existed was exercised partly through powers in public general Acts, *e.g.* the Advertisement Regulation Acts of 1907 and 1925, Section 47 of the Town and Country Planning Act, 1932, and partly through local Acts. The new statute repeals the public general legislation and contains (Section 113 (4)) a power to repeal or modify by Order in Council any local enactment dealing with advertisement control.

26. The detailed control of advertisements (which are defined in wide terms in Section 119) will be effected by means of regulations. Section 31 empowers the Minister to make regulations for restricting or regulating the display of advertisements so far as appears to him expedient in the interests of amenity or public safety. The regulations may provide (among other things) :

   (*a*) for requiring the consent of the local planning authority to be obtained for any display of advertisements ;

   (*b*) for enabling the local planning authority to require the removal of any advertisement contravening the regulations ;

   (*c*) for a right of appeal (either to the Minister or, if he should so decide, to an independent tribunal) from the decision of a local planning authority ;

   (*d*) for a special degree of protection for areas classed on grounds of amenity as " areas of special control ".

The regulations can be made to apply to advertisements already in existence on the date when the regulations come into force, but a period of grace must be allowed.

Delegation of Functions (*Section* 34)

27. Regulations may provide for delegating any of the functions of local planning authorities under Part III to the councils of county districts, or, in the case of a joint planning board, to the constituent authorities of the board. The extent of delegation can vary in different areas and at different stages in the preparation of plans, and the delegation can be either optional or obligatory.

Development by Local Authorities and Statutory Undertakers (*Section* 35)

28. Where a local authority or statutory undertaker have to obtain the authorisation of a Government department before carrying out development, the department may direct that the authorisation operates as if it were a planning permission granted by the Minister of Town and Country Planning. This avoids a separate application for planning permission. Administrative arrangements will be made to ensure that the local planning authority, and, where necessary, the Minister of Town and Country Planning, are consulted on the planning aspects. There is also provision on the lines of Section 32 of the 1944 Act enabling the Minister to exercise planning control over development carried out by a local authority on land for which they are themselves the local planning authority.

29. Statutory undertakers receive, as regards their operational* land, the same special treatment as in the 1944 Act ; that is to say, a refusal or revocation of permission to develop, or a requirement under Section 26 to remove a building, etc., must be embodied in an order which is made or confirmed jointly by the Minister of Town and Country Planning and the Minister concerned with the undertaking and which may be subject to special Parliamentary procedure. Compensation is assessed on the special basis in the Fourth Schedule of the 1944 Act.

Agreements with Landowners

30. Agreements made under Section 34 of the 1932 Act for restricting the development or use of land continue in force, but without prejudice to the exercise of any of the powers of the Act. The agreements can be varied or revoked by order of the Minister, on the ground that they are inconsistent with current planning requirements, or by an award of an arbitrator on the ground that it is just to do so in view of the effect of the Act or of action taken under the Act (10th Schedule, paragraph 10). Similar agreements can be made in future under Section 25.

Existing Schemes, etc.

31. For the effect of the Act on existing planning schemes and on permissions granted under previous Acts, see Appendix B.

4. Acquisition and Development of Land

Designation for Compulsory Acquisition

32. As stated in paragraph 12 above, a development plan may designate land as subject to compulsory acquisition. Land may be designated only if it is likely to be acquired within ten years, or seven years in the case of agricultural land (Section 5 (4)). The purpose of designation is thus to indicate a firm programme of development for a reasonable period ahead. For example, while a plan may show a considerable part of a town as an " area of comprehensive development ", i.e. as eventually due for reconstruction, only the area to be acquired in the first 10 years will be designated. Further land can be designated when the plan is amended (subject again to the 10-year and 7-year limitations which run from the date of the amendment), so that the programme of development can be kept up to date.

33. There are three categories of land which may be designated (Section 5(2)) :

(a) Land allocated by the plan for the functions of a Minister, local authority or statutory undertaker ;

(b) Land in an area of comprehensive development, e.g. an area of blitz, blight or overspill ;

(c) Any other land which may require compulsory acquisition in order to secure its use in the manner proposed by the plan.

* Operational land is that class of Statutory Undertaker's land which received special treatment in the 1944 Act. It is defined in Section 119, and, means, broadly, land used or held for the purpose of the undertaking, not being land which is comparable with land in general. Thus, a gas-works is operational land, but a gas company's showroom in a shopping centre would not be operational since it is comparable with any other shop.

Compulsory Acquisition of Designated Land (Sections 37 and 38)

34. Land in category (*a*) above may be acquired compulsorily under Section 37 by the Minister, local authority or statutory undertaker for whose functions it is allocated. Acquisitions by local authorities and statutory undertakers are authorised by the Minister concerned with the functions for which the land is being acquired. The Act does not repeal the powers of acquisition which public authorities already possess under other statutes. It is anticipated, however, that so far as practicable, they will make their requirements known in time for the land to be designated in a development plan.

35. Land in categories (*b*) and (*c*) may be acquired compulsorily under Section 38 by the council of the county borough or county district in which the land is situated, or, in certain circumstances by some other local authority. (For compulsory acquisition by the Central Land Board see paragraph 40 below.) The authorising Minister is the Minister of Town and Country Planning. This section reproduces the powers of acquisition in the 1944 Act, but it also covers a wider field:

(*a*) it applies to schemes of comprehensive development or redevelopment outside the blitz, blight, and other special categories covered by the 1944 Act ;

(*b*) it provides a general reserve power to acquire land in order to secure its use in the manner proposed by the plan.

36. If land is designated as subject to compulsory acquisition, it does not necessarily follow that it will all in fact be acquired compulsorily. The owner can himself develop, or he can sell for development, in accordance with the plan. Where land has been designated simply to ensure that it will be developed in accordance with the plan (see paragraph 35 (*b*) above), Section 9 (4) provides that the designation will lapse if development of the kind proposed in the plan is carried out privately. Section 9 also provides that, if the land is not acquired within twelve years of designation (eight years for agricultural land), the owner can serve a notice requiring it to be bought. Then, unless within six months notice to treat is served or an offer is made to acquire by agreement, the designation lapses.

Compulsory Acquisition before a Plan is in Operation (Sections 37 and 38)

37. Once a development plan is in operation, the powers of compulsory acquisition provided by Sections 37 and 38 of the Act apply only to land designated in the plan as subject to compulsory acquisition. The Act also provides certain powers of compulsory acquisition in the stage before a plan comes into operation:

(*a*) Section 37 (2) enables the Minister of Works and the Postmaster-General to acquire land for their purposes. The Minister of Town and Country Planning, as well as the acquiring Minister, must be satisfied that the acquisition is necessary. This provision came into operation on Royal Assent.

(*b*) Section 38 (2) enables the council of a county borough or a county district (or, in certain circumstances, some other local authority) to acquire:

(i) for any purpose which the Minister of Town and Country Planning is satisfied is immediately necessary in the interests of proper planning and which cannot be effected under other statutory powers (including the powers of the 1944 Act so long as they remain in force) ;

(ii) for the purposes covered by paragraphs (c) and (d) of Section 10 (1) of the 1944 Act.*

Section 38 (2) also came into operation on Royal Assent, but until the appointed day, when the acquisition provisions of the 1944 Act are repealed, those provisions will continue to be used where appropriate.

Acquisition by Agreement (Section 40)

38. Under Section 40 a county, county borough or county district council may, with the consent of the Minister, acquire land by agreement for any purpose for which they can acquire compulsorily under Section 38. This power applies both before and after a plan has come into operation, and whether or not the land is designated, but it is not available until the appointed day.

Acquisition by the Central Land Board (Section 43)

39. The Board have certain powers of acquisition for any purpose connected with their functions under the Act. Section 43 enables them to acquire land by agreement for such purposes, and also to acquire compulsorily (whether or not the land is designated) if the Minister is satisfied that the acquisition is expedient in the public interest and that the Board cannot acquire by agreement on reasonable terms. These powers will enable the Board to acquire land in order to dispose of it at an inclusive price including development charge. The Board could also be authorised to acquire compulsorily land which is needed for development but the owner of which refuses to sell on reasonable terms. Whenever the Board purchase land, they will dispose of it to a developer. They have no powers to carry out development themselves.

Procedure for Compulsory Acquisition

40. The procedure for compulsory acquisition under any of the powers in the Act is, in the main, that of the Acquisition of Land (Authorisation Procedure) Act, 1946. That procedure is, however, modified in the following respects (Section 45) :

(a) Where the land is designated, an objection may be disregarded if it amounts in substance to an objection to the provisions of the plan.

(b) A compulsory acquisition order submitted under Section 38 may be confirmed in part only and the remainder left for consideration later.

* These purposes are broadly as follows :
Paragraph (c) : to provide an alternative site for development which is desirable in the public interest but which on planning grounds ought not to be carried out on the site proposed.
Paragraph (d) : to provide accommodation for persons or undertakings who have left an area through war circumstances and whose re-establishment there would be contrary to planning requirements.

(c) There are changes in the special procedure for acquisition of land belonging to local authorities, statutory undertakers and the National Trust. Where the land is designated before acquisition, provision is made for special Parliamentary procedure at the designation stage instead of at the acquisition stage. (Section 5 (4)). In addition, the present Act, like the 1944 Act but not the 1946 Act, gives power to acquire the " operational " land of statutory undertakers even if no certificate is given by the appropriate Minister under paragraph 10 of the First Schedule to the 1946 Act that the land can be taken without serious detriment to the undertaking. If, however, the land is acquired without such a certificate, compensation is payable on the special basis of the Fourth Schedule of the 1944 Act. (For the meaning of " operational " land, see footnote to paragraph 29 above.)

41. The " speedy " procedure of Section 2 of the 1946 Act is available only for acquisitions under Section 37, *i.e.* acquisitions by Ministers, local authorities or statutory undertakers for the purpose of their functions.

42. The expedited completion procedure of the Sixth Schedule to the 1944 Act is available for acquisitions under Sections 38 and 43. This procedure enables the acquiring authority to obtain title to the land with a minimum of delay (Section 39).

Disposal of Development of Land (Section 44)

43. The Act provides powers of disposal and development of land acquired or held under its provisions by incorporating Sections 19–30 of the 1944 Act. Briefly, these sections enable a local authority to dispose of and appropriate the land and to carry out development outside the range of normal local government functions ; authorise development in spite of easements, restrictive covenants and other restrictions ; provide for the extinction of rights of way and rights as to apparatus over land acquired ; and require the local authority to secure provision of residential accommodation before people are displaced in the course of redevelopment, unless such accommodation is already available. The sections also provide for extending and modifying the powers and duties of statutory undertakers in the light of planning requirements and for relieving statutory undertakers of obligations which they cannot fulfil because their land is taken or planning restrictions are imposed on its use.

44. Sections 19–30 of the 1944 Act, as amended by the present Act, are set out in the Eleventh Schedule. The amendments are mainly drafting amendments to adapt the 1944 Act provisions to the wider powers of acquisition conferred by the present Act. Some of the provisions are needed only for land acquired or held by local authorities under Sections 38 or 40 for general planning purposes, while others are applied to all land acquired or held under the Act, by local authorities for whatever purpose, by Ministers, statutory undertakers, or the Central Land Board. Thus Section 19, enabling the Minister of Town and Country Planning to control the disposal of land, applies only to land held for the purposes of Sections 38 and 40, so that if, for example, a local authority acquire land under Section 37 for housing, there is no question of its disposal being subject to

the consent of the Minister of Town and Country Planning. The land would be subject to the same consents on disposal as land acquired under the Housing Acts.

45. There is an important amendment to Section 20 of the 1944 Act, the section which enables a local authority to carry out development outside their local government functions. Under the 1944 Act the local authority were, in the main, debarred from carrying out such development if some other person was able and willing to do so. This limitation is repealed by Section 44 (2) of the present Act.

Highways (Sections 47–49)

46. Part IV also contains certain provisions about highways:

(*a*) Section 47, which re-enacts Section 21 of the 1944 Act, enables a local highway authority to construct unclassified roads which are necessary on planning grounds and also enables contributions to be made by other local authorities to the expenses of local highway authorities and the Minister of Transport.

(*b*) Under Section 48 a local authority can declare to be a private street land designated for the purpose in a development plan. This brings into operation whatever enactments are in force in the locality concerning the execution of street works and the recovery of the costs from frontagers. By regulations under the section, these enactments can be modified in the same respects as they are usually modified by planning schemes under previous law.

(*c*) Section 49 gives a new power to the Minister of Transport to authorise the stopping-up or diversion of highways in order to enable development to be carried out in accordance with planning permission or by a Government Department.

5. COMPENSATION FOR COMPULSORY ACQUISITION

47. The Act introduces a new basis of compensation for compulsory acquisition and abolishes the 1939 standard. The new basis applies in all cases where notice to treat is served after Royal Assent, *i.e.* 6th August, 1947. The compensation will be based on existing use value only (see paragraph 48 below) calculated on current prices. This, however, is subject to the qualifications mentioned in paragraphs 49 to 52 below. Part V of the Act applies to all compulsory acquisitions by local and public authorities, statutory undertakers (see Section 57 (1)) and Government Departments, not only to acquisitions under the present Act.

Existing Use Value (Section 51)

48. Existing use value means the value of the land on the assumption that permission would be granted only for development of any of the classes mentioned in the Third Schedule, that is to say, broadly :

(*a*) the value of the land for agriculture, including the right to put up buildings required for general farming (but not dwelling-houses) and to work minerals required for agricultural purposes ; or

(*b*) where at the appointed day the land is built on, or is used for purposes other than agricultural, the value for the existing use in perpetuity, assuming, where there are buildings on the land:

(i) a right to replace buildings again and again as they wear out (including the right to make good war damage and to replace any building which was destroyed or demolished between 7th January, 1937, and the appointed day, 1st July, 1948) ;

(ii) a right to extend buildings up to 10 per cent. of cubic content measured externally), or, in the case of dwelling-houses, up to 10 per cent. or 1,750 cubic feet, whichever is the greater ;

(iii) a right to convert a house into flats.

NEW TOWNS ACT, 1946

The New Towns Act is to provide for the creation of new towns through the agency of development corporations established and financed by the Government.

Its main provisions include the following :

Clause 1 enables the Minister of Town and Country Planning, after consulting the local authorities concerned, to make an order designating an area as the site of a proposed new town.   Such an area may include as its nucleus the area of an existing town.   The procedure for making such an order follows substantially the provisions enacted by the Town and Country Planning Act, 1944, in relation to areas of extensive war damage as amended by the Town and Country Planning Act, 1947.

The Minister is enabled under Clause 2 to establish a corporation for the purpose of developing a new town once the area for the site has been designated.   In general, one corporation will be established for each new town, but the Minister may appoint one corporation to develop more than one town, or he may transfer the functions of a corporation already established to another corporation already in existence or specially created for the purpose.

The corporation may undertake any activity necessary for the purposes of the new town.   The establishment of a development corporation will not affect the powers and duties of local authorities in the area or the powers and duties of statutory undertakers operating in that area.   Corporations may, if necessary, undertake the provision of water, electricity, gas, sewerage, and other similar services.   But as far as possible, existing statutory undertakers or local authorities will provide the services which it would be their normal function to provide.

The corporation is not enabled to act otherwise than as any incorporated body could act ; where Parliamentary sanction is now required to enable any individual or incorporated body to become a statutory undertaker, the corporation would similarly have to obtain such sanction.

Each corporation will consist of a chairman and deputy chairman and up to seven other members.   All will be appointed by the Minister after consultation with the local authorities concerned.   The Minister will control the terms of appointment and provision is made for payment of the members with the consent of the Treasury.

Under Clause 3,* the corporation must obtain the Minister's approval of its plans for development, and before giving such approval the Minister is required to consult the local authorities concerned.

The corporation may, with the consent of the Minister, acquire land either by agreement or compulsorily.   " Such land may be in the area of the new town or if required for the purposes of the new town, elsewhere."   The procedure of the 1944 Act is followed and expedited.   Completion under that Act can be applied.   Temporary speedy acquisition under the Acquisition of Land (Procedure) Act is also available. " It would be used only very exceptionally and does not apply to purchase of dwelling-houses."

* Subsections (3) and (4) of Clause 3 have been repealed by Town and Country Planning Act, 1947.

The safeguards under the 1944 Act relating to the land of statutory undertakers and to open spaces are included. Inalienable National Trust land and land belonging to local authorities can only be acquired compulsorily by an order which is subject to special Parliamentary procedure if objection to acquisition is maintained.

The Minister has complete control over the disposal of land by the corporation. Generally, in England and Wales, disposal will be limited to leases of 99 years. But in exceptional circumstances, and if the disposal is to a Minister of the Crown or local authority, the Minister has power to agree to the transfer of the freehold, or the grant of a lease, for a longer term. Those living or carrying on business or other activities on land compulsorily acquired will have the opportunity to be rehabilitated on any land belonging to the corporation on terms settled with regard to the purchase price. Disposal of land in Scotland is adopted to suit the form of land tenure in that country.

Clause 7 states that a local highway authority and the Minister of Transport, in his capacity as highway authority for trunk roads, are enabled to acquire land compulsorily or by agreement for the purpose of providing or improving highways communicating with the new towns.

The corporations shall be deemed, under Clause 8, to be housing associations within the meaning of the Housing Act, 1936. Local authorities requiring houses in the new towns will thus be able to arrange for the corporation to build houses for them, and such houses will receive the Exchequer subsidy.

The corporation may also receive the Exchequer subsidy for houses built on its own account. When a corporation is wound up and its houses are transferred to local authority, the Minister of Health is enabled to continue to pay the subsidy to the acquiring authority.

It is expected that shortly after an area has been designated as the site for a new town, the area will (if it lies within the boundaries of two or more local authorities) be brought within the jurisdiction of a single local authority under the machinery of the Local Government (Boundary Commission) Act, 1945. For public health joint boards may be constituted by order of the Minister of Health under section 6 of the Public Health Act, 1936. Such an order is provisional only if objected to by any of the constituent authorities.

It is intended that wherever possible the sewerage of the new town should be undertaken by the local authority (or joint board), but the corporation may provide the service if the former are unwilling. The Minister of Health is enabled to make an order authorising the corporation to undertake sewerage services and apply them to the relevant provisions of the Public Health Act, 1936. No similar provision is required for water services, since the corporation, like any private individual, can be authorised to become water undertakers under the Water Act, 1945.

Clause 12 provides that the moneys required by a development corporation to meet the capital cost of developing a new town area will be advanced from the Consolidated Fund, and that such advances will be repayable on terms approved by the Treasury.

Provision is made for the payment of grant, as necessary, to enable the corporation to meet its expenses on revenue account.

A development corporation will be required to submit an annual report to the Minister, and this will be laid before each House of Parliament.

An order for the dissolution and winding-up of the corporation may be made by the Minister and such an order will require the approval by resolution of each House of Parliament. The Minister may then make an order, after consulting the local authority or statutory undertakers concerned, for the transfer of all or part of the corporation to the local authority or statutory undertakers, who will be required to pay a specified sum to the corporation. The local authority or statutory undertakers will have an opportunity of making an objection to the Minister within twenty-eight days of the service of notice of the proposed order, and if the objection is not withdrawn, the order will be subject to special Parliamentary procedure.   Any surplus remaining after winding up will be paid into the Exchequer.

The Act applies to Great Britain as a whole, with modifications to cover the different system of land tenure in Scotland.   The powers accorded under the Act to the Minister of Health in England and Wales are similarly vested in the Secretary of State for Scotland.

To establish a new town of 50,000 population may cost about £19,000,000, spread over ten years, according to a financial memorandum to the Act.   Of the sum estimated, about £15,500,000 would represent expenditure by the corporation (met by advances from the Consolidated Fund) and about £3,500,000 by local authorities. "A close estimate of the amount of advances which ultimately may be required from the Consolidated Fund is not possible", the memorandum says.   "Much depends on the future trend of prices and on the extent to which development will be undertaken by private enterprise."

The figures given are calculated on the assumption that services such as hospitals, gas, and electricity will not be provided by a development corporation, or by local authorities as such.   It is assumed that a large part of the construction of commercial buildings, shops, factories and middle-class houses will be undertaken by private developers.

Parliamentary authority is to be sought for advances from the Consolidated Fund up to £50,000,000 to enable the programme to be started.   It is estimated that this will cover requirements for about five years, after which it will be necessary to seek further Parliamentary authority for the continuance and expansion of the programme.

Housing Acts

The Housing Acts now mean the Housing Acts, 1936 and 1938, which consolidate the following Acts :

The Housing Act, 1914.

The Housing, Town Planning, etc., Act, 1919.

The Housing, etc., Act, 1923.

The Housing (Financial Provisions) Act, 1924.

The Housing (Rural Authorities) Act, 1931.

The Housing Acts, 1925, 1930, and 1935.

The Housing (Financial Provisions) Act, 1938.

The 1936 Act is in eight Parts, 191 Sections, and twelve Schedules, and sets up a Central Housing Advisory Committee, and the Minister of Health acts through the Housing, Slum Clearance, and Town and Country Planning Division of the Ministry.

Powers are given to a local authority to develop clearance areas, compulsorily acquire land, and to provide housing accommodation for the working classes, especially in overcrowded and unhealthy areas.

The Housing (Financial Provisions) Act, 1938, amalgamated the subsidies for slum clearance and overcrowding into a new composite grant, and increased the grant in respect of buildings on sites of high value.

THE HOUSING (TEMPORARY ACCOMMODATION) ACT, 1944

The Housing (Temporary Accommodation) Act is a measure designed to assist housing authorities in meeting the immediate shortage of housing accommodation by the speedy provision of temporary houses in large numbers.

A memorandum attached to the Act states : " Under present conditions no firm estimate is available of the cost of temporary houses, or of the number of such houses which it will be possible to construct for erection by 1st October, 1947, but it is anticipated that the amount of £150,000,000 should cover the cost of approximately 250,000 such houses.

Local Authorities' Part. The general scheme is that the housing authorities will find suitable sites and will develop them where necessary with the requisite roads and services.

The Ministry of Works, on behalf of the Ministry of Health and the Department of Health for Scotland, will arrange for the manufacture of temporary houses and their transport to and erection on the site provided. This power is limited to temporary houses erected or intended to be erected by 1st October, 1947.

Terms will be agreed between the Health Department and the housing authorities under which the latter will be responsible for the letting, management, and repair of the houses, and will pay to the Health Department a fixed sum per annum while the houses stand. The houses will be removed at the instance of the Health Department when the Housing situation warrants this course.

When a temporary house is dismantled or removed, the Minister may, if the local authorities desire, clear the land of substructure. The materials and fittings of the temporary houses, when removed, shall belong to the Crown.

The Act proposes that the cost incurred by the Ministry of Works in providing and erecting the houses shall be met out of moneys borrowed by the Treasury, the money being repaid by annuities spread over the years and provided out of votes of the Health Department.

The main cost to the Exchequer will be the excess of the annuities over the sums paid by local authorities under the agreed terms. The residual value of the fittings and materials will be a set-off against the cost of removal of the houses.

The cost to the local rates will be the excess of the loan charges on the site, acquisition, and development, together with the sums paid under the terms agreed with the Health Department, and the cost of management, repairs, etc., over the rents.

Until the terms to be agreed with the local authorities have been settled it is not possible to say more precisely what will be the actual costs to the Exchequer and the rates.

Clause 1 limits the power of the Minister of Health to supply temporary houses, unless Parliament determines otherwise, to those erected or intended to be erected by 1st October, 1947.

Housing (Rural) Workers Amendment Act, 1945

This Act proposes to :

(1) Increase the limits of grants which local authorities may make for the reconditioning of rural workers' cottages.

(2) extend the operation of the existing Housing (Rural Workers) Acts, as amended, for a further two years, to September 1947.

The present Act empowers local authorities to make grants or loans to owners towards reconditioning costing not less than £50 per cottage (the object of the £50 limit is to exclude works of ordinary repair, which the owner is under a statutory liability to carry out at his own expense). The cottages must be reserved for the occupation of agricultural workers for the next twenty years. Half of the grant made to the owner is borne by the Exchequer and half by the local rates.

The Act proposes the following changes :

(1) The minimum grant to be £75 instead of £50.
(2) The maximum grant to be £200 instead of £100 (or in cases where a further grant is given for abatement of overcrowding, £250 instead of £150).
(3) The present limit of £400 as the value of a cottage after reconditioning to be abolished.

Building Materials and Housing Act, 1945

This Act, which was passed on 20th December, 1945, is one " to make financial provision for the purpose of facilitating the production, equipment, repair, alteration, and acquisition of houses and other buildings, and to make provision for limiting the price for which certain houses may be sold and the rent at which certain houses may be let".

Its provisions fall into four parts, summarised by the Minister of Works at the second reading of the Bill in the House of Commons on 26th November 1945 as follows :

(a) Sections 1–4 provide for financing the operations of the Minister of Works in ensuring adequate supplies of building materials and components, including prefabricated houses, and in assisting local authorities in preparing housing sites and erecting houses ;

(b) Section 5 provides for increasing to £200,000,000 the £150,000,000 provided for in the Housing (Temporary Accommodation) Act, 1944, to cover the additional cost of the temporary housing programme ;

(c) Section 6 increases to £1500 the figure of £800 under the Small Dwellings Acquisition Acts and Section 91 (4) of the Housing Act, 1936 ; and

(d) Sections 7–8 contain provisions for enforcing the limitation of rent or purchase price, over a period of four years from the passing of the Act, on houses that are built under licence, and therefore subject to such conditions.

Provision of Prefabricated Houses under the Housing (Temporary Accommodation) Act, 1944

Section 5 of the Act provides for an increase of £50,000,000 to the sum of £150,000,000 provided under the Housing (Temporary Accommodation) Act, 1944, thus increasing to £200,000,000 the total sum available for the provision of temporary accommodation under that Act. The Minister of Works stated at the second reading of the Bill that the number of temporary houses allocated by the Health Departments to local authorities was about 165,000 ; 130,700 in England and Wales and 34,300 in Scotland. It was the Government's intention to meet this allocation in full, and on the basis of calculations as at the 26th November, 1945, the cost of this was estimated at about £191,500,000. Paragraph 10 of the White Paper on Temporary Housing showed a total expenditure of £184,669,470. This was related, however, to the provisional programme drawn up at that time of 158,480 houses. The estimate of £191,500,000 covered the full programme of 165,000 houses.

Powers of Local Authorities to loan money for the Acquisition or Construction of Houses

Section 6 increases to £1500 both in England and Wales and in Scotland, the present figure of £800 which may be advanced to owner-occupiers or would-be owner-occupiers by local authorities under the Small Dwellings Acquisition Acts and under Section 91 (4) of the Housing Act 1936.   It is interesting to note that this sum considerably exceeds the ceiling cost limit of £1200 (or £1300 in London) of houses built under building licence by private enterprise.

Housing (Temporary Accommodation) Act, 1945

The object of this Act, presented on 18th May, 1945, by the Minister of Health and the Secretary for State of Scotland, is to provide a speedier procedure by which local authorities may be authorised, in suitable cases, to erect temporary houses in their own parks and open spaces.

At present procedure by Provisional Order is necessary before a local authority can appropriate land vested in the Authority as an open space without providing equivalent land in exchange.   This procedure is slow. The Act proposes that for a limited period of two years, the Minister of Health (in Scotland, the Secretary of State) may authorise a Local Authority to use sites in parks or open spaces for temporary housing, but only on condition that :

(1) The Minister of Town and Country Planning (in Scotland, the Secretary of State) certifies that the use of the particular land is expedient in the public interest in the present emergency.

(2) The temporary houses must be removed after not more than ten years and the land restored.

    The application must come from the local authority and must relate only to land vested in the authority as an open space. The Planning Minister will not give a certificate until a special survey has been made reviewing all classes of unbuilt-on land in the area and he is satisfied that there are no alternative sites available having regard to sound planning.

Public Health Act, 1936

This important Act incorporated Public Health Acts, 1875 to 1932, and many new clauses and amendments, as well as repealed sections have been embodied in this Act.   The following list of provisions are mainly those affecting estate development :

Section 17.   Vesting of sewers in local authority.

Section 19.   Allows the local authority to provide for larger sewers to allow satisfactory drainage of adjoining areas to a development scheme, and extra cost of larger sewers is to be borne by the local authority. Duty is imposed upon the local authority to keep up-to-date record maps of sewers within their area.

Section 38.   The local authority may require buildings to be drained in combination by means of a private sewer.

Section 62–72.   Relates to building byelaws, model clauses, enforcement relaxation, and revision of byelaws.

Section 140.   Relates to byelaws for new streets by which the Minister of Health may prescribe a code of byelaws relating to the level, width, and construction of new streets.

RESTRICTION OF RIBBON DEVELOPMENT ACT, 1935*

This Act enables highway authorities to fix building lines and impose standard widths of roads and restricts accesses from estates adjoining main roads. It also gives power for compulsory purchase of land for road widenings.

Commission and Committee Reports

BARLOW REPORT

This was the Report of the Royal Commission on the Geographical Distribution of the Industrial Population, set up in 1937 under the chairmanship of Sir Montague Barlow. They inquired into the causes which have influenced geographical distribution of industrial population of Great Britain, considered what social, economic, or strategical disadvantages arise from the concentration of industries and population in large towns, and reported what remedial measures could be taken.

The Report was published in 1940 and the following principles were outlined by the Committee :

(1) National action is necessary.

(2) National central authority is necessary.

(3) National authority should have greater powers than those held by existing Government Departments.

(4) National authority should proceed with :
    (a) Re-development of congested areas.
    (b) Decentralisation or disposal of industries and population.
    (c) The securing of a balance of industry between regions and diversity of industry within regions.

(5) The movement of population to London and Home Counties is a matter requiring immediate attention.

(6) The National Central Authority determine immediately :
    (a) What urban areas should be decentralised.
    (b) Whether to develop garden cities or suburbs, satellite towns, trading estates, or use other methods. Municipalities should be encouraged to establish satellite towns, and trading estates on a regional basis.

(7) The National Authority should have the right to inspect all planning schemes, co-operate departments, study location of industry in order to prevent development of areas of depression, and maintain balance and diversity of industries.

SCOTT REPORT

A Committee, on Land Utilisation in Rural Areas, under the Chairmanship of Lord Justice Scott, made its Report in 1942. The Report gives a historical review of conditions which should govern building development in rural areas consistent with the maintenance of agriculture, location of industry, and preservation of rural amenities.

As many as 108 recommendations were made in the Report regarding Planning Control, Agricultural Considerations, Future Pattern of Road

* The Town and Country Planning Act, 1947, repeals Sections 1–3, 5–12, parts of various sections and Schedules 1–3.

and Rail considerations, Statutory Undertakers to be subject to Planning Control, Location of Industry, and greater control on preservation of National Parks, Rural Amenities, Holiday Facilities, etc.

It recommended the setting up of a central planning authority, and State Control of land in the interests of national planning, and suggested a five-years plan for Britain to carry out its numerous recommendations.

UTHWATT COMMITTEE

The Minister of Works and Buildings in 1940 appointed a Committee under the chairmanship of Mr. Justice Uthwatt to make an objective analysis of the subject of the payment of compensation and recovering of betterment in respect of public control of the use of land.

It was also asked to advise, as a matter of urgency, what steps should be taken to expedite reconstruction and planning work, and to ascertain means of stabilising value of land and powers needed to acquire land for development.

The final Report of this Committee was published in 1942, and is a lengthy and well reasoned document, and it gives many interesting recommendations, the chief of which are as follows :

(1) The immediate vesting in the State of the rights of development and all lands lying outside built-up areas on payment of fair compensation. Compensation to be based on a single sum representing the fair value to the State of the development rights taken as a whole.

(2) A central planning authority should be set up to manage all matters arising under planning schemes, with powers to purchase lands required for development.

(3) Simplification of procedure for obtaining and exercising powers of acquisition, and no public inquiry to be held unless the Planning Authority or Ministry think it desirable.

(4) Compensation for injurious affection and planning restrictions. The source of compensation by means of a levy on a proportion of increases in annual site values as revealed by quinquennial assessments.

(5) Betterment. The site values to be a fixed datum line from which to measure all future increases in values, and levies imposed to be borne by the person actually enjoying or capable of realizing the increased value.

(6) Proposed that a Minister for National Development should be set up with a Commission formed to deal rapidly and efficiently with local authorities, private developers, and land-owners.

Reference should be made to the Notes on pp. 157–168 on the Town and Country Planning Act, 1947, which adopted some of the above-mentioned recommendations, and which Act provides for the formation of a Central Land Board to assess compensation awards and betterment contributions on an approved formula.

12

CONTROL OF LAND USE

A Government White Paper on this matter was issued in June 1944, which sets out the Government's general scheme for the future control of land use in town and country, and especially for the solution of the problem of compensation and betterment, which the Uthwatt Committee examined.

In a foreword the Government explain that they recognise that the subject of the proposals is deeply controversial and raises problems on which widely divergent views are held with conviction. They feel that a determined effort should now be made to ensure some common measure of agreement upon the practical solution of these problems, so that planned reconstruction may go steadily forward. They therefore present their proposals in order to focus discussion in Parliament and among the public, and to assure themselves that there would be support for a solution on the lines proposed.

The Government accept as substantially correct the Uthwatt Committee's analysis of the problem. They do not feel able, however, to adopt the detailed recommendations of the Uthwatt Committee as to the manner whereby the compensation and betterment problem generally is to be dealt with. They therefore put forward a general scheme of their own, which differs in many important respects from the proposals of the Committee, and is, in the opinion of the Government, better adapted to provide the basis of a sound policy of land use.

That scheme includes :

(1) A universal requirement, making it necessary for landowners to obtain consent from the local planning authority before changing the use of their land.

(2) The imposition of a betterment charge, amounting to 80 per cent. of the increased value, in all cases where in the future the value of a particular piece of land is increased by the granting of permission for change of use.

(3) The payment of fair compensation for loss of development value to owners in cases where it can be shown that their land possessed such value on 31st March, 1939. The individual right to this compensation will be determined as soon as possible, but it will not be practicable to form a basis of calculation of the actual amount to be paid until the end of a five-year period, during which an expert Committee, specially appointed for the purpose, will work out a formula on which payment can be assessed. In the case of certain land, compensation will not be paid unless and until permission for change of use is sought and refused.

(4) The centralisation of the finances of compensation and betterment by the establishment of a Land Commission.

BURT REPORT

A Departmental Committee, under the Chairmanship of Sir G. Burt, was set up to consider alternative building materials and methods, and its first Report was published in 1944. It gives full technical details and illustrations—for alternative types of building, materials, and methods, to be used when standard materials are difficult to obtain. (See Chapter 6, p. 102, for details of this Report.)

DUDLEY REPORT

A Ministry of Health Central Housing Advisory Committee, under the chairmanship of Lord Dudley, was set up in 1943 to consider designs for dwellings. Its Report was published in July 1944, and gives in detail the views of this Committee, composed of housing experts, architects, and housewives, upon the most desirable type of house needed.

This is the typical house the Minister of Health's Central Housing Advisory Committee recommends for building by the million as speedily as possible after the war :

At least three bedrooms—two double, one single.

Two living-rooms, one always to be free for quiet recreation, social intercourse, or study. The other for meals and " the less private needs " of the family.

Separate access to each of the living-rooms from the hall.

A sunny aspect for the living-rooms, but with the larder on the shady side.

Bedrooms planned bearing in mind the shape and sort of furniture they are likely to contain.

Tiled bathroom with panelled bath.

Costs. Assuming the Government takes the Committee's advice and bring down building costs, a three-bedroomed house with all the improvements suggested should cost about £700, perhaps a little less.

The rent would be about 13s. 1d. a week without rates.

These improvements are recommended for all small houses over which the Government or local authorities have any control :

Better heating arrangements ; constant hot water ; improved cooking facilities.

Improved kitchen fittings and arrangements for washing and drying clothes.

More efficient plumbing and sanitary fittings.

More light and power points.

More storage room, including outhouses.

Kitchen Minimum. The minimum kitchen equipment which the Committee thinks essential as part of a house includes :

Sink, two draining-boards, work-table top, plate rack, store cupboard, fitted dresser, broom cupboard, and ample open shelving for pots and pans and so on. (See Figs. 87–89 of alternative plans of living-rooms.)

The Committee criticises the absence of cupboards from houses built since the first World War, and recommends that all bedrooms in the new home should have built-in cupboards and a full-length heated and ventilated linen cupboard.

Special attention is to be paid to the kitchens of the new house, where

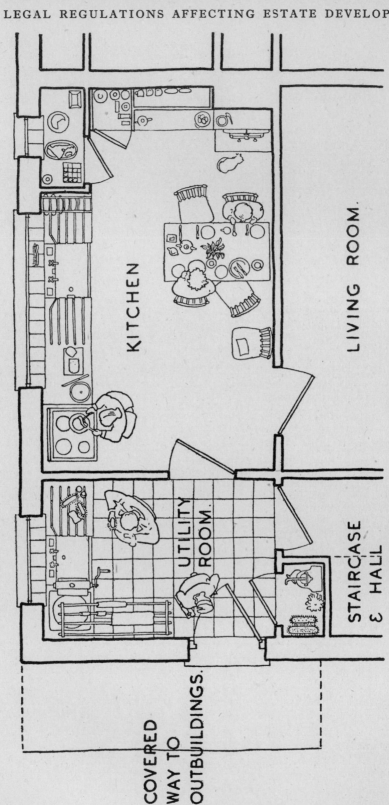

FIG. 87. Plan of kitchen, utility-room and living-room arrangement

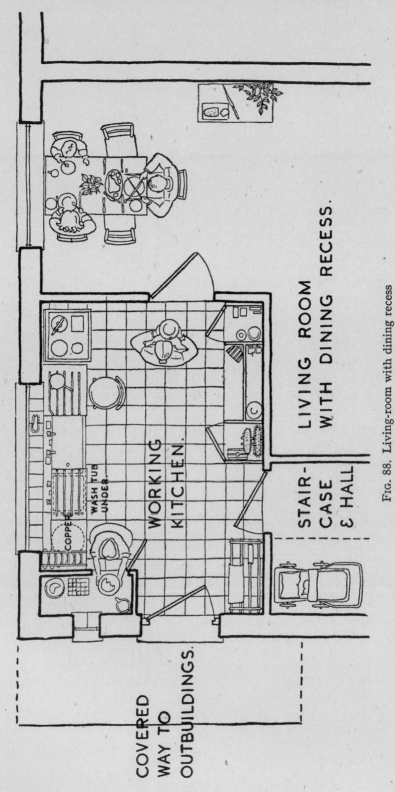

Fig. 88. Living-room with dining recess

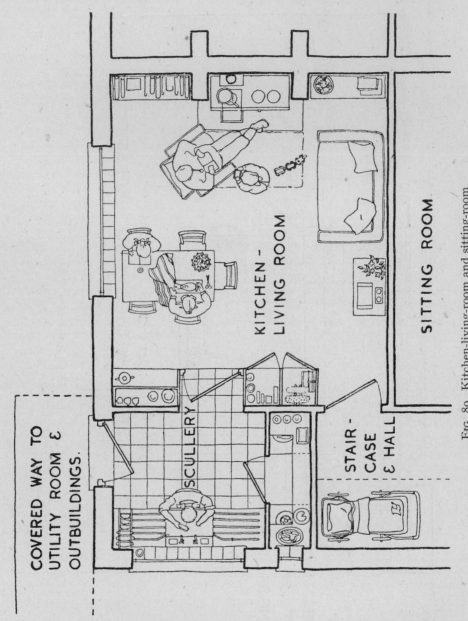

FIG. 89. Kitchen-living-room and sitting-room

the housewife spends so much of her day and where the family often takes its meals. It is suggested that the kitchen walls, like those of the bathroom, should be painted or finished in some washable material.

The floor too should be both attractive to look at and easy to clean— a " wide range of new materials will be available " for this.

Features. The new house should also be sound-proof, warm, and protected from vermin. It should have standardised fitments, to make replacements easier and cheaper—but not standardised external design.

" We hope ", says the Committee, " that in future local authorities will set out with the intention of adding positively to the beauties of the town and countryside, and not merely of making the housing estates ' unobtrusive '. "

A minimum overall floor space of 900 sq. ft. is recommended for the " standard type " of house. This is somewhat larger than the average small house at present ; and it is proposed that the second and third bedrooms—which are now normally 100 sq. ft. and 65 sq. ft. in area— should be increased to 110 and 70 sq. ft., including the area of built-in cupboards.

The parlour should go : it conveys an implication which is old-fashioned and obsolete ; and in its place should be the family sitting-room, where work, hobbies, or study can go on free of interruption from meals.

To ensure that best use is made of both living-rooms, the provision of a " utility room " is proposed. In this, washing and other home-disturbing work can be done with all the necessary tools and equipment to hand.

The bathroom should be upstairs, with a separate w.c., and in the bigger type of house there should be two w.c.s, one downstairs with a washbasin in it.

The fuel store should be easily accessible for fuel delivery, and reachable under cover from the back door.

In towns the outhouses, including a shed " for the innumerable things commonly kept in a shed ", should not be less than 70 sq. ft. in area ; in rural districts more.

Here is a comment on the garden path which will appeal to all mothers. It is false economy to save on paving ; it is especially objectionable to the housewives whose large families patter in and out all day long with muddy feet. Adequate flagging of all paths leading to outside doors and from the back door to the outbuildings is recommended.

The Committee knows that the experience of women in the Services and in industry will influence their attitude to housing.

War-time factories and hostels often provide high standards of services and equipment, which will make women intolerant of inferior conditions in their own homes.

On Terrace Houses. " We recommend a ground-floor passage between every two houses in the terrace—it is essential that no tenant shall have to pass a neighbour's back door to get to his own."

Flats. " Flats *v.* Houses " : The unattractive and dreary appearance of some blocks of flats can be avoided by more attention to gardens, varying the height and contour of buildings, and by arranging shopping centres, churches, public houses, and community centres so that they fit into the surroundings.

In the buildings there should be automatic passenger lifts. In a big block of flats at Leeds the adults sometimes cause the lift to break down by overloading it, and as the alarm whistles were all stolen by children in the first few months of the lifts' existence, adults sometimes get stuck in the lift, and have to bide themselves in patience until rescue comes. Says the Report dryly :

" It occurred to us that this enforced exercise of patience may not be so unsatisfactory as it sounds." The provision of lifts in all big blocks of flats is recommended. There should be constant hot water. All flats should have a balcony where the baby can sleep in the open air, and where flowers or vegetables can be grown in window-boxes.

For Old People. The courtyards should be laid out by an expert gardener. The number of old people in Britain is increasing, and by 1951 there will be about 5,500,000 over sixty-five, or $11\frac{1}{2}$ per cent. of the total population.

It is recommended that there should be special housing facilities for old people, within easy reach of churches, shops, and entertainments, and not separated from the houses of younger people. A few small dwellings might well be included in every street.

These old people's houses should consist of bedroom, living-room, bath-room, and small scullery, with unnecessary steps and too difficult cleaning avoided, and a handrail provided above the bath. As old people need more warmth than the young, there should be a fireplace in both rooms.

More accommodation for young and middle-aged single people is advocated ; the need is particularly acute in the case of single women, who much prefer a home of their own to the best of lodgings.

Rural housing, the Report recommends, should not be of a lower standard than urban housing, and better transport and higher wages make it no longer necessary to put houses near to farms and other places of work.

It is therefore suggested that they should be put in areas where modern amenities are available, and preferably form part of an existing village.

It is far better that the worker should have to travel some distance to his work than that his family should be remote from schools, shops, church, and all the other amenities of village life.

Country Cottages. It is also assumed that country cottages built after the war will have some form of piped water, and there is a strong need for laid-on gas and electricity.

Going into details about the equipment desirable for all the homes to be built after the war (the Government plans to build between 3,000,000 and 4,000,000 houses in the first ten to twelve years) the Committee proposes :

Bigger windows, with sills of the living-rooms not more than 2 ft. 9 in. from the floor ; in bedrooms not more than 3 ft. 3 in.

The worktable should have a hard, smooth, cold top on which pastry can be made.

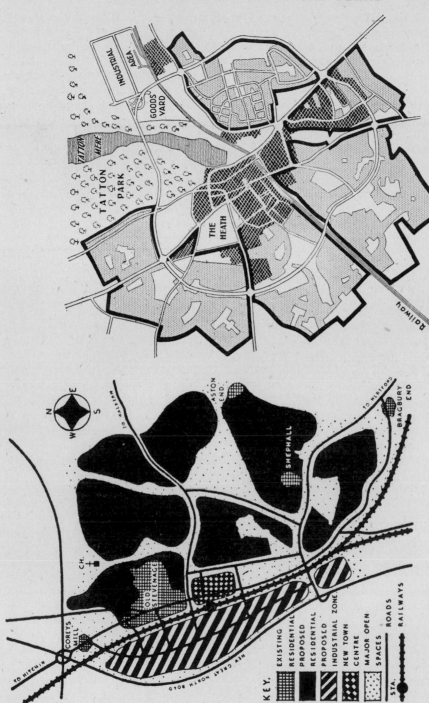

FIG. 91. Master plan of Knutsford scheme

Architects: F. R. S. Yorke, F.R.I.B.A., E. Rosenberg, and C. Mardall, A.R.I.B.A.

FIG. 90. Plan of Stevenage

The sink should be at least 24 in. × 18 in. × 10 in. The pipes should be hidden and neat. The sink is best placed under the window, and perhaps at right-angles to it if not too far from the light. The window-sill should be tiled.

Storage space should include accommodation for foods, utensils, cleaning materials, crockery, glass, ironing board, and other household necessities, and there should also be a fitted kitchen cabinet.

Bath, etc. The bath should be 5 ft. 6 in. long, with a hard-surfaced panel, and tiling at least 1 ft. high above it. The washbasin should incorporate a shelf. There should be a heated towel-rail in the bathroom.

Clothing cupboards should have a hat shelf and a rod for hangers. There should be a delivery hatch near the back-door.

It is proposed that great care should be given to the layout of areas where the new houses are to be built, so that they are made as attractive as possible, with the properly cared-for trees and hedges, wide roads, car parking facilities, and other modern amenities.

Numerous reports, memoranda, circulars, leaflets, etc., are published by His Majesty's Stationery Office from time to time dealing with all planning and building matters, and are furnished by various Government Departments.

Satellite Town Schemes

Several important satellite town schemes are in course of being developed by leading local authorities, as a result of the powers granted by Town Planning Acts, 1944 and 1947, and the New Towns Act, 1946, by which new towns are planned to provide accommodation for overspill population of big cities and towns. Such new towns have been considered by the L.C.C., Manchester, Liverpool, Birmingham, and several other large cities are also planning similar schemes.

It is proposed to establish twenty satellite towns including Harlow, Essex, and Hemel Hempstead. The former is intended for Londoners decentralised from Tottenham, Wood Green, Leyton, Walthamstow, and Edmonton.

Hemel Hempstead, the present population of which is 20,000, is intended in due course to take a population of 60,000, in particular from Acton and Willesden. This scheme was approved by the Minister of Town and Country Planning in February 1947.

L.C.C.—Stevenage Plan

Stevenage is one of ten sites recommended in the 1944 Abercrombie " Greater London Plan " for satellite towns to accommodate 1,000,000 of London's surplus population. The present population of Stevenage is to be increased from 6000 to 60,000, with industries and recreational amenities. Development is to proceed in advance of legislation under the New Towns Act, 1946.

It is proposed to acquire some 5500 acres of land by gradual process in order not to cause undue disturbance to farmers.

From the plan shown in Fig. 90 it will be seen that new residential

FIG. 92. Proposed swimming pool

FIG. 93. Civic centre and old town and waterfront

F .R. S. Yorke, F.R.I.B.A., E. Rosenberg, and C. Mardall ,A.R.I.B.A., Architects

KNUTSFORD

FIG. 94. Model of a neighbourhood unit

FIG. 95. Model of a proposed industrial estate

F. R. S. Yorke, F.R.I.B.A., S. Rosenberg, and C. Mardall, A.R.I.B.A., Architects

KNUTSFORD

neighbourhoods and industrial sites are to be provided. A new civic centre and shopping centre are also included, but the old town will be preserved almost entirely, although most of the streets and houses built between 1918–1939 will be demolished.

This scheme was approved by the Minister of Town and Country Planning in 1946, but the compulsory acquisition of 6100 acres required was quashed by the High Court in February 1947. A later appeal to the House of Lords upheld the decision of the Minister to proceed with this scheme.

MANCHESTER—KNUTSFORD PLAN

This scheme is an interesting essay in the replanning and expansion of a town, which was destined to take the " overspill " population of Manchester.

Knutsford was chosen as the most suitable town for development on account of its pleasant situation and because it is only 15 miles from Manchester. It is an ancient little town of 6000 people ; it is proposed to expand its population to 30,000. When the Government's policy of de-concentration from Manchester, Liverpool, and South Lancashire gets going, it will mainly be a dormitory to Manchester, but a small industrial site has been planned. The scheme consists essentially of opening up the old town to Tatton Mere (a lake now silted up), which will be drained, and so providing an area for five neighbourhood units, a new civic centre, and the new industrial area. Thus Knutsford is to be converted into a draining lakeside town with a charming surrounding tree-planted countryside. The scheme will also provide for grammar, modern, and technical schools, a county college, and cultural buildings. A ring road is designed to encircle the town centre at an average distance of three-quarters of a mile, which will link up all five neighbourhoods with the industrial area and enable through traffic to by-pass the town centre.

A key plan of this scheme is shown in Fig. 91 and Plate I is a preliminary sketch of the County College.

THE KNUTSFORD EXAMPLE—OUTLINE OF THE MASTER PLAN

Three maxims have been kept constantly in front of them by the five expert architect-planners and the committee who have consulted with them on the Knutsford plan—that in a town, as in a nation, freedom must be balanced with responsibility, work with leisure, and life in the home with a sense of good community. All these are necessary to the efficiency of a town, yet they fall within the framework of a much wider necessity. Just as in our private lives we take it for granted that decency, good manners, beauty of spirit, and comeliness of person are ideals worthy of much effort in achievement, so increasingly the modern man has come to see that similar qualities are worthy to be fostered in the home, the street, and the town.

The master plan for Knutsford sets out deliberately to attack the notion that bricks and mortar mean either confinement of the individual spirit or dreariness and meanness in physical shape. The idea has been to show how the freedom and grace which are the essence of the surrounding country can be induced to flow through the town, and at the same time to demonstrate how landscape well handled enhances urban architectural dignity and beauty to produce a result that is urbane in the very truest sense of the word.

The first of the adopted maxims means, of course, that if Knutsford is to become a more or less self-sufficient community, it must continue to rule itself. A leading proposal in the plan is therefore a protective green belt enabling it to retain its separate identity as an administratively self-contained town.

In this, Knutsford is particularly fortunate. A vast area of agricultural land surrounding it on all sides already forms a natural barrier which has only to be zoned as rural land in order to be permanent. Within the green belt thus formed are four fine private parks, some of great extent and ancient origin—Tatton, Tabley, Toft, and Norbury Booths. It is recommended that in none of these parks should building development be allowed. Tatton Park, *i.e.* up to the new ring road which crosses the south spur of it, and Norbury Booths Park, should be taken into public use.

To fulfil the need of local work for all who want it, the plan provides for the creation of a small industrial estate, sponsored municipally or by a suitable public body, along the lines of such well-known trading estates as Hillington, Team Valley, and Treforest. For the ultimate stages of expansion, it is proposed that the present unsatisfactory council housing estate at Shawheath, immediately opposite the industrial site on the south side of the railway line, should give way to factories. When the whole scheme is completed, Knutsford can look forward to having diversified light industry enough to employ 6000 people—in other words, to be virtually self-supporting. This is in itself a safeguard against any form of industrial, social, or administrative domination by the town's big neighbours.

Fulfilling the third maxim, the home is married to the community by the decision that when all rebuilding and new building is completed the town should form five residential neighbourhoods, each self-contained in the sense that it will have its own schools, own churches, own community centre, own shops, own pubs, and own open spaces : all the immediate needs of a good life, in fact, for some six thousand people in each neighbourhood.

The first neighbourhood unit to be developed is at Crosstown. It is conveniently close to the industrial site ; the general disposition and slope of the land make it easy for work to begin without delay and its natural features provide the planner with a chance to show how natural beauty and housing can be blended. As elsewhere the scheme is for stage-by-stage development. Thus errors can be eliminated and new ideas incorporated as the work proceeds. All these neighbourhoods and the industrial estate will link in the town centre, where the chief public buildings will still be located, where the cinemas and theatre will very properly continue to consort with the principal shops, where the buses will collect and the new enlarged railway station arise.

In addition, all the town's children will have the opportunity to win a way eventually to a new county technical college sited south of the railway ; and town playing-fields will appear mid the green belt. So far, so good.

If Knutsford is to be developed safely, however, it is evident that the only traffic coming into it should be that which concerns the town itself. Therefore, the proposal is to divert all through traffic between the Midlands and the north to two new roads well clear of Knutsford, one passing to the west for Warrington and beyond, and the other, a regional road, forking south from the first to pass east of the town towards Manchester.

Both these roads have been planned for provisionally under the Cheshire Advisory Planning proposals. Thus the way is made clear for traffic entering and circulating in Knutsford itself, and for this purpose the principal proposal is a ring road running around the town and connecting its parts at an approximate radius of three-quarters of a mile from the centre.

This ring road stands as C.-in-C. to the whole town plan—it serves Convenience-in-Communication. Beside it are to be sited the new residential neighbourhoods and the industrial estate. As a parkway it forms in some degree part of a continuous green belt. The civic and commercial centres are contained inside it. By means of it the ebb and flow of traffic into, out of, and around Knutsford is canalized and regulated. The proposed local traffic roads form the skeleton figure on which the flesh is to be filled in.

How the plan proposes this should be done—the neighbourhood units, the industrial estate, the civic, entertainment, and commercial centres, and the green belt laid out in detail—is dealt with fully.

According to a statement which appeared in *News-Chronicle* of 3rd April, 1947, the Knutsford-Mobberley New Town Plan which was dropped by the Minister of Town and Country Planning December 1946, following an adverse report on the possibility of subsidence due to salt deposits, is to be reconsidered.

Three deep borings have been made between Knutsford and Mobberley, at the request of the Minister of Town and Country Planning.

The report of geologists who have examined the core brought up from 400 ft. below the surface is that there is no rock salt—and no serious danger of subsidence.

At Booth Mill, near Knutsford, an additional check will be made by drilling down to 775 ft. Other minor borings will be made where necessary.

The latest news about the geological conditions in the area, which would now apparently make the building of a new town possible, has been reported by letter from the Ministry of Town and Country Planning to Manchester City Council, Lancashire and Cheshire County Councils, and the authorities of Salford, Stretford, Knutsford, Wilmslow and Bucklow.

The letter concludes as follows : " The Minister hopes to be able to convey to the authorities very soon the results of the whole series of borings, together with his proposals for subsequent action to accommodate overspill population and industry from Greater Manchester."

For the time being, therefore, the scheme is in suspense.

13

CHAPTER 10

GARDEN CITY AND PRIVATE DEVELOPMENT ENTERPRISES

A LITTLE book which first propounded the idea for the erection of garden cities was written in 1898 by a reformer named Ebenezer Howard. He advocated " towns designed for healthy living and industry ; of a size that makes possible a full measure of social life, but not larger, surrounded by a rural belt ; the whole of the land being in public ownership or held in trust for the community ". Some eight months later the Garden City Association was formed, and they started a limited company, called " Garden City, Ltd.", with a share capital of £50,000, of which £5000 was to be a first issue, with a cumulative 5 per cent. dividend.

As a result of meetings of various borough councils, co-operative and friendly societies, and progressive industrial organizations, a new company called " Garden City Pioneer Company ", was registered in 1902, with a capital of £20,000.

This company decided on an estate at Letchworth, comprising some 4562 acres, for their first garden city development ; and later another garden city was developed on similar lines at Welwyn.

Important industrial concerns then provided model housing estates for the benefit of their own workers, and these include Port Sunlight, Wirral, promoted by Lord Leverhulme ; Messrs. Cadbury made an industrial village at Bournville, some four miles outside Birmingham, and it was later made over to the Bournville Trust ; Messrs. Rowntree established the Garden Village of Earswick near York ; Ealing Garden Suburb and Hampstead Garden Suburb are housing estates for better-class houses, and tenants have shares in the company, and are called co-partnership tenants.

Many local authorities have since developed garden city type of estates, notably Manchester with its large estate at Wythenshawe. (Plate XI.)

A brief description of various public and private housing estates already provided are now given which will convey some idea of housing development made in recent years. The following is a list of housing estates described and illustrated on information kindly supplied by the Authorities concerned and to whom the Author is indebted.

Private Enterprises :

First Garden City, Letchworth.
Welwyn Garden City.
Port Sunlight, Wirral.
Bournville Village Trust.
Hampstead Garden City Trust.
Ulster Garden Villages Ltd.

Local Authorities :

London County Council.
City of Birmingham.
City of Liverpool.
City of Glasgow.
City of Manchester.
City of Leicester.
City of Nottingham.
City of Edinburgh.

FIG 96. The Crescent

FIG. 97. Aerial view of Letchworth Hall hotel

LETCHWORTH

13†

FIG. 98. A quiet corner amongst working houses

FIG. 99. Leys Avenue : principal shopping centre

LETCHWORTH

Fig. 100. Pixmore Avenue

Fig. 101. Group of cottages in Eldefield

LETCHWORTH

FIG. 102. Entrance drive to Sollershott Hall

FIG. 103. Type of houses in which children grow up healthy and strong

LETCHWORTH

THE FIRST GARDEN CITY OF LETCHWORTH

It is some forty years since Sir Ebenezer Howard's scheme for a new planned industrial and residential town achieved reality in the formation of Letchworth—the first garden city to be so created.

The 4562 acres of agricultural land, on which the first sod was cut by Earl Grey in 1903, now have as their nucleus a manufacturing and residential town with an area of 1528 acres, the balance of 3034 acres constituting the green belt acting as a buffer between Letchworth and the surrounding towns and villages. (See layout plan in Plate II, facing this page.)

(1) What sort of a town has been built during the past three decades ? Here, in bare statistical form, is the result :

Population	20,220
Houses and cottages	5,148
Shops	190
Factories and workshops	143
Employed in factories—12,000 including temporary influx	12,000
Daily influx of workers from villages to factories	4,500
Places of worship	18
Schools	12
Theatres and cinemas	4
Hotels	6

Area of parks, commons, playing-fields, open spaces, sports grounds, etc.,
270 acres, plus reserved area of about 200 acres for future open spaces,
sports, etc.

(2) So much for the skeleton of the town. What of the human and social factors ? Has life in this planned town conferred any benefit upon the inhabitants which is distinct from that in any other town ?

Let us take the vital statistics first, which invariably reflect the degree to which A1 or C3 people are being created within the borders of a town.

The 1945 death rate was 8·2 per 1000, as compared with a rate of 11·4 for the whole of England and Wales. The infantile mortality rate was 18·7 per 1000 births, as compared with a rate of 59 per 1000 for the whole of England and Wales and 87 per 1000 in the case of Gateshead. It is obvious, therefore, that a progressive policy of good housing, abundant open spaces, and proper zoning for industrial, residential, and other purposes is highly advantageous in terms of human life and well being.

Letchworth's low death rate and infantile mortality rate are remarkable ; and they apply not to a health resort, such as Bournemouth, nor to a garden suburb, but to a thriving and busy factory town.

At Letchworth there is an engineering factory, covering 26 acres, which is the largest producer of carbon steel castings in the United Kingdom and employs 1500 men. Several other factories each employ from 500–1000 workers. The effect of the industrial prosperity on the economic life of Letchworth is indicated by the high annual pay-roll amounts.

The disparaging reference once made by John Burns to " miles of brick boxes with slate lids " certainly would not apply to Letchworth.

Every house has a garden, and many of the factories are set in gardens. There is plenty of fresh air inside and around both houses and factories. When our present King was Duke of York he visited Letchworth, and very aptly summarised what he saw as " The Factory in the Garden Movement ".

(3) Some of the more recent developments at Letchworth include the provision of a new ozone swimming-pool in the 60-acre Norton Common, which during the recent season was used by 77,921 people ; new tennis courts and bowling greens are also laid in Norton Common.

(4) The principal peacetime trades are : electrical tabulating and costing machinery, steel casting, general engineering, printing machinery, aircraft components, tool making, parachutes, corsets, compressors, mining machinery, coppersmiths, commercial vehicles manufacture, scientific instrument manufacture, printing, bookbinding, publishing, photographic papers, furniture making, embroidery and lace manufacture, lenses, baby carriages, etc.

(5) Imposing new council offices have been erected by the Letchworth Urban District Council, and these were opened on 24th July, 1935, by the then Minister of Health, Sir Kingsley Wood. A fine grammar school has been provided by the Hertfordshire County Council, and this Authority has now bought 1¼ acres of land on which to build a Technical School at a cost of £50,000 to serve Letchworth and North Hertfordshire. The Education Authority have also provided in their budget for an additional council school and an infants' school for Letchworth. In order to meet the cultural needs of the town the Urban District Council have erected a free library at a cost of £10,000 in the town square.

(6) A Ministry of Labour Training Centre is firmly established and continuing under war-time conditions. Men are trained in the following fifteen trades and absorbed into industry : bricklaying, plastering, carpentry, electric welding, house painting, panel beating and sheet metal work, gas and hot-water fittings, hairdressing, wood machining, oxywelding, metal polishing, motor mechanics, machine operating, fitting and turning, and instrument making.

The value of this scheme to the town's industries lies in the fact that during the concluding months of their training the youths at the training centre can have a general " shaping " given to their tuition to meet any special local industrial needs. The gain to the men is immeasurable. Many of them arrive after having been workless for months or years and hundreds having never done a day's work since they left school.

(7) Thousands of real " homes " for Letchworth's factory workers have been built by different agencies, both public and private, and every effort is being made to meet the continuous demand for new dwellings. Excellent three-bedroomed cottages have been erected by a housing association and let at a gross rent of 11s. 6d. per week, while the Urban District Council has built 1313 houses under the different Housing Acts.

One of the main aims of Ebenezer Howard's scheme when he formulated the garden city idea was to combine urban and rural life, and to a considerable extent this aim has been achieved at Letchworth.

(8) The daily influx of 4500 workers, was a pre-war rough estimate. It is now far more, but it is impossible to give accurate figures.

Workers come from the adjacent towns and villages, and practically all these surrounding rural areas, which prior to the development of Letchworth were becoming de-populated, have now received a new lease of life. The old people remain in the villages, but the young folk flock to Letchworth by bicycle, bus, or train, to find profitable employment in the various factories. Many of them marry and settle down in Letchworth itself, but the population figures of all the adjacent rural districts show an increase rather than a decrease. Rural de-population has, in fact, been checked, and the development of Letchworth has been the principal factor.

(9) One of the most convincing proofs of a town's commercial prosperity is indicated by the comparative consumption of electricity, gas, and water over a period of years. The figures for Letchworth are very striking:

	1920	1936	1939	1945
Electricity	2,545,508 units	17,991,517 units	22,675,992 units	24,900,000 units
Gas	94,757,000 cu. ft.	132,930,000 cu. ft.	140,820,000 cu. ft.	187,196,000 cu. ft.
Water	149,448,000 galls.	283,458,000 galls.	305,166,000 galls.	498,292,000 galls.

These figures show an increase of 797 per cent., 98 per cent., and 233 per cent. respectively, the electricity figures reflecting in a remarkable manner the rapid industrial development of the town. The supply of all these public services is in the hands of the company responsible for the creation of the town.

(10) The total mileage of roads in Letchworth is now 35, of which 29 miles have been constructed by the First Garden City.

(11) The rateable value of Letchworth in 1945 was £167,613.

The foregoing brief statement of facts surely affords simple testimony that Letchworth has made good ; and, indeed, garden city enthusiasts can rightly claim that Letchworth's example might well be followed in many other parts of the country.

(12) *Future Observations.* Plans have been prepared and are now being considered by the Regional Town Planner and other interested parties for the development of two areas, one on the north side of the town area, to be known as the " Grange Estate ", the other to the south—" Jackmans Estate ".

Each of these areas has been planned as a neighbourhood unit according to the latest ideas on town planning. A further area, to be known as the " Lordship " Estate is being planned for building by private enterprise.

The preparations are being made for building the first batch of cottages on the " Grange " immediately conditions permit.

Schemes are also being considered for a community building in the centre of the town, a youth centre, and schemes for new shops in the shopping area, also new schools by the County Council.

Photographs of Letchworth are given in Figs. 96–103.

WELWYN GARDEN CITY

The development of this town on completely open country was commenced in 1920.   The population in 1943 was about 17,000 within the area of the present urban district council.

Although the commencement of building this town was as recent as 1920, the changes in the requirements of living during the past twenty years have been substantial.   In the light of experience and the changing requirements for certain particular purposes, it has been necessary to keep the plan flexible, so that each further advance in knowledge can be reflected in the development.   For example, the size of the site which the Local Education Authority thought necessary for an elementary school when the first school was built in 1923 was only 3½ acres ; for sites for schools required immediately after the war, the area of land required for the same number of schools has doubled.   Again, during the last twenty years the development of labour-saving machinery in industry has been such as to require a substantially larger floor area of factory per 100 persons employed than was the case at the beginning.

The development has now gone sufficiently far for an approximate estimate to be given of the ultimate population within the area of the urban district council and what proportion of land will be required for various purposes.

The total area of the urban district is 2597 acres.

The estimated ultimate population within the urban district will, if the land is developed in accordance with the most recently revised plan, be about 30,000.

Land is allocated to the following groups in this manner:

	Acres
Residences, schools, community centres, main civic centre, shops and offices, including minor open spaces of under 1 acre	1369
Industrial, including gravel and brick works, and public utility undertakings, such as sewerage, waterworks, and reservoirs	413
Railway, including land at present not utilised for railway purposes, but reserved for such use in future	91
Major open spaces, including 40 acres of railway land likely to remain as open space and not be required for railway purposes	724
Total	2597

See layout plan in Plate III and photographs in Figs. 104–109.

It will be noted that nearly one-third of the whole of the urban district is reserved as open space.   Part will be for playing-fields and the remainder for general amenities, including woods and parks.   Some will continue to be used for pasture or agricultural purposes, but it is important to emphasise that in the opinion of those responsible for the plan, the proportion reserved as open space is really necessary if the fullest opportunities of life are to be available for the urban population.

Ultimately, the over-all density of population within the urban district will be approximately 11 persons per acre, and the density of the residential areas about 22.

Louis de Soissons, A.R.A., Architect

FIG. 104. The Parkway, Welwyn Garden City

Louis de Soissons, A.R.A., Architect

FIG. 105. The community centre

Louis de Soissons, A.R.A., Architect

FIG. 106. Fretherne road

WELWYN GARDEN CITY

Louis de Soissons, A.R.A., Architect

FIG. 107. Parkway Close

Louis de Soissons, A.R.A., Architect

FIG. 108. The Orchard

WELWYN GARDEN CITY

Louis de Soissons, A.R.A., Architect

FIG. 109. Corner of Digswell Road and Walden Road, Welwyn Garden City

It is calculated that the area reserved for industry would be approximately the quantity required if all those inhabitants of the town as were gainfully occupied actually worked in the town. In practice, of course, already at any given time there will be a proportion of the inhabitants working elsewhere, and a certain number of those working in the town for one reason or another prefer to live elsewhere. Roughly speaking, it is calculated that these will approximately balance each other.

The expansion of the town is shown by the following statistics :

	No. of Houses Completed	Approximate Population
December 31st, 1920	86	328
December 31st, 1925	1147	3575
Census April 26th, 1931	2496	8586
December 31st, 1934	2804	10,200
December 31st, 1937	3554	13,500
October 1943	4500	17,000

THE NEW TOWNS ACT, 1946
Administration of New Towns

It is interesting to note that the set up of the administration for the development of the New Towns by Development Corporations is largely similar to the administration set up by Welwyn Garden City, Limited.

The New Towns Committee, in its report to the Minister of Town and Country Planning, recommended that a Director General or Chief Executive Officer should lead the team. This officer should not be a member of the Board. In the case of Welwyn Garden City, Limited, there is a Managing Director as leader of the team.

This officer should be a man of initiative and proved organising ability, able to inspire and lead the team. The other five members of the team would be as follows :

Business Manager (or Chief Accountant)

Responsible for general administration especially from the financial angle. He will provide other members of the team with factual information.

Chief Architect

A man of imagination, courage and artistic judgement. Able to harmonise work of other architects into the general plan.

Chief Engineer

Responsible for physical development, i.e. surveys, supervision of provision of roads, sewers, and services.

Estate Manager

In control of management of land and buildings, leasing of sites and devising and enforcing covenants in leases.

Public Relations Officer

He will have the task of presenting the work of the Corporation to the residents, and taking back their reactions to the Corporation. He will watch only the social and cultural development of the New Town.

The author is indebted to Welwyn Garden City, Limited, and its Officers for these notes on their Garden City.

PORT SUNLIGHT, WIRRAL

What most impresses itself on those who study the industrial village of Port Sunlight is the fact that it is the definite outcome of a genuine ideal. Whether its present state has surpassed the hopes of its founder, the late Lord Leverhulme, or has failed to realise them, we can at any rate see that this was meant to be something better than what had been before, and that no effort was wanting to secure this. We are sure that the inconsequent charm and the haphazard picturesqueness of an old English village were not the main objects in view, but that the aim was a conveniently planned and healthy settlement laid out with all possible artistic thought on sound business lines. Garden grounds, roads, and open spaces were to be ample without being wasteful, houses were to be picturesque but sensibly planned. Avenues were to be planted and gardens laid out with needful limitations as to size and direction. The individuality of separate gardens was to be subordinated to a definite idea of communal amenity. Variety of plan was to be obtained only within a certain economic range.

The Plan. The general plan of Port Sunlight now shows an inhabited area nearly a mile long by nearly half that wide, bounded on the longer sides by the new Chester Road (on the east) and the main railway lines to London and Greendale Road (on the west). (See Plate IV facing p. 210.)

There is enough variety of level to avoid the monotony of an entirely flat area, and one piece of natural dell, well grown over with trees and shrubs, forms a delightful feature near the works end of the village. Goods from the works are loaded on the one side into railway wagons and on the other into barges on the Bromborough Pool, from which they emerge into the River Mersey. From this pool there used to be gutters or ravines, up which the muddy tidal water flowed right up into where the village now stands ; but these have all been cut off from the tide and, with the exception of the dell above referred to, filled up.

One very notable innovation on the common practice of estate development is the fronting of houses towards the railways, instead of the long lines of unlovely backs which usually exhibit all their unhappy privacies to the railway passengers. Though one long thoroughfare, the Greendale Road, runs alongside the railway embankment for the greater part of a mile, one cannot feel it to be other than one of the pleasantest roads on the estate.

Every intelligent student of town planning knows that you cannot rule out a number of rectangular plots arranged on axial lines without due consideration of varying levels and a proper expression of local features. Moreover, the planning of many right-angled plots is not in itself a very desirable aim. But at Port Sunlight it was possible to create some rectangular spaces, with the art gallery and the church on their axial lines, in such a way as to make a striking and orderly scheme as a central feature in the estate. There are numbers of winding or diagonal roads which give variety and interest and afford pleasant lines of perspective to the groups of houses.

In an especial way one might claim that the best results in the planning

Fig. 110. A Bridge Street group, Port Sunlight

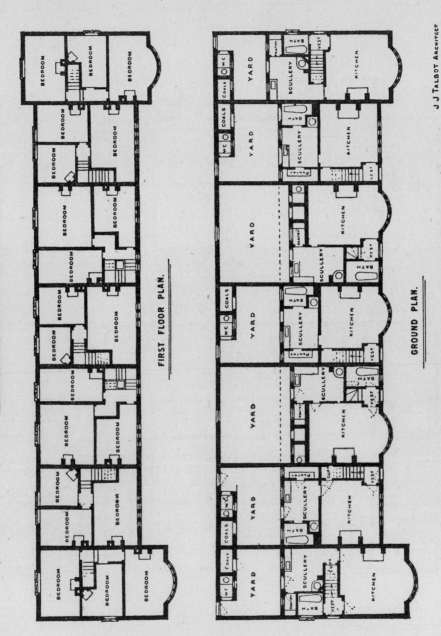

COTTAGES, PORT SUNLIGHT.

FIRST FLOOR PLAN.

GROUND PLAN.

J J TALBOT Architect

Fig. 111. Kitchen Cottages

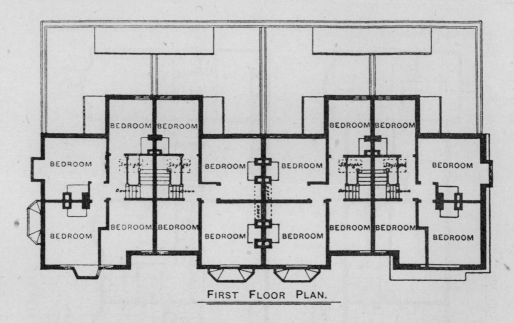

FIRST FLOOR PLAN.

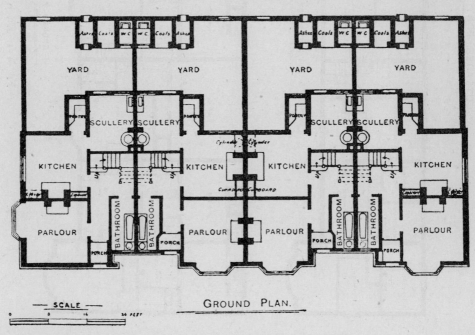

GROUND PLAN.

FIG. 112. Parlour Cottages, Port Sunlight

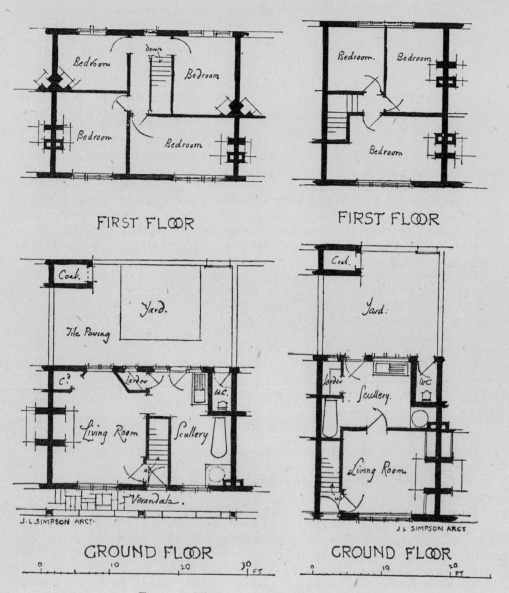

FIRST FLOOR FIRST FLOOR

GROUND FLOOR GROUND FLOOR

FIG. 113. Kitchen Cottages, Port Sunlight

of a new village will be obtained through bearing in mind the classical saying *ars est celare artem*. In such a scheme we do not wish to be confronted with buildings of ponderous dignity or a big display of formal lines and places. Anything approaching ostentation or display is surely out of place, and what we want is something expressing the simplicity and unobtrusiveness which is the tradition handed down to us through the charm of the old English village. This is best attained by variety in direction of roads and shapes of houses by forming unexpected corners, recessed spaces, and winding vistas.

General Scheme. Port Sunlight Village (founded in 1888), apart from the works covers 160 acres, on which the houses may approach 1500 for a population of 10,000. The tenancies of the houses are limited to employees of the works. Already over 1300 houses have been built or are in process of building, and the length of broad roadways exceeds 5 miles. The first block of cottages, built in 1888–1889, was reproduced at the Brussels Exhibition of 1910 and was awarded the Grand Prix. It is intended to limit the number of cottages to 10 per acre, and it is hoped to keep below that maximum.

The general width of the roadways is 40 ft., giving 24 ft. to the road and 8 ft. for each footpath ; but there are roads 48 ft. wide, including footpaths. The paths are flagged along the central portion only.

In a progressive world, and especially in such a progressive part of it as Port Sunlight, one cannot hope to give a record which will for long represent existing facts. The arrangements which have been made for the benefit of the inhabitants of this village have necessarily been altered or modified. At the present time the buildings for general use include : Christ Church, an admirable late-Gothic building in a central position ; the schools, which accommodate about 1600 children ; a lyceum ; a cottage hospital ; a gymnasium ; an open-air swimming bath ; a post office ; a village inn ; a village stores ; a fire station ; a library and savings bank ; the Gladstone Hall ; the Hulme Hall ; men's club, with billiard rooms and bowling-green ; a village fountain ; and, finally, the Lady Lever Art Gallery, which holds a fine collection of pictures, pottery, and furniture.

Port Sunlight has been an object of attraction to visitors for years as a model for town planners the world over, and this is due not only to the interest and variety of its cottage houses, but also to the whole-hearted endeavour to meet all the practical and social needs of everyday life which is expressed in its various public buildings.

See illustration and plans of cottages on the estate in Figs. 110–113, pp. 205–209.

This account of this estate has been kindly supplied by Messrs. Lever Brothers, Port Sunlight, Limited, Estate Office.

BOURNVILLE VILLAGE TRUST

The following account of this Trust's Bournville Estate has been given by courtesy of the Estate Office of the Bournville Village Trust, Birmingham.

The Bournville Estate has an area of 1086 acres and is situated about four miles south-west of the centre of Birmingham. It was founded by George Cadbury in 1895, when he began to build houses on a piece of land adjoining the newly built factory of Cadbury Brothers, Ltd., which had been moved from the centre of Birmingham. The houses were intended as an experiment in housing reform, designed to avoid the defects of the speculative building of that period. Even at that time, tenancy was not confined to employees of the firm, and this principle has been maintained.

In 1900 George Cadbury handed over the estate to Trustees under the control of the Charity Commissioners. The area which he had then acquired was 330 acres, upon which 313 houses had been built.

The trust deed contained the following stipulations :

(1) That dwellings built by the Trust should be accessible to the labouring and working classes, without, however, placing the tenants in the position of being recipients of a bounty.

(2) That the houses should not occupy more than one-quarter of their sites.

(3) That at least one-tenth of the land in addition to roads and gardens, should be reserved for parks and recreation grounds.

(4) That such factories as might be erected should not occupy more than one-fifteenth of the estate.

In addition it stipulated that the Trustees should not benefit financially from the estate, and that all profits arising from its management should be devoted to estate development and to housing reform, either at Bournville or elsewhere. Bearing in mind, however, that the example of Bournville was to be of general application, the founder also insisted that the undertaking should be made to pay a fair return on the capital invested.

Since 1900 the estate has been continuously developed and improved, and at the present time, in addition to the area of land at Bournville, the Trustees own over 1500 acres of land adjoining the south-west boundary of the City of Birmingham. This is being maintained in its present use, and it is hoped that it will ultimately form part of an agricultural belt around the City.

The Trust retains the freehold on all land on its estates and grants 99-year building leases to public utility societies and private individuals.

Development has been carried out in a number of ways. The Trustees have themselves built a large number of houses of all types for sale and for renting. In addition, the following five housing societies have been responsible for the development of different parts of the estate:

Bournville Tenants', Ltd. (founded 1906). This society leased 20 acres

15

of land upon which it built 145 houses, all of which are let to tenant-shareholders.

Weoley Hill, Ltd. (*founded* 1914).   This society builds houses of various sizes for sale at prices varying from £235 (in 1914) to over £2000.

Woodlands Housing Society, Ltd. (*founded* 1923).   This society builds houses for sale.   Every purchaser is a shareholder of the society.

Bournville Works Housing Society, Ltd. (*founded* 1919).   This is the only society the membership of which is confined to employees of Cadbury Brothers, Ltd.   Capital for the construction of the houses was advanced by the firm, and large numbers of dwellings have been erected with subsidy under the various Housing Acts.   All tenants are members of the society and hold shares.   If a tenant leaves the employment of the firm he does not sacrifice his tenancy.

Residential Flats, Ltd. (*founded* 1924).   This society has a building known as " St. George's Court " which contains thirty-two self-contained flats for business and professional women.   The tenants are shareholders of the society.

The total number of houses on the Trust's estate is nearly 2500 ;   the population is approximately 8750.

The public buildings provided include one Anglican, four Free churches, three village halls, elementary schools, day continuation schools, school of arts and crafts, and shopping centres.   In addition, adjoining the estate, there are many religious and other colleges, which contribute to the social life of the estate.

Great attention has been paid to the maintenance of open spaces in various parts of the estate.   As will be seen from the general plan (see Plate V), these traverse the estate in three directions and for the most part are linked together in well defined parkways following the valleys.

Strict architectural control is maintained by the Architects' Department, stress being laid upon good planning and landscape treatment as the essential bases of good appearance.   Plans of all houses are prepared by the Architects' Department of the Trust.   (Typical views are shown in Figs. 114–118.)

FIG. 114. A view at Bournville

FIGS. 115, 116. Weoley Hill

BOURNVILLE

The above views of Weoley Hill, showing the road planned so as to preserve a row of
hedgerow trees as the principal feature of this part of the Estate

Fɪɢ. 117. The Valley pool

Fɪɢ. 118. Subsidy houses built in 1923

BOURNVILLE

Fig. 119. Lodge Avenue, looking south. L.C.C. Becontree Estate

HAMPSTEAD GARDEN CITY TRUST

This Trust was responsible for the development of the Hampstead Garden Suburb. They acquired land and developed it on garden city principles, and provided houses for the middle and working classes, on the condition that the tenant must take a number of shares in the company, and before disposing of them must give the company the first refusal.

Many housing estates were developed on these lines, and undertakings are affiliated to public utility societies, which provide houses on co-partnership tenant methods. The tenants pay rent, and there is a limitation of dividend, and any surplus is applied to providing further amenities for the estate. (Plan is shown in Fig. 10 on page 18.)

L.C.C. BECONTREE ESTATE

Becontree, developed by the London County Council, is the largest municipal housing estate in the world. Covering over four square miles (2784 acres) within the county of Essex, it includes large areas of the Boroughs of Ilford, Barking, and Dagenham: nearly one-fifth of the total area (505 acres) is devoted to open spaces and playing-fields, and over 200 acres reserved for industrial development. The estate provides accommodation for 110,742 persons in 25,825 dwellings, made up of the following types of cottages and cottage-flats (see plan on Plate VI):

	1 room	2 rooms	3 rooms	4 rooms non-parlour	4 rooms parlour	5 rooms	6 rooms	Total
Cottages	–	–	8872	7019	5138	3599	138	24,766
Cottage-Flats	8	749	208	42	31	21	–	1059

In addition there are 21 dwellings reserved for superintendents' quarters.

The greater part of the construction was carried out by Messrs. C. J. Wills & Sons, Ltd., over a period of years from 1920 to 1930, the value of the original contract being £13,455,170 : subsequently over 800 houses of a better class, designed for letting at remunerative rents, were erected by other contractors on various scattered sites. Further sites are now in course of development and 305 cottages and flats (including 94 flats for aged persons) are to be built at a cost of over £300,000. The rebuilding of over 400 dwellings destroyed or damaged beyond repair by enemy action is also in hand.

In the development of the estate, the construction of public buildings was provided for and sites reserved : 27 churches, 30 schools, 400 shops, 14 doctors' houses, 3 clinics, 7 institutes, 2 cinemas, 9 licensed premises, a hospital, and 6 other public buildings have been erected, and sites for a community centre and 22 shops are in process of development. Many forms of social activity are available to the tenants, and at Pettits Farm, Heathway, there is a social settlement established in 1929 and now the headquarters of over thirty educational, cultural, and social organisations.

The estate is served by two railway companies : by the L.N.E.R., with Chadwell Heath station just beyond the northern boundary, and by the L.M.S. with stations at Becontree and Heathway within the estate, and

Dagenham and Dagenham Dock just outside. The time by train to Liverpool Street or Tower Hill is approximately half an hour. There are also various bus and coach services.

An out-patients' department of the King George Hospital at Ilford has become established on the estate, the site being leased by the L.C.C. to the hospital authorities at a nominal rent, together with a donation of £6500 towards the cost of the building.

Thirty-two acres of the estate have been reserved for development by private enterprise, and there were a number of small scattered sites unbuilt upon.

In 1934 the L.C.C. decided to proceed with the development of these, and contracts for about 800 houses had been given, by January 1937, to four firms of private builders. This development permits of the building of houses for letting at remunerative rents to people able to pay more for the housing accommodation than the tenants of the L.C.C. houses.

Photographs are shown in Figs. 119–124.

These notes have been given by kind permission of The Director of Housing and Valuer, London County Council.

FIG. 120. Church Elm Lane, looking east. L.C.C. Becontree Estate

FIG. 121. Four-room parlour and non-parlour type

FIG. 122. Halbutt Street and Beverley Road

L.C.C. BECONTREE ESTATE

FIG. 123. Houses in Gale Street

FIG. 124. Junction of Fanshawe Crescent and Springpond Road

L.C.C. BECONTREE ESTATE

BIRMINGHAM—SHELDON ESTATES

The following notes have been kindly supplied by the City Engineer and Surveyor of Birmingham, J. J. Manzoni, Esq., C.B.E., M.Inst.C.E.

This group of estates on the eastern boundary of the City is about five miles from the centre and has open country to the east. It is approximately three square miles in area and is reached from the City by four main roads—Old Chester Road to northern end—Bordesley Green and Washwood Heath Road to the centre and Coventry Road to southern end. The main routes on the site are sub-arterial in character and designed with due regard to the interests of vehicular traffic and give no encouragement to pedestrians to cross other than at properly prepared points. Subsidiary local roads entering the sub-arteries are kept to the minimum. The other roads are local in character and laid out to discourage use by through traffic and designed only for vehicles having business in the locality. The main L.M.S. London line intersects the site and a station has been erected to serve the district.

The estate, the first section of which was commenced in 1932–3 has been designed to accommodate 44,000 persons in 11,000 houses. Four thousand six hundred of these dwellings were completed prior to the outbreak of hostilities and varied considerably in size according to the number of bedrooms provided, one bedroom type bungalows being erected for old folk without children living with them, and houses with bedrooms up to five in number for those with families.

During the war period the estates have been divided into four " neighbourhood units " of approximately 10,000 persons designed so that each is reasonably self-contained and is not split by any railway, main road, or other impediment. The units are " A " which is almost complete and bounded by the railway, river and Lea Villages ; " B " south of, and bounded by the railway, main roads, and private development ; and " C " lies between Old Chester Road, City Boundary and river ; and " D " north of and bounded by the railway, river, city boundary, and Lea Village.

Each unit has, or will have, it own " neighbourhood centre " consisting of a shopping centre, schools, religious buildings, library, welfare centre, doctors' and midwives' homes, public houses, social and communal centres within ten minutes walk of any part of the neighbourhood and is adjacent to but not actually fronting main roads. One centre at least will also have a swimming bath establishment.

One of these units " C " has been designed by the Birmingham and Five Counties Architectural Association and is on similar lines to the other three.

A total of 283 acres has been reserved for industry in the four areas and located so that although separated from the dwellings it is within 15 minutes travel of the unit. Over a third of this area had been developed. Two of the sites are adjacent to the railway and the others near, but all of them are easily accessible from main roads.

Three hundred acres have been set aside as permanent open space for recreational, school playing-fields and allotment garden purposes.

17

A wide river walk is planned along the Cole. Trees, old hedge-lined grassy lanes and other natural features have been preserved and utilised as far as possible. The old " Kents Moat " which at one time probably surrounded a fortified farmhouse is preserved intact and the enclosure is now a bird sanctuary.

The whole estate has and will be developed at a density of 10 to 12 houses per acre generally though the area adjacent to Sheldon Hall will be developed with larger types of houses at densities of 6 and 8 per acre to preserve the amenities of the Hall. Local names have been utilised as far as possible to maintain old associations for roads such as Billingsley Road, Blakenhale Road, Este Road, Averill Road, and Hengham Road chosen in conjunction with the Vicar of St. Edburghs, Yardley Old Parish Church, which lies on the fringe of the estate.

A portion of the area that is developed has open forecourts along the roads providing continuous grassed spaces between roads and building and avoiding the monotony of small wood fences. This treatment will be extended. The house elevations are varied considerably and different colours and types of walling and roofing add to the variety. For old folk a small colony of bungalow dwellings has been built and more are planned in each area. The houses which have 2 to 5 bedrooms will vary in size and incorporate the latest development in house design and be suitable for varying income groups to produce a balanced community.

(See illustrations in Figs. 125–132.)

FIG. 125. Perspective of centre of neighbourhood " C " Sheldon. Shard End Estate

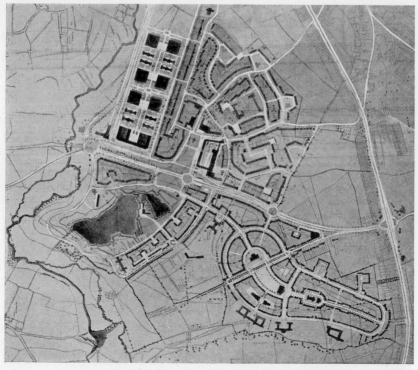

FIG. 126. Layout of neighbourhood " C " Sheldon

BIRMINGHAM

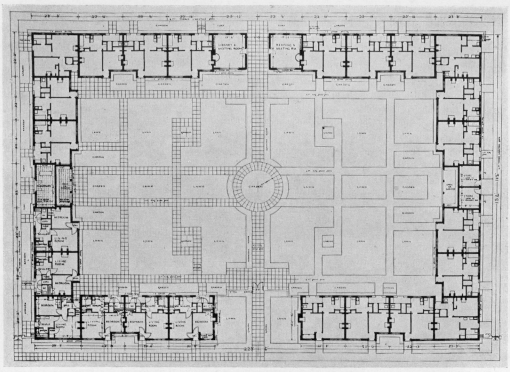

FIG. 127. Plan of bungalows for old people

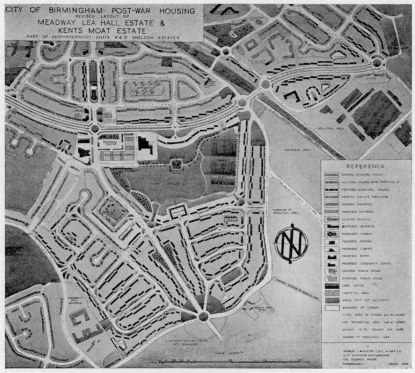

FIG. 128. Meadway Lea Hall Estate and Kents Moat Estate

BIRMINGHAM

FIG. 129. Non-parlour houses, Lea Hall Estate

FIG. 130. Parlour type houses, Lea Hall Estate

BIRMINGHAM

FIG. 131. Non-parlour type houses, Lea Hall Estate

FIG. 132. Non-parlour type houses, Lea Village

BIRMINGHAM

PLATE VII

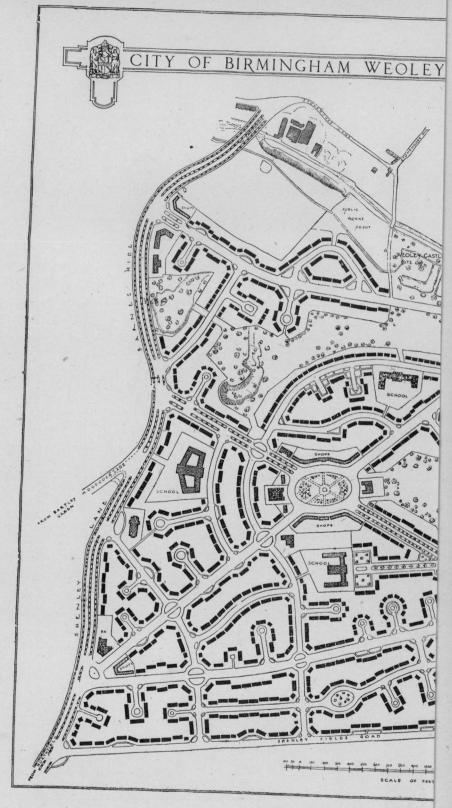

PLAN OF WEOLEY CASTLE

Weoley Castle Estate—Birmingham

Weoley Castle Estate, which is 312 acres in extent, is approximately oblong in shape, three-quarters of a mile long by nearly two-thirds of a mile wide. It lies about a third of a mile to the west of Bristol Road beyond Selly Oak, a little over four miles from the centre of the City.

The estate accommodates 2718 houses, together with central and other shopping areas, public recreation areas, etc. The central shopping area is planned to contain also the civic buildings required in connection with a community of such a size.

The layout of the estate has been designed to conform, as pleasingly as possible, with the natural topographical features of the site, great care being taken to preserve all the old sound trees and to add extensively to their number. (See Plate VII.)

There are several areas on the estate which, for various reasons, are impracticable for building upon, and they are being retained as public open spaces. These are connected by parkways or parkway roads which will form very pleasant features. Amongst these spaces is the site of the very interesting ruins of the old Weoley Castle, dated from the thirteenth century, which have recently been brought to view mainly through the exertions of Mr. G. M. Bark, of the town clerk's department.

An interesting innovation has been to design some of the roads with open forecourts to the houses, which not only adds to the spacious appearance of the setting of the houses but also gives the roads beautiful parkway effects.

The houses have been constructed in pairs and blocks of four and six, designed with variety of both layout and elevation.

Parlour type	Floor area within containing walls, sq. ft.	Contract Price, £	Total No. of type
Parlour type	920	398	303
Non-parlour " A "	820	328	} 2063
Non-parlour " B "	760	300	
Small non-parlour (3 bedrooms)	652	280	168
Small non-parlour (2 bedrooms)	620	270	152
Maisonnettes (2 bedrooms)	536	233	32

Situated on this estate is the 40,000th house completed by the Corporation, No. 30, Hopstone Road, which was opened by the Right Hon. Neville Chamberlain, M.P., Chancellor of the Exchequer, on 23rd October, 1933. It is a small type non-parlour three-bedroom house.

CITY OF LIVERPOOL—SPEKE

The following description of this estate has been very kindly submitted by Sir Lancelot Keay, K.B.E., M. Arch., P.R.I.B.A., former City Architect and Director of Housing.

This estate is planned as a self-contained community and comprises 2208·5 acres, of which 626 acres is allocated to factories, approximately 626 acres to housing, 430 acres to the airport, 101·75 acres for railway sorting sidings, and 709·73 acres to open spaces and including an Institutional area. (See plan in Plate VIII.)

Factory development commenced in 1934 and to-day roughly 318 acres have been sold or let as follows :

271·14 acres —sold on lease for 999 years (10 factories and 17 sites).
  35·05 ,, —sold on lease for 999 years (8 factories) with Corporation mortgages.
  11·06 ,, —on which 11 factories have been erected by the Corporation for tenants.

These twenty-nine factories now employ approximately 11,000 persons. Of the eleven factories erected by the Corporation five were erected to the requirements of lessees and six were put in hand to meet possible requirements. These latter are now all taken up.

The estate is now a thriving industrial area with well over half the available industrial land occupied by up-to-date factories, including industries new to Liverpool and undertakings formerly carried on in the congested parts of the city. The estate is ideally situated, and has all modern services. Although railway siding accommodation could be provided, it has not been necessary so far, as most transport has been by road ; excellent road facilities were made available before the development of the estate.

This estate will eventually be served by the proposed Speke-Widnes arterial road.

In addition to the factories erected there is a large Corporation Housing Scheme which will eventually contain about 6000 houses, made up approximately of :

  250 Cottage Flats for aged persons.
  2129 Houses with living-room and dining-room, and 2 or 3 bedrooms.
  3014 Houses with sitting-room, dining-room, and 3 or 4 bedrooms.
  92 Flats for single persons.
  221 Larger flats with living-room, dining-room, and 2, 3, or 4 bedrooms.
  294 Large houses with garage and 4 bedrooms for professional men, managers, etc.
  ____
  6000

At the moment Speke cannot be said to be a self-contained community unit, but it is the intention that it will be when completed, and it is because the development has been deliberately designed as such, that it is unique among housing estates developed by local authorities.

In February 1947, 1815 houses and flats have been completed. Building operations have recommenced and since the cessation of hostilities 110 houses have been completed. Approximately 100 are now in course of erection and a contract has been let for 560 dwellings. The layout makes provision for eight schools, a fine civic centre in which will be situated the main shopping centre, the community centre, churches, public library, baths, post office, estate offices, and cinema, and in fact all the modern amenities of a township of 20,000 people.

The rents of the houses, which inclusive of rates range at present from 12s. 6d. to 15s. 6d. a week for non-parlour houses and from 18s. 6d. to 23s. 6d. per week for parlour houses, are economic rents based on the immediate pre-war cost of building, as the scheme was designed to be self-supporting, calling for no financial assistance from either State funds or the rates. Higher post-war building costs, however, may entail a re-consideration of policy—whether to continue to build as an unassisted scheme and raise rents to a new economic level or to seek financial assistance from the Government with the object of retaining rents at something like their present level.

THE COMPLETION OF SPEKE

The next stage of the development, working towards the town centre, will include the first of the larger houses to be provided in accordance with the plan. The City Architect realises that on first thought that the whole of the resources of the building industry in this district should for the present be concentrated upon the erection of the greatest number of houses, each using the smallest amount of the labour and materials available. But the shortage of houses to-day is not confined to houses of any particular size, and discrimination and limitation on these lines would defeat entirely the whole principle upon which Speke has been planned. It would be directly contrary to the aim of Parliament as expressed in the New Towns Act, and to the opinions of many who are best qualified to judge. In the development of new industries the housing of managers and key men is as important as that of operatives and there is little doubt that the expansion of industry has been handicapped already by the lack of suitable housing accommodation for key men to act as instructors of new operatives. Speke is isolated from the City and though there are less than two thousand families on the estate, continuous representations are being made for the provision of the essential amenities. The City Architect is, therefore, very strongly of the opinion the final details for the completion of the township and upon reaching their decision should approach the Ministers concerned for approval to proceed with the development in its entirety and, so far as may be, simultaneously.

So that the Council may appreciate the completeness of the development contemplated, a plan and scale model of the town centre have been prepared showing the siting of the various buildings to be accommodated in it. To prepare the plan in the detail essential it was found necessary to make sketch designs of each of the various buildings. Whether the

18

council will themselves erect all or most of these buildings, as appears to have been contemplated by the special powers of the Liverpool Corporation Act, 1936, is a matter upon which a decision should be reached. Whatever the decision may be, the preparation of the designs will ensure the proper siting and indicate the general outline, size, and kind of buildings which the City Architect would be prepared to recommend for approval.

GLASGOW CORPORATION HOUSING DEPARTMENT

The Director of Housing, Ronald Bradbury, P.H.D., F.R.I.B.A., A.M.T.P.I., has very kindly supplied the following information regarding his department.

The activities of the housing department can be summarised briefly as follows:

Since 1919 Glasgow Corporation has built 56,000 houses under the various Housing Acts on land of an extent of approximately 9250 acres, which is equal to 14·46 sq. miles and represents about 23 per cent. of the total acreage of the City. The developments to date have not only comprised cottage estates but also a considerable amount of flatted dwellings, mainly of a three-storey character. The larger housing schemes completed include the Knightswood Estate, the Carntyne Estate (north west and east of the City respectively), and many other smaller estates too numerous to mention.

At the outbreak of war in 1939 work was suspended on the Pollok Estate, but at that date only 194 out of a total of 3780 houses had been completed. One of the most interesting developments is the Penilee Estate, which has been completed during war-time to war-time specifications. It comprises a number of large blocks of three-storey flats, terraced and two-storey flatted houses, all with flat roofs, and shops. Sites have been reserved for public buildings, schools, etc., and a community centre. One of the largest developments which the corporation have in hand is the Castlemilk Estate on the southern boundary of the City, which will eventually provide approximately 9000 houses and is to be planned on the most modern lines with all the necessary amenities required by a large modern development of this kind. This is a pleasantly wooded area of rolling country which affords great possibilities for development. The provision of a number of blocks of multi-storey flats with central heating and automatic lifts has been mooted. The development of this area is, however, still at the sketch design stage. It offers possibilities, however, for a very interesting solution and will add considerably to the residential amenities of the City.

Various photographs are given in Figs. 141–150 illustrating the constructional details of buildings.

PENILEE HOUSING ESTATE

The housing scheme recently completed at Penilee Estate was erected by the Glasgow Corporation and all the architectural work carried out under the direction of Mr. J. H. Ferrie (now retired), the Chief Architect,

FIG. 133. Perspective of three-storey tenement block.   Penilee Estate

DIRECTIONS OF SPAN OF FIRST FLOOR SECOND FLOOR & ROOF

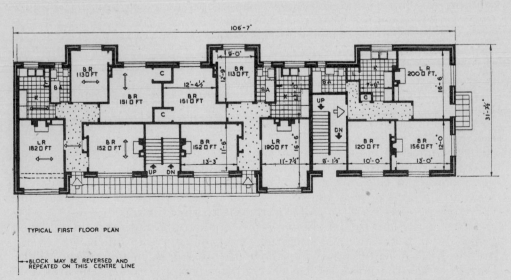

TYPICAL FIRST FLOOR PLAN

BLOCK MAY BE REVERSED AND
REPEATED ON THIS CENTRE LINE

FIG. 134. Typical plan of three-storey tenement block.   Penilee Estate

and of the architectural staff of the housing department. The estate consists of some 1900 dwellings, in three-storey tenements and two-storey blocks of flats and cottage houses. Plans and perspective of each of these types are shown in Figs. 133–138 and Figs. 139–140 and show respectively the finished appearance of a tenement block and of a block of cottages.

The scheme is of particular interest because it is the most advanced of the larger war-time housing schemes, and because of the careful preparatory research which was undertaken before the scheme was initiated.

Shortly after the outbreak of war restrictions on the use of timber were imposed, and the Glasgow Corporation housing department, realising that new housing would have to be erected for war workers, immediately set up a research department to investigate methods of construction which would eliminate timber. Concrete was the obvious material, and so the research department examined many varieties of concrete floors, with a view to selecting the most suitable types. The question of floor finish and roof finish were also studied, and the final scheme was the outcome of this research.

It was, of course, impossible without practical experience to determine which type of concrete floor was the most suitable, and for this reason and in order to spread responsibility over a number of firms, no less than eight different types of concrete floors were incorporated in the scheme. The value of this large-scale experiment in the use of concrete for housing is considerable, but it is obvious that some time must elapse before final conclusions can be reached as to which is the best type of concrete floor.

Throughout the scheme it has been the policy of the Housing Department to employ specialist firms to supply and erect concrete floors and roofs, but the remainder of the pre-cast work, such as stairs, kerbs, window-sills, lintels, and parapet copings has been executed by the Glasgow Corporation's own pre-cast product works.

See Plate IX of layout plan of this estate.

POLLOK ESTATE

This is part of the lands of Pollok, acquired by the Corporation of Glasgow in 1935 from Messrs. Nether Pollok, Ltd., a company formed by Sir John Stirling Maxwell, Bart., K.T., of Pollok, to administer and develop his estates.

It lies immediately south of the White Cart River, extending southwards to the Barrhead Road, with an area of about 60 acres south of that road not included in the present development, but which area will ultimately form an integral portion and is intended to furnish the playing-fields for the large population that will be brought to the district.

The site is bounded on the west by Crookston Road, and on the east generally on a line ranging with the extension of Corkerhill Road.

The Levern Water into which flows the Brock Burn joining the White Cart River at the north-west corner of the scheme, divided the area and along the banks of all these waters the layout indicates possibilities for

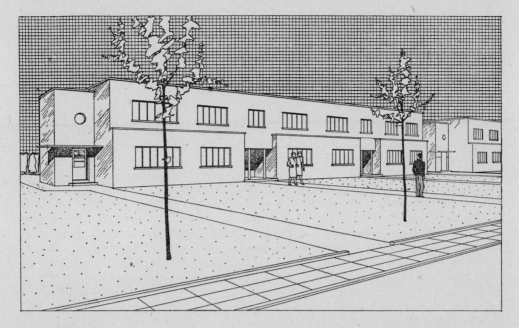

FIG. 135. Perspective view of two-storey cottage block. Penilee Estate

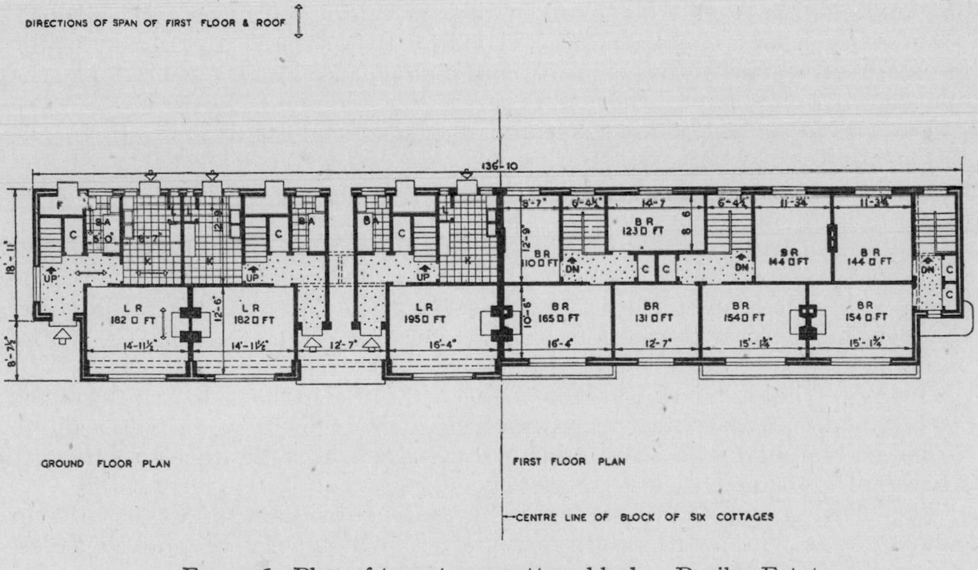
DIRECTIONS OF SPAN OF FIRST FLOOR & ROOF
136'-10
GROUND FLOOR PLAN
FIRST FLOOR PLAN
CENTRE LINE OF BLOCK OF SIX COTTAGES

FIG. 136. Plan of two-storey cottage block. Penilee Estate

the landscape gardener to exercise his skill in the formation of pleasure walks and gardens plot which will give health and delight to many.

The ruined Castle of Crookston, taken over by the Government as an Ancient Monument (the scene of many a fight and foray), is incorporated in a large open space, which could be laid out as pleasure gardens or romping space for children. From its high position it can be seen from most parts of the site, and will stand out in strong contrast as between the old and the new.

The site is undulating in character, with extensive woodlands, and advantage has been taken of this to leave the hill-tops clear of buildings and as places of rest and viewpoints.

The fine plantations for the most part have been left untouched, although two subsidiary main roads lay them open and for fully half a mile will form very fine picturesque avenues.

Altogether the scheme has been devised with the idea of the virgin nature of the site, with its varied sylvan beauties, being conserved and incorporated in the housing development.

The area extends to 754 acres and the present amended development provides for the erection of 5105 houses at an average gross density, including the playing-fields mentioned, of 7·2 or a nett residential density of 15·34 houses per acre.

Many public building sites are provided, which could be utilised for community purposes.

Particular attention and care has been exercised in selecting four large school sites (about 6 acres each) to be as near as possible centrally placed, so as to avoid children having to cross main arterial roads and to be in as close proximity as possible to public playing-fields.

Six shopping centres well distributed over the scheme are provided, and they are expected to be on or in close proximity to main bus routes.

Provisional arrangements are in hand to provide a cinema, while inquiries and arrangements are being made to take up ground by the church, post office, and other bodies.

The layout developed, with three main arterial roads linking up the Barrhead Road with Crookston and Hillington districts on the west and Corkerhill and Mosspark areas on the east, has necessitated the provision of 24 miles of subsidiary roads. (See layout plan in Plate X.)

The engineering development work includes the building of an 80-ft. wide bridge over the White Cart River, two 80-ft. wide bridges and one 70-ft. wide bridge over the Levern Water, and an 80-ft. wide bridge over the Brock Burn ; also another bridge over the White Cart River, whose width has not yet been determined, as well as various footbridges.

Owing to the physical features of the site the construction of the sewers formed a difficult task : the sewers ranged from 9 in. in diameter up to 30 in. in diameter and were laid in some cases at a depth of 30 ft. At such depths tunnelling was necessary.

The arterial roads and some of the main subsidiary roads have twin carriageways with a dividing grass plot, in which may be planted trees, which should well merge into and unify the scheme.

FIG. 137. Perspective of two-storey flatted type house. Penilee Estate

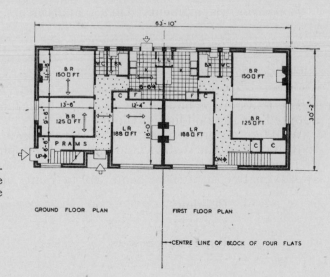

FIG. 138. Plan of two-bedroom flatted type house. Penilee Estate

These roads are from 60 ft. to 80 ft. in width, while the lesser main roads are as a rule 36 ft. in width.

Effect has been given to the Ministry of Transport's principle of installing roundabouts at main crossings, and it is intended to make special features of the central island roundabouts.

The whole of the engineering work, including the building of one of the bridges, was undertaken by the housing department.

The central idea by which the scheme was planned was to make of Pollok the foremost garden suburb in the city, and with this object in view 50 per cent. of the total area has been set apart as open spaces.

Many new ideas in the treatment of the houses externally and internally, as well as in the grouping of various architectural types, are embodied, and many different types of buildings are used in various settings.

The layout, types, and grouping of houses have been decided in close collaboration with Sir John Stirling Mawell, Bart., K.T., of Pollok, and his advisers, Professor Sir Leslie Patrick Abercrombie, M.A., M.T.P.I., John Stewart, F.R.I.B.A., of Messrs. Stewart and Paterson, Architects, and in conjunction with John Wilson, F.R.I.B.A., Chief Architect, Department of Health for Scotland, and Robert Bruce, B.Sc., A.M.I.C.E., A.M.T.P.I., the City Engineer and Master of Works. Of the 5105 houses, 1072 will be of three apartments, 3353 of four apartments, and 560 of five apartments, as detailed in the following table :

Cottage type, 3 apartments, 84 ; 4 apartments, 342 ; 5 apartments, 308.

Terrace type, 3 apartments, 188 ; 4 apartments, 660 ; 5 apartments, 252.

Flatted 4-in-block type, 3 apartments, 60 ; 4 apartments, 678.

Tenements, 3 apartments, 740 ; 4 apartments, 1673.

Single Persons Flats, 1 apartment, 100.

Old Persons Bungalows, 2 apartments, 20.

The rents of the houses have not yet been fixed, nor the method to be adopted for the building of the houses.

While an accurate figure at this date cannot be given, it is estimated that, including the cost of land and all development charges for building of houses and the construction of bridges, roads, and sewers, the total approximate cost of the scheme will be made up as follows :

Buildings	£6,250,000
Land	115,000
Roads and Sewers	600,000
	£6,965,000

FIG. 139. Finished appearance of a tenement block. Pollok Estate

FIG. 140. Finished appearance of a block of cottages. Pollok Estate

GLASGOW

FIGS. 141, 142. Constructional views of houses, Penilee Estate

GLASGOW

FIGS. 143, 144. Constructional views of houses, Penilee Estate

GLASGOW

FIGS. 145, 146. Constructional views of houses, Penilee Estate

GLASGOW

Figs. 147, 148. Constructional views of houses, Penilee Estate

GLASGOW

Figs. 149, 150. Constructional views of houses, Penilee Estate. Glasgow

FIG. 151. Typical housing development, Manchester

Fig. 152. " Mansard " group of houses, Manchester

MANCHESTER—WYTHENSHAWE ESTATE

The author is indebted to the City Surveyor of Manchester, Mr. R. Nicholas, C.B.E., B.Sc., M.Inst.C.E., M.T.P.I., for the following information relating to Wythenshawe.

HISTORY

The Corporation acquired its first interest in the estate in 1926 when Lord and Lady Simon (then Sir Ernest and Lady Simon) generously presented Wythenshawe Hall and Park, comprising 250 acres, to the City. In the same year the Corporation purchased the Tatton Estate of 2500 acres and further purchases were made in 1928 and 1929.

At present, the Corporation own some 4118 acres and the Ministry of Health have consented to the compulsory acquisition of a further 535 acres.

The development of the estate has been progressing since 1926, and a total of 8715 dwellings have been built by the Corporation.

Figs. 151 and 152 show typical houses erected under the Housing Act, 1930.

The present estimated population of the built-up area of the Wythenshawe Estate (including Northenden) is about 43,000.

The original planning proposals formulated in 1930 envisaged the development of Wythenshawe as a satellite town and were considered as a model for planning at that time.

However, in the light of recent experience and legislation, it has been necessary to revise the original plan to keep abreast with modern standards of planning. (See Plan on Plate XI facing p. 248.)

REVISED PLANNING PROPOSALS

(1) *Basis of the Scheme*

The principles of the revised planning proposals formulated in 1944 were as follows :

(a) The recognition that modern conditions require a planned road system based on the segregation of different classes of traffic.

(b) The adoption of the neighbourhood principle in residential development to counteract and forestall the tendency towards social disintegration.

(c) The fostering of a full urban life by the provision, not only of homes, but also of workplaces, medical services, and opportunities for recreation, education, and cultural pursuits.

(d) The use of landscaping as a means of emphasising undulations and natural features and securing variety of treatment.

(2) *The Road Pattern*

The plan provides for two major parkways :

(a) The extension of Princess Parkway southwards from the Altrincham–Stockport Road (A.560) to meet the proposed London–Glasgow motorway south of Lymm.

(b) The Western Parkway, skirting the western and southern boundaries of Wythenshawe. This forms part of the Outer Ring Road for the Manchester Region, and provides a direct route to Trafford Park from the north and south.

20

From east to west, Wythenshawe is traversed by the Cheshire Lines Railway and the existing Altrincham–Stockport Road (A.560) which is to be widened and reconstructed.

Connections to the major highways are provided at a limited number of points by a system of major local roads which traverse the area, linking together the proposed residential neighbourhoods, industrial areas, and civic centre.

(3) *Residential Neighbourhoods*

Wythenshawe will comprise nine residential neighbourhoods when fully developed which are designed to accommodate about 24,100 dwellings with an estimated population of 84,000.

Space does not permit a comprehensive description of each neighbourhood but the provisions of the Baguley Hall Neighbourhood can be quoted as typical. (See Plan on Plate XII following Plate XI.)

(4) *The Civic Centre*

The site of the proposed Civic Centre comprises about 62 acres, and will constitute the main shopping and commercial hub of Wythenshawe.

It has been planned to form a focus for social life and includes a Civic Hall, community centre, main health centre, public baths, library, theatre, dance hall, shops, cinemas, etc.

The layout is based on the principle of precincts for shops and offices, amusements, cultural and administrative buildings, and aims at providing an urban setting with adequate variety and interest.

The area is to be served by a number of local roads giving an easy access to all parts of the estate.

(5) *Industrial Areas*

Three areas are zoned for light industry comprising in total 419 acres, one area of which is already partly developed.

At present no less than 68 per cent. of the employed persons work outside the ward, and spend about one and a half hours per day in travelling.

From detailed calculations it is estimated that 33,000 persons of the ultimate population will be engaged in industry for whom employment will have to be found.

The reservation gives 61·5 square yards per employee which can be compared with 63·6 square yards in the industrial section of Welwyn Garden City.

(6) *Post War Progress in Roads and Sewers*

All roads and sewers are completed on the Baguley Hall Neighbourhood, and in the case of the Newall Green Neighbourhood all sewers are completed together with 95 per cent. of the concrete roads.

Work on roads and sewers is also in progress on the Woodhouse Park and Moss Nook Neighbourhoods.

A total of 15·50 miles of roads and 20·49 miles of sewers have already been laid.

Fig. 153. Homes of the aged, Braunstone Estate

Fig. 154. Elmthorpe Rise from Winstanley Drive, Braunstone Estate

LEICESTER

20*

FIGS. 155, 156. Gooding Avenue at junc

FIG. 157. Houses 65–71 Winforde Crescent, Braunstone Estate

LEICESTER

ith Camville Road, Braunstone Estate

FIG. 158. Houses on Wynthorpe Rise, Braunstone Estate

LEICESTER

Fig. 159. Junction of Peverel Road and Waltham Avenue, Braunstone Estate, Leicester

City of Leicester—Braunstone Estate

The following description of this estate is given by the courtesy of Leicester's Housing Architect, J. S. Fyfe, A.R.I.B.A.

The estate of Braunstone was purchased by the Leicester Corporation in 1925. It contained in all about 1200 acres, of which 235 acres were then within the city boundary. Included in the estate is the pleasant parkland (about 170 acres in extent) of Braunstone Hall, which has been maintained as a public park. (See Plate XIII for the plan of this estate as originally planned.)

The hall, which was the residence of the late owner, Major Richard Winstanley, is a handsome brick building of the Georgian period, built about 1777, has a commanding position in the midst of the Park, and has now been converted into a school.

Within the bounds of the estate lies also the quaint old village of Braunstone, which has been preserved. The stone-built church of St. John the Baptist, though it is the one property in the village which does not pass into the possession of the City, provides the central point of interest by reason of its architectural features and its centuries of historical association.

A portion of the estate (154 acres) was allocated for a municipal aerodrome.

The estate also contained a number of spinneys and groups of fine trees, and the layout was planned so as to retain these natural features.

The estate is now fully developed and contains 4340 houses. Of this number 1773 houses were for rehousing of families from the slum clearance areas. Photographs of houses are shown in Figs. 153–159.

A number of sites were reserved for schools, shops, churches, clinics, community centres, open spaces, and allotments, etc.

City of Leicester's Post-War Housing Estates

The City Engineer and Surveyor of Leicester, John L. Beckett, Esq., M.Inst.C.E., has very kindly submitted the following notes on Leicester's post-war housing schemes.

The City Council is adopting in its post-war reconstruction programme certain principles to form the basis of planning of its future housing estates. Briefly, they are as follows:

(a) Adequate passenger transport routes that will serve the residential neighbourhoods efficiently but at the same time divide the estates into precincts.

(b) Educational and play facilities for younger children, recreational facilities for older people, and subsidiary shopping centres to be included within these precincts.

(c) Full neighbourhood facilities to be provided together with modern recreational and educational facilities in close proximity if possible.

The Council's first post-war permanent housing estate, which is the New Parks Estate, will provide for about 3000 houses and a population of about 10,000 persons. The layout and arrangements of this estate are forming the basis of experiment in the new conception of estate planning, covering the points mentioned and other departures in detail, such as alterations in design of front fences ; communal gardens ; expert tree planting ; variation in size of plots catering for the garden enthusiast and his opposite ; variation in street design ; variation in housing types ; intermixture of classes, etc. (See Plate XIV for layout of this estate as originally planned.)

The estate, which is illustrated in Plate XIV, is laid out on two sides of a large existing park, which is being redesigned to incorporate all modern recreational facilities including open-air swimming-pool and baths and a boating lake. Types of housing will include a large colony for aged persons' homes and a hostel for single persons, both in close proximity to the recreational facilities and the neighbourhood centre. The neighbourhood centre will include health centre, library, communal buildings, churches, cinema, and shops.

An existing golf-course is to be reinstated elsewhere, so as to provide an educational centre for the new estate and part of the surrounding built-up area. This will include two modern schools (girls and boys), boys' grammar school and technical schools, and a county college.

CITY OF NOTTINGHAM—WOLLATON PARK ESTATE

The following notes have been kindly supplied by the City Engineer and Surveyor of Nottingham, R. M. Finch, Esq., O.B.E., M.Inst.C.E., in respect of Wollaton Park Estate.

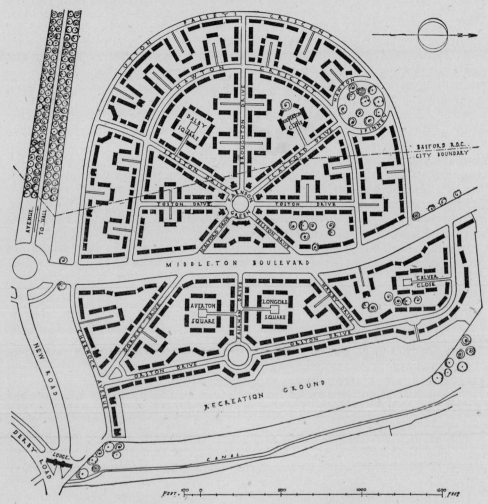

FIG. 160. Wollaton Park Estate, Nottingham

Few housing estates throughout the country have such a desirable environment as this particular estate, forming part of 744 acres of beautiful park land, purchased by the corporation in 1924, containing Wollaton Hall, an Elizabethan building now used as a public museum, a municipal golf-course, and a lake available for public fishing by permit ; while a greater portion of the park is free of access to the public. (See plan in Fig. 160.)

21

The portion allotted for municipal housing comprises an area of approximately 93 acres and is located on the western side of the city at a distance of 2½ miles from the city centre.

Middleton Boulevard, 120 ft. wide, with dual carriageways and generous verges planted with trees, runs through the estate between Derby Road and Wollaton Road, both of which give direct access to the City centre.

The estate was laid out by Mr. T. C. Howitt, the Corporation Housing Architect at that time, and building operations were commenced in 1926.

At this period the demand for houses far exceeded the supply, and the housing committee realised that some other form of construction than the traditional type would have to be introduced to cope with the increasing demand.

After examining various types of demonstration houses, the committee came to the conclusion that the most suitable type was that known as the " Crane " composite bungalow. The general method of construction consisted of light steel stanchions and roof trusses at 6-ft. centres, with walls consisting of concrete and plaster slabs resting on a concrete raft. 500 of these bungalows, detached and semi-detached, were erected.

The accommodation provided included a living-room, two bedrooms, and a room adaptable as a sitting or third bedroom. Alternative designs were used for north and south aspects.

In addition to the " Crane " bungalows, 313 brick houses and bungalows were erected, creating a variety in design. These were of the non-parlour type with three bedrooms. Photographs of houses are shown in Figs. 161–165.

A shopping centre consisting of six shops with living accommodation was provided in a central position, from which roads radiated to serve all parts of the estate. (See photograph in Fig. 161.)

Sites on the north and south sides of the municipal housing have been made available for private housing development and a rigid control exercised on the type of house to be erected.

A modern school with room for future extension has been built on the north side of the estate and a large school playing-field provided on the eastern boundary.

The main roads on the north and south sides form a natural boundary for a neighbourhood unit, and a well-organised social centre run by the residents is established on the estate, using the school for community purposes.

It is hoped in the post-war period to provide separate accommodation for social activities.

While no sites have been allocated for industrial purposes, the estate is in close proximity to modern factory development, and the amenities of the estate as a whole have been carefully preserved. Transport for the residents is well provided for by a trolley vehicle service on the Derby and Ilkeston Roads and along Middleton Boulevard.

FIG. 161. Aerial photograph of Wollaton Park Estate, Nottingham

FIGS. 162, 163. Brick bungalows, Wollaton Park Estate

NOTTINGHAM

FIGS. 164, 165. Brick houses and bungalows, Wollaton Park Estate

NOTTINGHAM

EDINBURGH CORPORATION HOUSING DEVELOPMENT

The following notes have been kindly supplied by M. Murchison, Esq., Housing Executive Housing Architect to the City of Edinburgh to whom the Author is indebted.

Since 1919 Edinburgh Corporation has built 16,000 houses in its own developments, apart from having feued considerable areas of land for the erection of houses by private enterprise, both for letting and for sale, the total number of new houses being over 30,000.

Whilst some of the earlier schemes included cottages, the majority of the new houses built were of the flatted type, including a large number in three- and four-storey blocks, the latter on central cleared areas within the city. The main feature of these central developments is that a successful attempt has been made to retain the old traditional appearance of the tenements by using natural stone on the front elevations and gables, and by the adoption of a design essentially Scottish in character, and in keeping with surrounding buildings.

The number of families which could be rehoused on these central sites was only about 20 per cent. of the number removed from the old houses, and for the balance, new estates were built in the outer parts of the city.

These large new developments, consisting as they do of a very large number of families, all of the same economic status, have not been entirely satisfactory, apart from the fact that the houses themselves are of a good type and provide accommodation of a very much higher standard than that to which the tenants had been accustomed. Such large schemes as Lochend, Niddrie Mains, and to a lesser degree Granton Mains, suffer from the lack of some of the essentials and incentive necessary to the development of well-balanced communities.

Before the outbreak of war, work had been begun on a new large scheme of approximately 2300 houses at West Pilton. For the first time, a large development had been planned as a self-contained community with sites being planned for all the ancillary requirements such as community centre, recreation grounds, children's play areas, public buildings, schools including nursery schools, shopping centres, etc. Cottages, flatted houses and tenements blocks were all included in the proposals, and the houses on the main frontages were intended to have natural stone fronts, and to be built in terraced blocks.

Work on this scheme was, however, suspended in 1939, and although operations were restarted later, amendments in the design and construction of the houses due to wartime restrictions and shortages caused major changes to be made and, to some extent at least, the high hopes which had grown up round the West Pilton scheme have not been realised. In addition, a large portion of the site has had to be used for the erection of 364 temporary houses. Whilst these temporary houses meet a very urgent want, the necessity to use a large part of the site in this way has somewhat complicated the original proposals.

THE FUTURE

Attention is now being given to Edinburgh's future housing developments, and to this end a housing and social survey has recently been carried out of all housing in the City, so that a reasonably accurate assessment may be made of the City's requirements from a planning point view to cover all sections of the community, including housing, industry, recreation, education, transport, etc.

Complete results of this survey are not yet fully known, but meantime, to provide a working pool of new housing, a limited number of new schemes are being proceeded with on sites, the use of which will not prejudice the long-term plan and report, at present in course of preparation.

THE INCH HOUSING AND COMMUNITY DEVELOPMENT (See Plates XV and XVI and Frontispiece.)

Perhaps it will be sufficient to describe this development generally as being indicative of the Corporation's intentions in the provision and planning of new schemes in the future.

The site, which is in the southern part of the City, extends to over 200 acres, and includes the large partly seventeenth-century mansion house known as the Inch with its 90 acres of very attractive and well-wooded policies. The ground rises gradually southwards and from all parts excellent views can be obtained of the City and the Firth of Forth to the north. Although there has been a certain amount of residential development in the general area, the site in the main has been used for farming.

Realising the importance of the site and the need for getting the best possible plan, the Corporation decided to invite competitive layout plans. Nearly 70 schemes were received, and the assessor ultimately awarded first place to the scheme submitted by Messrs. Stratton Davis and Yates, FF.R.I.B.A., of Gloucester.

In his designs for both the development of site and the actual houses, the architect has been particularly successful in that he has retained the semi-rural character of the site by providing an informal layout with due regard to the contours, and with the complete absence of a rigid and formal pattern. Although there will be approximately 1740 houses, almost 1200 of these will be in the form of 4-apartment and 5-apartment cottages, the remainder being in two-storey flatted blocks, and a small number in three-storey blocks grouped in selected parts of the area. Provision is also made for special houses for elderly persons and for single women, the latter not being in special blocks, but forming part of the general development. Good use is also to be made of terrace development to give repose and ample opportunity for good architectural design.

Ample provision is also made in the plan for schools, churches, playgrounds, shopping centres, etc., while the mansion house with its delightful policies and amenities are to be used for communal purposes including library, clinics, recreation, etc. In the layout plan all the very delightful natural features of the site have been very carefully retained.

Traffic through the site is discouraged by there being no direct through roads in the development, and the transport services will be restricted to the use of the existing main roads.

In the design of the houses, Messrs. Stratton Davis and Yates have relied on simple lines and on good proportion of wall surfaces and openings. Interest will be encouraged rather by the use of the colour and texture of natural materials than by a use of revolutionary design and construction.

It is intended to commence site operations in the early summer, and the results of this development are keenly awaited.

Schedule of Houses

Cottage Types

4-apartment ..	..	..	709
5 ,, ..	..	..	487

Flatted Types (Two-storey)

4-apartment	..	..	110

Flatted Types (Three-storey)

4-apartment	..	..	310
Single persons flats ..	..	..	50

Flats over Shops	..	..	35

Old people's dwellings ..	..	..	40

1741

MULTI-STOREYED BLOCKS

Plans are now being completed for the erection of a seven-storey block containing 88 houses, and with an addition of a part eighth storey containing a nursery school. The majority of the houses in this block will be of four apartments, with a small number of specially planned 2-apartment houses for elderly couples and single women. Communal accommodation for social functions is included, and each house will have a drying chamber. Lifts will be provided in addition to staircases for each group of fourteen houses with two special lifts to serve the nursery school and playground on the top floor. No solid fuel fires are being installed, and heating and hot water will be centrally supplied.

The structure of the block will consist of a reinforced concrete frame covered externally with bright coloured precast concrete slabs.

Ample open space will be provided adjacent to the new block with a bowling green and children's playground as central features.

It is expected that similar multi-storeyed blocks will be erected not only on central sites in Edinburgh, but also in outer areas as a means towards economising in the use of agricultural land, always provided, of course, that the proper amount of open space is allocated to such blocks.

22

THE MERVILLE ESTATE, BELFAST, FOR THE ULSTER GARDEN VILLAGES, LIMITED

There can hardly be any phase of the landscape architect's work that calls for more thought than the layout of housing estates. In the past, little attention has been paid to the creation and preservation of landscape features so essential to the surroundings of small houses. Almost everyone has witnessed in his own locality the slaughter of well-grown timber, simply because little or no imagination has been used in trying to work those features, which have taken a lifetime to produce, into the scheme of things as the centre of a courtyard or village green. Too often, estate development seems to be treated as some form of jigsaw puzzle with serried rows of uninteresting sameness ; whereas every feature of the site should be carefully considered and the road plan adjusted to the contours.

In this Estate the designer, Mr. E. Prentice Mawson, F.R.I.B.A., M.T.P.I., has produced an outstanding example that should set a new standard both in layout and in the grouping and design of the units.

As will be seen on reference to the plan (Plate XVII), the site is long and narrow, flanked on the one side by a fine belt of timber (which is scheduled for preservation in the local town-planning scheme) and on the other by a magnificent well-timbered glen, with a charming stream and walks running through it, which is to be preserved as an open space for the benefit of the village.

Flanking the main entrance on the south-east is a large group of flats and shops with access roads on each side, climbing to the higher ground, on which the main development is placed on each side of a central double roadway in the form of groups of flats and of small houses. The flats are of three storeys high, of two- and three-bedroom type, and have been so arranged to take full advantage of the magnificent views over Belfast Lough.

The cottages (Figs. 166–168) are interesting both in the simplicity of their design and grouping into courts. One particular feature is the placing of cottage flats at the external angles of the courts, thus avoiding the usual unpleasant view into the back gardens. Equally, each block of houses is joined by a flanking wall or pergola, giving a continuity that is most effective.

In the whole scheme, the layout provides that the estate company shall have the upkeep of all the front gardens, which can, therefore, be laid out on broad lines with effective grass and planted areas.

The cottages shown in Figs. 166–168 are all of the usual three-bedroom type, but also contain many interesting features not usually found in the ordinary housing schemes. For example, the kitchens have been especially well-planned and equipped, each having ample cupboard space, with fitted refrigerator. Cooking is by gas or electric stove, according to the preference of the tenants. In every case, hot water is provided by an independent " Taco " stove, with the addition of an immersion heater for summer use.

Each courtyard is treated as an entity, and all groups of houses forming

FIG. 166. One of the courtyard

FIG. 167. Blocks of houses

THE MERVILLE ESTATE, BELFAST

owing flanking walls between houses

FIG. 168. A row of cottages

)R ULSTER GARDEN VILLAGES, LTD.

E. Prentice Mawson, F.R.I.B.A., M.T.P.I., Architect

a courtyard have the same type of roofing material, texture of wall finishings, colour, etc.

The number of flats is 256, cottage flats 28, and houses 146. The old mansion on the site will ultimately be turned into a community centre for the village.

PLATE XVII

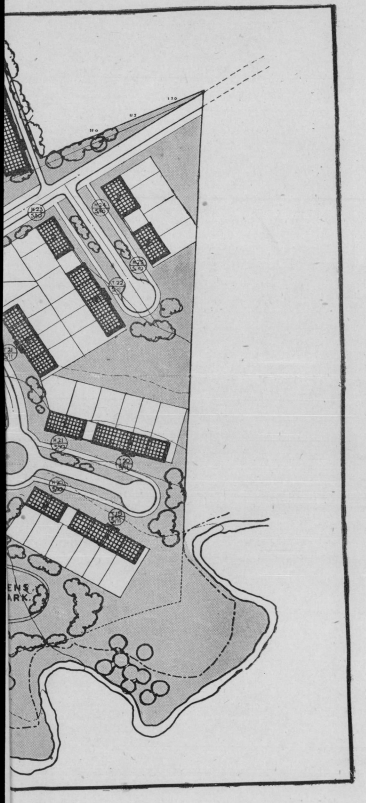

APPENDIX

THE APPEARANCE OF HOUSING ESTATES

REPORT OF CENTRAL HOUSING COMMITTEE PUBLISHED BY HIS MAJESTY'S STATIONERY OFFICE, JUNE, 1948

To improve the appearance of local authority housing estates, 26 recommendations are made in a Report presented to the Minister of Health, Mr. Aneurin Bevan, by the Central Housing Advisory Committee. The recommendations were made by a Sub-Committee which, under the chairmanship of Lord Faringdon, was appointed " to consider means of improving the appearance of local authority housing estates, particularly by enlisting the help of tenants ".

Among them are :—

1. Creepers of all kinds should be more freely planted and colour-washing of walls should be more frequently used to provide variety.
2. Planting of forest trees should be regarded as an essential part of housing estates ; a greater variety of trees should be used for roadside planting and they should be planted in front gardens as an alternative to the pavement.
2. Maximum height for front hedges and fences should be three feet.
4. Adequate shed or store should be provided for every local authority house.
5. Advice on simple garden layouts should be available to tenants.
6. Window boxes should be provided in blocks of flats and arrangements made for the renewal of soil.

Minister's Recommendation. In sending a copy of the Report to housing authorities, the Minister of Health has generally endorsed the Committee's recommendations and hopes that they will give them early consideration. Saying that he would welcome experiments on the lines suggested, the Minister has pointed out that the majority of the recommendations involve work of a kind that can, in general, be undertaken at present without drawing on labour and materials needed for house-building or for work of national importance.

POST-WAR ESTATES BETTER DESIGNED

Stating their general view of the problem, the Committee emphasized that they found many local authority estates which are well laid out, attractive in appearance, and which clearly form a pleasant and neighbourly background for real community life. The layout of post-war estates by many of the leading housing authorities showed improvements in all directions on previous standards.

" But we have come across many other estates where all individuality and homeliness have been lost in endless rows of identical semi-detached houses," they state.

The Committee were also struck by the desolate appearance of the back gardens on some estates. Here there were tenants who appeared to take little pride or interest in the external appearance of their houses and in some cases had had little incentive to do so from the local authority. Even where the Council planted trees and provided grass verges in the early days, many of the young trees were soon destroyed by the children, and those that survived had, with constant lopping and pollarding, " degenerated into knobs of foliage which add nothing to the beauty of the estate. Frequently, too, the grass verges, which at best were possibly scythed only once or twice a year, have long since disappeared and only tufts of grass and small distorted shrubs remain to show where the green places were."

It was clear that the defects evident on many estates depended for remedy upon the authorities themselves and the major part of the Report deals with suggested remedies dependent on their initiative, but the recommendations also cover remedies lying with the tenants themselves.

23
271

ACTION BY LOCAL AUTHORITIES

Trees. The importance of designing layouts in relation to existing trees and, above all, the paramount necessity of planting more forest trees, are emphasized. There was need for much wider choice among the numerous varieties available where small trees are to be used. The white beam and bird cherry are two varieties recommended. The presence of a tree in a garden, provided it can be planted where it will not darken rooms or interfere unduly with cultivation, was likely to encourage the tenant's pride and interest both in his own garden and in other trees on the estate.

Hedges. Front hedges and fences should be regarded as a frame for the garden and kept low—three feet as a maximum height. Those round the back garden, on the other hand, should provide for the greatest possible measure of privacy in order to encourage the full use of the back garden for the family's pleasure and recreation. With the exception of close-board fencing or a brick wall, nothing made so successful a screen as a good hedge of sufficient height.

Creepers. The Committee do not feel that these constitute a danger to the structure or an expense so serious as to outweigh their advantages. While there is some conflict of evidence, the balance goes to show that creepers, with the exception of ivy, do no real injury to the structure of the house. In appropriate cases, tenants should be encouraged to plant suitable light creepers and fruit trees against their houses.

Gardens. It is a general experience that the standards of gardening deteriorated considerably during the war, principally because of the absence of men in the Forces, and recovery seems to be slow. The importance of a good start is urged. It is suggested that both front and back gardens should be dug over for the tenant of a new house before he moves in and that, where possible, a lawn should be laid out in the front garden. If a tenant is unable or unwilling to cultivate his garden, the work might be carried out by the local authority at his cost.

Grass verges. Discussing the difficulties of preserving grass verges, the Committee state that footpaths and verges both need to be wider than has often been the case in the past, and it is clear that, generally speaking, verges must not be planned close to bus stops, school entrances and shopping centres. In the case of both verges and greens, if they are maintained as lawns by frequent mowing instead of being left as rough grass scythed only once or twice a year, they are much more likely to be respected by adults and children alike.

Colour-wash. Colour-wash can give variety and freshness to the appearance of an estate. Regarding external painting, the Report urges that drab colours and graining of all kinds should be avoided. While the Committee agreed that tenants should not undertake the painting of eaves-gutters, down-spouts and window frames, " some of us would like to see an exception made in the case of the front door, feeling that the appearance of this is a matter in which the tenant and his wife very readily take a pride."

Window boxes. Suggestions for flats include the freer use of trees on the site and the provision of window boxes to be cultivated by the tenant. To encourage good use of window boxes, arrangements should be made for frequent changes of soil.

ACTION BY TENANTS

Recommendations relating to tenants are largely concerned with the maintenance of gardens in good condition. Tenants who are inexperienced gardeners should be able, it is suggested, to turn to the Housing Manager for encouragement and help.

The Committee consider that horticultural societies and garden competitions are better organized by the tenants themselves than by the local authority, but in cases where the latter course is adopted, it is preferable to offer prizes for the best roads rather than the best individual gardens. Part of the prizes should be in kind rather than in cash.

Among other matters discussed are the advantages of garden associations and the extended use of municipal nurseries.

A booklet entitled " Our Gardens," designed to emphasize pictorially many of the points made by the Committee, will be published by H.M. Stationery Office at a later date.

INDEX